INSTRUCTOR'S RESOURCE GUIDE

Billstein • Libeskind • Lott

A Problem Solving Approach to

MATHEMATICS
for Elementary School Teachers
FIFTH EDITION

INSTRUCTOR'S RESOURCE GUIDE

Billstein • Libeskind • Lott

A Problem Solving Approach to

MATHEMATICS
for Elementary School Teachers
FIFTH EDITION

ADDISON-WESLEY PUBLISHING COMPANY
Reading, Massachusetts • Menlo Park, California • New York
Don Mills, Ontario •Wokingham, England • Amsterdam • Bonn • Sydney
Singapore • Tokyo • Madrid • San Juan • Milan • Paris

TABLE OF CONTENTS

INSTRUCTOR'S RESOURCE GUIDE

Billstein • Libeskind • Lott

A Problem Solving Approach to

MATHEMATICS

for Elementary School Teachers

FIFTH EDITION

Sample Test

1. List the terms that complete a possible pattern in each of the following:

    (a)   6, 8, 10, 12, 14,____,____,____
    (b)   38, 33, 28, 23, 18,____,____,____
    (c)   640, 320, 160, 80,____,____,____
    (d)   7, 8, 15, 23, 38,____,____,____
    (e)   4, 8, 16, 32, 64,____,____,____
    (f)   0, 7, 26, 63, 124,____,____,____
    (g)   1,____,____,____,25, 36, 49

2. Classify each of the sequences in Problem 1 as arithmetic, geometric, or neither.

3. Find the nth term in each of the following:

    (a)   7, 11, 15, 19, ...
    (b)   2, 9, 28, 65, ...
    (c)   5, 25, 125, 625, ...

4. Find the first five terms of the sequences with the nth term given as follows:

    (a) $5n + 4$
    (b) $n^2 + n$
    (c) $3n + 7$
    (d) $n(n + 7)$

5. Find the following sums.

    (a) $6 + 8 + 10 + 12 + \ldots + 100$
    (b) $71 + 72 + 73 + 74 + \ldots + 89$

6. (a)   Determine a possible pattern in the following sequence if the tenth term is supposed to have four digits.

          101, 212, 323, 434, 545, 656, 767, ...

    (b)   What is the 100th term of the sequence in (a)?

▶ 7. A person writing a book numbered the pages consecutively starting with 1 and had written 4553 digits. How many pages had she numbered? Explain your reasoning.

8. Place the numbers 3, 4, 7, 9 in the squares below to obtain the greatest product.

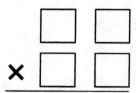

9. John is responsible for seating arrangements at a dinner party. He has seven tables which individually seat six people as shown. He wants to make one large table by pushing them together. He expects a total of 15 couples.

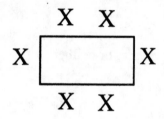

   (a) Can he accommodate all the expected guests if he lines the tables up side-to-side?

   ▶ (b) Can he accommodate all the expected guests if he lines the tables up end-to-end? Explain your answers.

10. Given the eight numbers 2, 3, 4, 5, 6, 7, 8, 9;

   (a) Choose six of them whose product is 20,116.

   ▶ (b) How many solutions are there? Explain your answer.

11. A novice rabbit breeder started with two pregnant females. One delivered six female young, the other delivered three males and five females. He recently bred all the females he owned and each delivered five young. If he has kept all of the rabbits, how many does he have?

12. A rectangle is 6 cm wide. The length is 1 cm less than 3 times the width.

   (a) What is the length of the rectangle?

   (b) What is the perimeter of the rectangle?

13. How many different ways can you make change for a $100 bill using $5, $10, $20, and $50 bills?

14. How many rectangles are in the following figure?

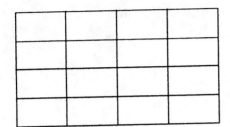

15. The third term in an arithmetic sequence is 11 and the 11th term is 35. Find the first term.

Sample Test

1. List the terms that complete a possible pattern in each of the following:

    (a)   2, 3, 5, 8, 12,___,___,___
    (b)   47, 87, 67, 107, 87,___,___,___
    (c)   100, 300, 900, 2700, 8100,___,___,___
    (d)   2, 10, 50, 250, 1250,___,___,___
    (e)   8, 15, 22, 29, 36,___,___,___
    (f)   4, 0, 8, 0, 16, 0,___,___,___
    (g)   5, 9, 13, 17, 21,___,___,___
    (h)   0, 15, 80, 255, 624,___,___,___

2. Classify each of the sequences in Problem 1 as arithmetic, geometric, or neither.

3. Find the nth term in each of the following:

    (a)   4, 9, 14, 19, 24, ...
    (b)   6, 12, 24, 48, 96, ...

4. Find the first five terms of the sequences with the nth term given as follows:

    (a) $4n + 7$
    (b) $n^2 + 2n$
    (c) $3n + 1$

5. Find the following sums:

    (a) $3 + 6 + 9 + 12 + ... + 84$
    (b) $183 + 182 + 181 + 180 + ... + 17$

6. In order to divide a P.E. class into two teams, the gym teacher has the students stand in a circle and count off 1, 2, 3, ... all the way around the circle. If the teacher divides the circle in half between the numbers 3 and 4 and between the numbers 12 and 13, how many students are on each team?

7. Place the letters A, B, C, and D in the grid below so that no letter shows up twice in any row, column, or in either diagonal.

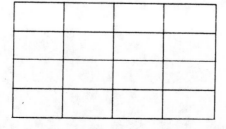

▶   8.   A 200 ml test tube collects 25 ml of condensation every night and loses 9 ml to evaporation every day. When will the test tube overflow? Explain your reasoning.

▶   9.   Charlie is designing an 80' x 120' rectangular fence. He wants to put posts 10' apart along one of the 120' sides. The posts will be 8' apart along the other three sides of the fence. How many posts does Charlie need? Explain your reasoning.

10.   Catarina had $2.00. This money was the value of the same number of nickels, dimes, and quarters only. How many of each did she have?

11.   Joey attached a popsicle stick to one of his bicycle spokes. Then he attached a bell to his front fender so that the popsicle stick would ring the bell with each revolution. If a complete turn of the wheel moves his bicycle forward 5 feet, and his friend lives ½ mile away, how many times will his bell ring?

▶   12.   What is the 200th letter in the sequence A, B, C, D, E, F, A, B, C, D, E, F, ...? Explain your reasoning.

13.   Gerald and Betty Joggette ran 5 blocks on their first day out. They increased their run by 3 blocks each day until they were running 35 blocks. How many days did it take to do this?

14.   Place the digits 2, 3, 4, 5, and 6 in the squares below to obtain the product shown.

$$\begin{array}{r} \square\square\square \\ \times\ \ \square\square \\ \hline 10695 \end{array}$$

15.   How many numbers are there between 100 and 1000 that contain the digits 7, 8, or 9?

Sample Test

1. Write the set of vowels in the name of the creator of "set theory" using set-builder notation.

    List all the subsets of $\{2, o, t\}$.

3. Let $U = \{x | x \text{ is a female}\}$;
    $A = \{x | x \text{ is a mathematician}\}$;
    $B = \{x | x \text{ owns a pickup}\}$;
    $C = \{x | x \text{ owns a dog}\}$;

    Describe in words a member of each of the following:

    (a) $\overline{B}$ (b) $B \cup C$ (c) $A - C$
    (d) $\overline{A \cup C}$ (e) $B - A$ (f) $\overline{A}$

4. Let $U = \{u, n, i, t, e\}$;
    $A = \{n, i, t\}$;
    $B = \{n, e\}$;
    $C = \{u, n, i, t, e\}$;
    $D = \{u, e\}$;

    Find each of the following:

    (a) $A \cap B$ (b) $C \cup D$
    (c) $\overline{D}$ (d) $\overline{A \cup D}$
    (e) $B \cap \overline{C}$ (f) $(B \cap C) \cap D$
    (g) $(A \cup B) \cap (C \cup D)$ (h) $(C - D) \cap \overline{A}$
    (i) $n(C)$ (j) $n(C \cup D)$

5. Indicate the following sets by shading.

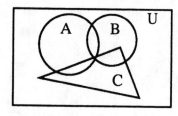
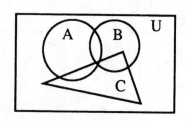

    (a) $(A \cup B) \cup C$ (b) $A \cap (B \cup C)$

6. Let $C = \{p, l, u, s\}$. How many proper subsets does C have?

7. How many possible one-to-one correspondences are there between sets D and E if $D = \{w, h, y\}$ and $E = \{n, o, t\}$?

8. How many elements are there in the Cartesian product of sets D and E in Problem 7?

9. Use a Venn diagram to determine whether $A \cup (B - C) = (B \cup A) - C$ for all sets A, B, and C.

10. Describe using symbols, the shaded portion in each of the following:

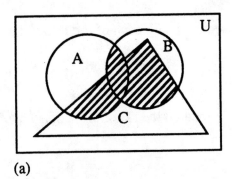

(a)

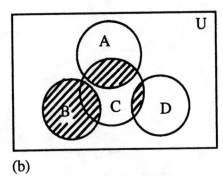

(b)

11. Use $A = \{o,n,e\}$, $B = \{t,w,o\}$, $C = \{z,e,r,o\}$, to illustrate the equality
    $A \times (B \cup C) = (A \times B) \cup (A \times C)$.

12. Classify each of the following as true or false. If false, tell why or give an example showing that it is not true.

    (a) For all sets A and B, $A - B = B - A$
    (b) For all sets A, $\emptyset \subseteq A$
    (c) For all sets A, $A \subseteq A \cup \emptyset$.
    (d) The set $\{r,s,t,\ldots,z\}$ is a finite set.
    (e) No set can be equivalent to all of its subsets.

13. In an interview of 50 math majors,
    12 liked calculus and geometry
    18 liked calculus but not algebra
    4 liked calculus, algebra, and geometry
    25 liked calculus
    15 liked geometry
    10 liked algebra but neither calculus nor geometry
    2 liked geometry and algebra but not calculus.
    Of those surveyed, how many liked calculus and algebra?

14. Which of the following relations are functions from the set of first components to the set of second components?

    (a) $\{(b,a),(d,c),(a,e),(g,f)\}$
    (b) $\{(a,b),(b,a),(c,c),(a,c)\}$
    (c) $\{(b,a),(c,a),(b,b),(c,b)\}$

15. Given the following function rules and domains, find the associated ranges.

   (a) $f(x) = 5x + 3$;   Domain = $\{0,1,2,3,4\}$
   (b) $f(x) = x^2 - 1$;   Domain = $\{1,9,4\}$
   (c) $f(x) = 2x + x^2$;   Domain = $\{1,0,2\}$

16. If $f(x) = 3x - 10$, find the element of the domain associated with each of the following functional values:

   (a)   2   (b)   8

17. What properties do each of the following relations defined on the set of all people have?

   (a)   uses the same brand of toothpaste
   (b)   has more teeth than
   (c)   is a teacher of
   (d)   is the paternal grandmother of

18. The following graphs show the cost and revenue functions in dollars for producing cameras. From the graphs estimate the following.

   (a)   The break-even point — that is, the number of cameras that must be sold to meet expenses exactly.
   (b)   The profit or loss on the first 25 cameras produced and sold.
   (c)   The number of cameras that must be sold to gain a $2000 profit.

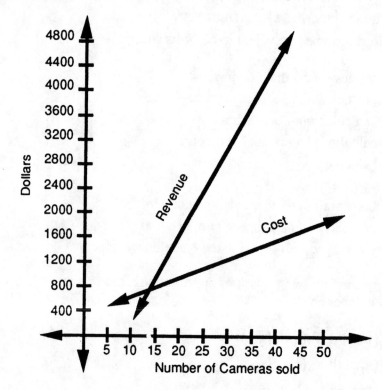

* 19. Which of the following are statements?

    (a) Emily Dickinson won a Nobel Prize in physics.
    (b) How many cars does it take to create parking lot?
    (c) It takes 3 book editors to screw in a light bulb.
    (d) $x + 3 = 15$

* 20. Negate each of the following:

    (a) Butterflies are animals.
    (b) Whitney Houston always says "How de do Boo Boo."
    (c) Some umpire calls are correct.
    (d) $7 + 3 = 10$.

* 21. Write truth tables for each of the following:

    (a) $[p \wedge (q)] \to p$ (b) $[q \vee (\sim q)] \to q$
    (c) $[p \to (\sim q)] \leftrightarrow [(\sim q) \to q]$ (d) $p \to p$

* 22. Decide whether or not the following are equivalent:

    (a) $q; (p \to q)$ (b) $\sim q \leftrightarrow p; \sim (\sim p \to q)$

* 23. Write the converse, inverse, and contrapositive of the following. If the host was the Jay Leno, the director was Doc Sevrinson.

* 24. Find a valid conclusion for the following arguments.

    (a) If I don't get an increase in salary, I will quit. I do not quit.
    (b) If the map is in the plane, it takes no more than four colors to color it. It takes more than four colors to color the map.
    (c) All women mathematicians are well known. Gloria Hewitt is a woman mathematician.

* 25. Write the following argument symbolically and then determine its validity.

    If a nail is lost, then a shoe is lost.
    If a shoe is lost, then a horse is lost.
    If a horse is lost, then a rider is lost.
    If a rider is lost, then a battle is lost.
    If a battle is lost, then a kingdom is lost.
    Therefore, if a nail is lost, then a kingdom is lost.

*   26.   Determine whether or not each of the following arguments is valid.

    (a)   All larch trees are conifers.
        All conifers keep their needles all year long.
        Therefore, all larch trees keep their needles all year long.

    (b)   No spiders are insects.
        All insects are not arachnids.
        Therefore, no spiders are arachnids.

    (c)   If a cat is spayed, then it cannot have kittens.
        My cat has kittens.
        Therefore, my cat is not spayed.

    (d)   If John works in stained glass, then he makes butterflies.
        If John does not make butterflies, then he is not a glazier.
        John works in stained glass.
        Therefore, John is not a glazier

Sample Test

1. Use set notation to write the months having six letters in their name.

2. Write the set $M = \{1,3,5,7,9\}$ using set-builder notation.

3. List all the nonempty proper subsets of $\{a,b,c\}$.

4. Let $U = \{x|x \text{ is an American}\}$
    $C = \{x|x \text{ is an smoker}\}$
    $D = \{x|x \text{ has a health problem}\}$
    $E = \{x|x \text{ is a male}\}$

    (i)   Describe a person who is an element of each of the following sets:

    (a) $\overline{C}$ (b) $\overline{C} \cap \overline{D}$ (c) $C \cap D$

    (d) $D - C$ (e) $D \cup C$

    (ii) Use the sets above, along with the set operations to describe a set of which each of the following is a representative number.

    (a)   A healthy American male   (b)   An unhealthy male smoker
    (c)   A nonsmoking healthy female
    (d)   An American who is either a female or a nonsmoker

5. Classify the following as true or false, where A and B are any two sets. If false, give a counterexample.

    (a)   If $A \cup B = A$, then $B \subseteq A$
    (b)   If $A \subseteq B$, then $A \cup B = B$
    (c) $(A \cup B) \cup C = A \cup (B \cup C)$
    (d) $A \cap \overline{A} = \emptyset$
    (e) $A \cup \overline{A} = \emptyset$
    (f) $A - \overline{A} = \emptyset$
    (g) $A \times \overline{A} = U$
    (h) $\emptyset \subset \emptyset$

6. If $U = \{q,u,e,s,t\}$, $A = \{s,e,t\}$, $B = \{s,u,e\}$, and $C = \{q,u\}$, find each of the following:

    (a) $A \cup B$
    (b) $A \cap \overline{C}$
    (c) $A \cup (\overline{B \cap C})$

6.   (cont.)

    (d) $\overline{A} \cap \overline{B}$

    (e) $A - B$

    (f) $(A \cup B) \cap (A \cup C)$

    (g) $A \cup \overline{A}$

    (h) $n(B - A)$

7.   Let $A = \{1,2\}$ and $B = \{a\}$. Find the following:

    (a) $n(A \times B)$

    (b) $n(B \times A)$

    (c) $B \times B$

    (d) $A \times A$

    (e) $\varnothing \times A$

    (f)   Is $A \times A$ a function from A to A?

    (g)   Is $B \times B$ a function from B to B?

    (h) $n(A \times \varnothing)$

8.   (a)   Illustrate a one-to-one correspondence between the following sets:

$$N = \{1,2,3,4,\ldots,n,\ldots\}$$
$$F = \{4,9,14,19,24,\ldots\}$$

▶ (b)   In your correspondence, what number corresponds to 57? Explain why.

    (c)   In your correspondence, what element of F corresponds to n?

9.   Given the function rules and domains, find the associated ranges.

    (a) $f(x) = 2x + 3$, domain = $\{1,2,0\}$

    (b) $f(x) = 0$, domain = $\{0,1,2\}$

10.   Shade the Venn diagram to illustrate $\overline{A} \cup \overline{B}$.

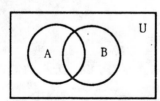

11. Describe in symbols the shaded portion of the Venn diagram below.

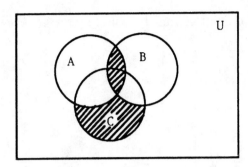

▶ 12. A survey was made of 200 students to study their use of the public library system. The findings were as follows:

60 used the Reader's Guide.

28 used both the card catalog and the information booth.

68 used the information booth.

83 did not use the library.

43 used only the card catalog.

Explain how the above information can be used to conclude that some students must use both the information booth and the Reader's Guide.

13. If there are 36 different flavors of ice cream and two types of cones are available, how many choices for a single scoop of ice cream on some type of cone do I have?

14. If $A = \{a,b,c,d\}$ and $B = \{1,2,3,4\}$, how many different one-to-one correspondences can be made?

15. Which of the following relations are functions from the set of first components to the set of second components?

(a) $\{(1,2),(2,1)\}$

(b) $\{(5,10),(10,10),(15,10),(20,10)\}$

16. What properties do each of the following relations defined on the set of all people have?

(a)   uses the same mouthwash as
(b)   drinks more orange juice than
(c)   is an uncle of
(d)   is the grandmother of

17. The following graphs show the cost and revenue functions in dollars for producing dishwashers. From the graphs estimate the following.

(a)   The break-even point — that is, the number of dishwashers that must be sold to meet expenses exactly.
(b)   The profit or loss on the first 20 dishwashers produced and sold.

17. (cont.)

   (c)   The number of units that must be sold to gain a $6000 profit.

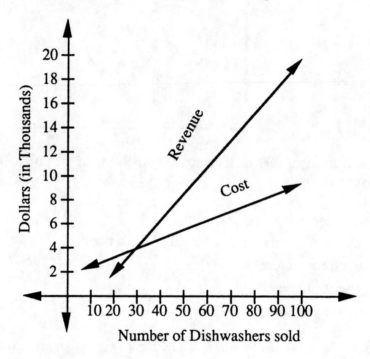

*   18.   Which of the following are statements?

   (a)   Bishop Desmond Tutu won a Nobel Peace Prize for Literature.
   (b)   Is there a Nobel Prize for physics?
   (c)   All people who work for the government are bureaucrats.
   (d) $15 + x = x + 15$

*   19.   Negate each of the following:

   (a)   *The Valley of the Horses* was written by Jean Auel.
   (b)   All realtors get commissions on houses that they sell.
   (c)   There exists a dishonest used car salesman.
   (d) $5 - 2 \neq 3$

*   20.   Write truth tables for each of the following:

   (a) $(p \vee q) \leftrightarrow (p \rightarrow \sim q)$
   (b) $(p \rightarrow q) \rightarrow (p \wedge \sim q)$
   (c) $(p \vee q) \wedge (r)$

*   21.   Decide whether or not each of the following are equivalent.

   (a) $[(\sim q \rightarrow \sim p) \wedge \sim q]; \ p$
   (b) $(p \rightarrow q) \wedge \sim q; \ p$

* 22. Write the converse, inverse, and the contrapositive of the following: If Michele Pfeifer is Catwoman, then she came from Gotham City.

* 23. Find a valid conclusion for the following argument:

    (a) If you do not understand a problem, then you can solve it.
         You cannot solve a problem.
    (b) No students like 8:00 classes.
         You like 8:00 classes.
    (c) It always snows in Montana.
         I will go skiing if it snows in Montana.
         If I go skiing, then I will get cold.

* 24. Write the following argument symbolically and then determine its validity.

    If I pay attention to my job, I will get a salary increase.
    If I shirk my job, then I will not get a salary increase.
    I shirk my job.
    Therefore, I did not pay attention to my job.

* 25. Determine whether or not each of the following arguments is valid.

    (a) If you do not understand this test, then you enjoy logic.
         You do not enjoy logic.
         Therefore, you understand this test.
    (b) No dogs are cats.
         All cats are finicky.
         Therefore, no dogs are finicky.
    (c) If I eat a piece of fudge, I will gain weight.
         I will not gain weight.
         Therefore, I ate a piece of fudge.

Sample Test

1. Convert each of the following to base ten.

    (a)   MXLV   *(b) 211_{four} *(c) $T20_{twelve}$
    *(d) 101_{two} *(e) 210_{six} (f)   CMII

2. Convert each of the following base ten numerals to numerals in the indicated system.

    (a)   128 to Roman   *(b)   346 to base five
    *(c)   440 to base eight   *(d)   127 to base twelve

3. Simplify each of the following, if possible. Write your answers in exponential form, that is, a^b.

    (a) $3^3 \cdot 3^5 \cdot 3^5$ (b) $3^{13} \cdot 3^{13}$ (c) $4^3 + 3 \cdot 4^3$

4. For each of the following, identify the whole-number properties which are illustrated.

    (a) $2 \cdot (3+4) = 2 \cdot (4+3)$ (b) $5+7 = 7+5$
    (c) $1 \cdot 14 = 14 = 14 \cdot 1$ (d) $5 \cdot (9+3) = 5 \cdot 9 + 5 \cdot 3$
    (e) $2 + (3+2) = (2+3) + 2$ (f) $5 \cdot (3 \cdot 4) = (5 \cdot 3) \cdot 4$

5. Using the definition of less than or greater than, prove that each of the following inequalities is true.

    (a) $5 < 7$ (b) $18 > 14$

▶ 6. Explain why the product $12 \cdot 100$ namely, 1200 has zeroes in the tens and unit places.

7. Use both the scratch and traditional algorithms to perform each of the following.

    (a)   542   *(b) 312_{five}
           889   434_{five}
        + 611   + 311_{five}

8. Use both the lattice and traditional multiplication algorithms to perform each of the following.

    (a)   512   *(b) 213_{six}
         x   32   x 52_{six}

9. Use both the repeated subtraction and the traditional algorithms to perform each of the following.

    (a) $12\overline{)312}$ *(b) $101_{two}\overline{)10011_{two}}$

10. Use the division algorithm to check your answers in Problem 9.

11. For each of the following base ten numerals, tell the place value for each of the circled digits.

   (a)   3⑥7 2   (b)   5③9 1 0   (c)   2 3④2

12. For each of the following, find all possible whole-number replacements that make the following statements true.

   (a) $5 \cdot \square + 27 < 48$ (b) $944 = \square \cdot 48 + 32$
   (c) $\square \cdot (8 + 3) = \square \cdot 8 + \square \cdot 3$ (d) $28 - \square \geq 14$

13. Use the number line to perform each of the following operations.

   (a) $10 - 3$ (b) $5 + 3$
   (c) $3 \cdot 3$ *(d) $3_{\text{five}} + 4_{\text{five}}$

14. Use the distributive property of multiplication over addition and addition and subtraction facts to rename each of the following, if possible.

   (a) $2x + 4x + 7x + 5x$ (b) $6x^3 + 7x^3$
   (c) $a(b + c + d)$

15. Joyce sold 48 student tickets to the play at $3.00 each and 37 adult tickets at $5.00 each. Expenses for the play were $300. How much money was left in the account after expenses were paid?

16. What number comes after each of the following:

   *(a) $\text{T0E}_{\text{twelve}}$ *(b)   XXIX

17. Hugo's checking account at the beginning of the month had a balance of $250. During the month he wrote five checks for $15 two checks for $12, and one check for $107. He made one deposit of $62. What is his new balance?

18. Use numbers to illustrate each of the following properties of whole numbers.

   (a)   Associative Property for Addition
   (b)   Distributive Property of Multiplication over Addition
   (c)   Identity Property for Multiplication

19. Tom, Dick, and Mary decided to share expenses for a class party. Tom bought $28 worth of pizza, Dick bought $20 worth of ice cream, and Mary bought $15 worth of soft drinks. How much should each person pay in order that each of them spend the same amount and how might they accomplish this?

20. Kim's new bicycle cost $390. She paid $120 down and was to make nine equal size payments on the balance. If no interest was charged, how much were her monthly payments?

21. Jim was paid $800 a month for his first 6 months of work and then received a $20 per month raise for his next 6 months. How much money did he make for the year?

22. Sue argued that $0 \div 0 = 1$ because any number divided by itself is 1. What would you tell her?

23. Find the missing numbers in each of the following.

    (a)
    ```
      _ 4 5 _
    + 2 _ 7 2
    ─────────
      4 0 _ 8
    ```

    (b)
    ```
      _ 3 _ 2
    - 2 1 9 _
    ─────────
      3 _ 9 1
    ```

24. Which is greater $2^{10} + 2^{10}$ or 2^{20}? Explain why.

25. I am thinking of a number. If I multiply it by 8, then add 5 and subtract 9, I get 52. What is my number?

Sample Test

1. Convert each of the following to base ten.

    (a) $\overline{\text{MCD}}$ *(b) 1413_{five} *(c) $\text{T10}_{\text{twelve}}$
    *(d) 1011_{two} *(e) 101_{three} (f)   CCXXIV

2. Convert each of the following base ten numerals to numerals in the indicated system.

    (a)   454 to Roman   *(b)   200 to base five
    *(c)   590 to base twelve   *(d)   9 to base nine

3. Simplify each of the following, if possible. Write your answers in exponential form, that is a^b.

    (a) $3^4 \cdot 3^3 \cdot 3^8 \cdot 3$ (b) $4^{14} \cdot 4^{79}$ (c) $5^6 + 4 \cdot 5^6$

4. For each of the following, identify the whole-number properties which are illustrated.

    (a) $4 \cdot (6+7) = 4 \cdot (7+6)$ (b) $5 \cdot (7 \cdot 3) = (5 \cdot 7) \cdot 3$
    (c) $5 \cdot (7+3) = 5 \cdot 7 + 5 \cdot 3$ (d) $5 \cdot 1 = 5 = 1 \cdot 5$
    (e) $0+1$ is a whole number   (f) $5 \cdot (7 \cdot 3) = 5 \cdot (3 \cdot 7)$

5. Using the definition of less than or greater than, prove each of the following is true.

    (a) $18 < 22$ (b) $1 > 0$

6. June claims that $1 \div 0 = 1$ because one divided by nothing is still one. How would you help her?

7. Use both the scratch and traditional algorithms to perform each of the following.

    (a)   362   *(b) 214_{five}
             78 232_{five}
            534 $+ 223_{\text{five}}$
          $+\ \ 79$

8. Use both lattice and traditional multiplication to perform each of the following.

    (a)   518   *(b) 212_{five}
          $\times\ 342$ $\times\ \ 23_{\text{five}}$

9. Use both the repeated subtraction and the traditional algorithms to perform each of the following.

    (a) $8\overline{)3648}$ *(b) $12_{\text{three}}\overline{)2021_{\text{three}}}$

10. Use the division algorithm to check your answers in Problem 9.

11. For each of the following base ten numerals, tell the place value for each of the circled digits.

    (a)   2 5 2⑧4   (b)   1 3②5 8 3   (c)   5 2 8⓪

12. For each of the following, find all possible whole-number replacements that make the following statements true.

    (a) $5 + \square = \square + 5$ (b) $123 = 7 \cdot 17 + \square$
    (c) $2 \cdot \square + 15 < 27$ (d) $18 - \square \geq 13$

13. Use the number line to perform each of the following operations.

    (a) $2 + 4$ (b) $8 - 4$
    (c) $4 \cdot 2$ *(d) $3_{five} \cdot 2_{five}$

14. Use the distributive property of multiplication over addition and addition and subtraction facts to rename each of the following, if possible.

    (a) $5x^2 + 2x^2 + 7x^2$ (b) $8x + 9x + 11x + 9x$
    (c) $(a + b)(c + d)$

15. What number comes before each of the following?

    (a)   DCLXV   *(b) $E0E_{twelve}$

16. Use numbers to illustrate each of the following properties of whole numbers.

    (a)   Identity Property for Addition
    (b)   Associative Property for Multiplication
    (c)   Commutative Property for Addition

17. Sam's operating expenses for driving a car are $40 per week. If his expenses for driving a motorcycle for 52 weeks are $1650 how much did he save for the 52 week period?

18. Christen scored 6 more points in a basketball game than Molly. If Molly doubled the number of points she scored, the result would equal Christen's points. How many points did Molly score?

19. Tina had $103 in her checking account. She wrote 3 checks for $5 and 2 checks for $18. She then deposited $19. What was her balance?

20. Sandy took a seven day trip on which she drove 120 miles the first day. Each day after the first she drove 20 miles more than the day before. How many total miles did she drive?

21 . Find the missing numbers in each of the following.

(a)
```
    _3_5
  + 482_
    7_89
```

(b)
```
   865_
  -_2_2
   5_72
```

22. Which is greater $2^{20} + 2^{20}$, $3 \cdot 2^{20}$, or 2^{21}? Why?

23. I am thinking of a number. If I add 3, multiply the result by 15 and then subtract 25, I get 200. What is my number?

24. Why is a front-end estimate before doing the adjustment always less than the actual answer?

25. If 10 is removed from the set of whole numbers, is the set closed with respect to multiplication? Why?

Sample Test

1. Find the additive inverse of each of the following.

   (a) $^-7$ (b) x (c) $2 + x$ (d) $x - y$

2. Perform the following operations:

   (a) $(^-12 - {}^-18) + 4$ (b) $-3(-2) - 2$ (c) $^-12 - 3(^-4) + 2\,(^-8)$

   (d) $(3)6 + (^-3)2$ (e) $(-4)4 - 44$ (f) $(^-7 - 3)(7 - 3)$

3. For each of the following find all integer values of x, that make the equation or inequality true.

   (a) $x + (^-5)$ (b) $x^2 = 9$ (c) $|x| = 7$

   (d) $|^-x| = 5$ (e) $4 - 3x < 2x + 84$ (f) $|x + 2| = 7$

   (g) $-3(^-2x + {}^-7) = -3 + 7$ (h) $(x - 3)^2 = 64$

▶ 4. Use a pattern approach to explain why $(^-3)\cdot(4) = {}^-12$.

5. Factor each of the following expressions.

   (a) $5x - 3x^2$ (b) $25 - x^2$

   (c) $(a +1)(a - b) + (a + 1)$ (d) $5 + 5x$

▶ 6. Use any method to demonstrate that $(^-1)(^-1) = 1$.

7. Use the concept of the additive inverse to explain why $^-(^-a) = a$.

▶ 8. Evaluate the following when $x = {}^-3$, if possible.

   (a) ^-x (b) $|x|$ (c) x^2

   (d) $^-x^2$ (e) $(^-x)^2$ (f) $0 + x$

9. Multiply each of the following and simplify your answer.

   (a) $(b + 3d)(b - 3d)$ (b) $(^-4j + 2k)(^-4j - 2k)$

▶ 10. Classify each of the following as true or false, where a and b are any integers. If false, tell why.

   (a) If $ac > bc$, then $a > b$.

   (b) If $^-x > {}^-7$, then $x > 7$.

   (c) If $^-3x + 72x + 14 = 0$ then
   $^-3x +7 + {}^-72x +14 + {}^-7 = 0$.

   (d) $|x|$ is always equal to x.

   (e) $-12 - {}^-7 = {}^-5$.

   (f) $a^2 + b^2 = (a + b)(a + b)$

   (g) $a^2 - b^2 = (a + b)(a - b)$

11. Solve each of the following for x, if x is an integer:

(a) $x + 7 = 34 - 2x$ (b) $|x + 3| = 13$ (c) $5x - 6 > 3x + 4$

12. Classify each of the following as true or false. If false, tell why.

(a)   All whole numbers are integers.
(b)   Subtraction is commutative on the set of integers.
(c)   Multiplication is associative on the set of integers.
(d)   The set of integers is closed with respect to division.

13. What conditions must be satisfied so that the product of two integers is positive?

14. Find a counterexample to disprove each of the properties on the set of integers.

(a)   The inverse property of multiplication.
(b)   The commutative property of subtraction.

15. In the football game, O.J. Simpson gained 5 yards on each of 2 plays, gained 16 yards on one play, made no gain on one play and lost 9 yards on one play. How many total yards did he end up with for the day?

16. The temperature dropped 15 degrees from the high temperature to $^-6°$ C. What was the high temperature?

17. Two cars have the same size fuel tank. Each car starts out on a trip with a full tank and after 345 miles, one car has used 10 gallons while the other has used 13 gallons. One car now has twice as much fuel remaining as the other. What size are the fuel tanks?

18. After Freon was added to a freezer, the temperature dipped from $10°$ to $^-30°$. What was the change in temperature?

19. A pound of rose food costs $2. A pound of enriched compost costs $6. If Jernigan's Greenhouses wishes to sell 20 pounds of a mixture of the two as fertilizer at $3 per pound, how much of each should they use?

20. Nancy has a collection of quarters and pennies. She has nine fewer pennies than six times the number of her quarters. If she has $4.56, how many of each type of coin does she have?

21. The sum of two integers is 14. Their difference is 8. What are the integers?

22. Demonstrate the addition $^-5 + ^-3 = ^-8$ using each of the following models:

(a)   Number line
(b)   Charged field
(c)   Chip

Sample Test

1. Find the additive inverse of each of the following.

   (a) 13   (b) ⁻x   (c) ⁻3 + x   (d) ⁻x + y

2. Perform each of the following operations:

   (a) 5 - ⁻3 + 13   (b) 6·(⁻8) + (⁻5)   (c) ⁻8 + 3·(⁻2) - (⁻8)·(⁻2)

   (d) $(⁻5)^8 + (⁻5)^6$ (e) $8^3 + (⁻8)^3$ (f) (⁻8 + 6)·(⁻8 - 6)

3. For each of the following find all integer values of x, if they exist, that make the equations true.

   (a) ⁻x − 3 = ⁻8   (b) $x^3 = ⁻27$

   (c) $|x| = 16$ (d) $|x| = 9$

   (e) $8 − 5x < 2x − 20$ (f) $|⁻x + 5| = 8$

   (g) ⁻6·(3x + ⁻2) ≤ 2x − 48   (h) $(x − 2)^4 = 16$

4. Factor each of the following expressions.

   (a) $9x^2 − 3x$ (b) $4x^2 − 9$

   (c) $(a + 1)·x + (a + 1)$ (d) $11x − 11$

5. Solve each of the following for x, if x is an integer.

   (a) $|x − 1| = 20$ (b) $4x + 3 > 0$ (c) ⁻1(x − 6) < ⁻1(2x − 2)

6. Use the concept of the additive inverse to prove that (⁻a)b = ⁻(ab).

7. (a) Show that $(x + y)·(x + y) = x^2 + 2xy + y^2$

   (b) Use the result in (a) to compute $(⁻5 + 2a)(⁻5 + 2a)$

8. Evaluate the following when x = ⁻2, if possible.

   (a) ⁻x^2 (b) $|⁻x|$ (c) ⁻$|x|$

   (d) x^3 (e) $(⁻x)^3$ (f) $2x^3$

9. Classify each of the following as true or false. If false, tell why.

   (a) If a > b then a+c > b+c.   (e) ⁻5 - 8 · 3 = ⁻39

   (b) If ⁻x > 2 then x > ⁻2.   (f) $a^2 · b^2 = (ab)^2$

   (c) If 3x = 6 then ⁻6x = 12.   (g) $a^2 − b^2 = (a − b)(a − b)$

   (d) | ⁻x | is always equal to ⁻x.

10. Classify each of the following as true or false. If false, tell why.

    (a) Every integer is a whole number.
    (b) Subtraction is associative on the set of integers.
    (c) Multiplication is closed on the set of integers.
    (d) Addition is commutative on the set of integers.

11. Find a counter-example to disprove each of the properties on the set of integers.

    (a) The associative property of division.
    (b) The distributive property of division over addition.

12. What conditions must be satisfied so that the product of two integers is negative?

13. Use a pattern approach to explain why $(^-2)(^-4) = 8$

14. Ann had a balance of $25 in her checking account. She wrote three checks for $5.00 each, one check for $28, and two checks for $22 each. What was her new balance?

15. The temperature was 18° C and it dropped 37° C. What was the new temperature?

16. The temperature dropped 37° C from the high temperature to reach a low of $^-8$° C. What was the high temperature?

17. Nathan has 86 stuffed envelopes to mail, some of which weigh three ounces each and some which weigh five ounces each. If the total weight of the envelopes is 19 pounds, 12 ounces, how many envelopes of each weight does he have?

18. Bill mixes 40 pounds of nuts worth 60¢/pound with 60 pounds of nuts worth 45¢/pound. How much should he sell them for in order to make the same amount of money as when he sold the nuts separately?

19. Lakeside High School has 178 students. There are twice as many juniors as freshmen. There are as many sophomores as there are freshmen and seniors combined. There are eight more seniors than freshmen. How many freshmen, how many sophomores, how many juniors and how many seniors are there at the high school?

20. The difference between two integers is 22. The greater integer is equal to three times the smaller integer plus 8. What are the two integers?

21. Demonstrate $^-8 + 2 = ^-6$ using the following models.

    (a) Number line
    (b) Charged field
    (c) Chip

Sample Test

1. Determine all possible digits to fill in the blanks to make each of the following true.

   (a) $7|728\_$ (b) $9|482\_$ (c) $11|5\_63$

   (d) $6|24\_35$ (e) $4|63\_$ (f) $8|632\_$

2. Let N be the three-digit number whose hundreds digit is a, tens digit is b, and units digit is c. If $3|(a + b + c)$, prove that $3|N$.

3. Classify each of the following as true or false. If false, give a counterexample or tell why.

   (a) If a and b are different, then GCD(a, b) = 1.
   (b) If a and b are even, then GCD(a, b) = 2.
   (c) If $a|b$, then LCM(a, b) = a.
   (d) If $6|a$ then $12|a$.
   (e) $0|a$ for all natural numbers a.
   (f) $a|0$ for all natural numbers a.

4. Circle the given numbers that divide 888,888.

   2, 3, 4, 5, 6, 7, 8, 9, 10, 11, 12, 15, 22, 25

▶ 5. Find the least whole number with exactly seven positive divisors and explain why it is the least.

6. Determine whether each of the following numbers is prime or composite.

   (a) 219   (b) 791
   (c) 1001   (d) 91

7. Find each of the following

   (a) GCD(38, 57)   (b) LCM(38, 57)
   (c) GCD(12, 26, 65)   (d) LCM(12, 26, 65)

8. Use the Euclidean Algorithm to find the GCD of 76 and 19,192.

9. If $a = 2^3 \cdot 3^7 \cdot 5^3 \cdot 11^4$ and $b = 2^2 \cdot 3^5 \cdot 7^2 \cdot 11 \cdot 13,$, find the following.

   (a) GCD(a, b)   (b) LCM(a, b)

10. What is the greatest prime that must be checked in order to determine if each of the following is prime?

    (a) 1317   (b) 241

11. Find all positive divisors of 280.

12. Describe a divisibility test for 35.

13. Jane cut her cake into 6 pieces of equal size. Lori cut her cake into 8 pieces of equal size. If the cakes must now be cut so that they are identical, into how many pieces should each cake be cut?

14. In their freshman years, Jacqueline took 43 credit hours and Jean took 47 credit hours. If Jacqueline took only 5-credit courses and Jean took only 3-credit courses after their freshman years, how many credits did they have when they had the same number?

* 15. Christmas falls on Monday this year. On what day will it fall next year if next year is a leap year?

* 16. Find the remainder for each of the following.

(a) 7^{100} is divided by 9

(b) 19^{1990} is divided by 14

(c) 19^{1991} is divided by 20

Sample Test

1. Determine all possible digits to fill in the blanks to make each of the following true.

   (a) $3|\_543$ (b) $9|24\_3$ (c) $11|8\_61$
   (d) $6|7\_4$ (e) $4|28\_20$ (f) $5|37,28\_$

2. Prove the test for divisibility for 4 for a 3-digit number n such that $n = a \cdot 10^2 + b \cdot 10^1 + c$.

3. Classify each of the following as true or false. If false, give a counterexample or tell why.

   (a) GCD(a, a) = a for all a $\in$ W.
   (b) LCM(a, a) = a for all a $\in$ W.
   (c) If LCM(a, b) = ab, then GCD(a, b) = 1.
   (d) If LCM(a, b) = 1, then a =1 and b = 1 if a, b $\in$ W.
   (e) If 6|a and 2|a, then 12|a.
   (f) If 2|a, 3|a and 7|a, then 42|a.

4. Circle the given numbers that divide 653,430.

   2, 3, 4, 5, 6, 7, 8, 9, 10, 11, 12, 15, 22, 25

5. Find the least whole number with exactly 3 distinct prime divisors.

6. Determine whether each of the following numbers is prime or composite.

   (a) 231   (b) 393   (c) 1141   (d) 199

7. Find each of the following.

   (a) GCD(67,75)   (b) LCM(67,75)
   (c) GCD(156, 84, 292)   (d) LCM(156, 84, 292)

8. Use the Euclidean Algorithm to find the GCD of 120 and 468,468.

9. If $a = 5^2 \cdot 7 \cdot 11 \cdot 13$ and $b = 2^3 \cdot 5^2 \cdot 7^3 \cdot 17$, find the following.

   (a) GCD(a, b)   (b) LCM(a,b)

10. What is the greatest prime that must be checked in order to determine if each of the following is prime?

    (a) 231   (b) 1811

11. Find all positive divisors of 244.

▶ 12. Describe a divisibility test for 33.

13 . Becky's class size will be either 16, 24, or 32 students. She would like to bring exactly enough treats to have available an equal number for each student. What is the minimum number she should bring?

14. Joel's dog barks every 9 minutes. Billy's dog barks every 15 minutes. They both barked at exactly 2:00 P.M.. When is the next time they will bark at the same time?

* 15. Christmas is on Tuesday this year. In how many years will it be on Friday if no leap years are involved?

* 16. Find the remainders for each of the following.

   (a) $13^{100} \cdot 12^{88}$ is divided by 11
   (b) 2^{64} is divided by 4
   (c)   100! is divided by 98!

Sample Test

1. For each of the following, draw a diagram illustrating the fraction.

    (a) $\dfrac{1}{6}$

    (b) $\dfrac{5}{7}$

2. Write three rational numbers equal to $\dfrac{4}{5}$.

3. Reduce each of the following rational numbers to simplest form.

    (a) $\dfrac{36}{48}$

    (b) $\dfrac{\left(cy^3\right)^2}{dy^2}$

    (c) $\dfrac{0}{3}$

    (d) $\dfrac{204}{51}$

    (e) $\dfrac{b^2 + x}{b^3 + bx}$

    (f) $\dfrac{29}{57}$

4. Place $>$, $<$, or $=$ between each of the following pairs to make true sentences.

    (a) $\dfrac{4}{5}$ and $\dfrac{120}{150}$

    (b) $\dfrac{3}{4}$ and $\dfrac{5}{6}$

    (c) $\dfrac{^-6}{5}$ and $\dfrac{^-7}{6}$

    (d) $\dfrac{^-4}{20}$ and $\dfrac{4}{^-20}$

    (e) $\dfrac{0}{10}$ and $\dfrac{0}{3}$

    (f) $\left(\dfrac{6}{5}\right)^{30}$ and $\left(\dfrac{5}{4}\right)^{30}$

5. Perform each of the following computations. Leave your answers in simplest form.

    (a) $\dfrac{2}{3} + \dfrac{4}{5}$

    (b) $\dfrac{3}{4} - \dfrac{2}{3}$

    (c) $\dfrac{5}{3} \cdot \dfrac{27}{40}$

    (d) $\dfrac{14}{5} \div \dfrac{2}{3}$

    (e) $\left(3\dfrac{1}{4} + 7\dfrac{1}{8}\right) \div 8\dfrac{1}{2}$

6. Find the additive and multiplicative inverses for each of the following.

    (a) 8

    (b) $3\dfrac{1}{2}$

    (c) $\dfrac{^-1}{4}$

    (d) $\dfrac{8}{3}$

7. Simplify each of the following. Write your answer in the simplest form .

    (a) $\dfrac{\dfrac{2}{3} + \dfrac{3}{4}}{\dfrac{1}{5} - \dfrac{1}{6}}$

    (b) $\dfrac{\dfrac{2}{3} \cdot \dfrac{3}{5}}{\dfrac{1}{5}}$

8. Solve each of the following for x, where x is a real number.

   (a) $5\left(\dfrac{1}{x}+\dfrac{1}{3}\right)=5$

   (b) $\dfrac{2}{3}x-\dfrac{3}{4}\le\dfrac{1}{2}(2-3x)$

9. The ratio of boys to girls in Mr. Joiner's class is 5 to 7. If there are 15 boys in the class, how many total students are in the class?

10. Write each of the following in simplest form with nonnegative exponents in the final answer.

    (a) $\left(\dfrac{1}{3}\right)^{5}\cdot 3^{-5}$

    (b) $5^{4}\div 5^{-4}$

    (c) $16^{2}\cdot 8^{-2}$

    (d) $\left(a^{-2}+b^{-2}\right)^{-1}$

11. Sunflower seeds are packed in packages each weighing $3\dfrac{1}{4}$ ounces. If there is a supply of $15\dfrac{1}{2}$ pounds of sunflower seeds, how many packages of seeds can be packed? How many ounces of sunflower seeds will be left over? (16 oz. = 1 pound)

12. A student says that he found a quick way to divide mixed numbers. He demonstrates his method as follows

$$9\dfrac{1}{4}\div 3\dfrac{3}{4}=3\dfrac{1}{3}\text{ since }9\div 3=3\text{ and }\dfrac{1}{4}\div\dfrac{3}{4}=\dfrac{1}{3},$$
$$20\dfrac{3}{5}\div 4\dfrac{3}{5}=5\dfrac{1}{1}\text{ since }20\div 4=5\text{ and }\dfrac{3}{5}\div\dfrac{3}{5}=1$$

   Is the student correct? Why or why not?

13. Estimate each of the following, indicating if the actual answer is greater than (+) or less than (-) the estimate.

    (a) $\dfrac{199}{198}+\dfrac{35}{17}$

    (b) $4\dfrac{10}{11}+3\dfrac{8}{9}+\dfrac{13}{14}+\dfrac{1}{20}$

    (c) $5\dfrac{19}{20}-2\dfrac{9}{10}+1\dfrac{1}{100}$

14. Estimate by rounding the fractions.

    (a) $7\dfrac{8}{9}\cdot 5\dfrac{1}{13}$

    (b) $3\dfrac{19}{39}\cdot 4$

    (c) $\dfrac{34\dfrac{9}{10}}{4\dfrac{9}{10}}$

    (d) $\dfrac{14\dfrac{19}{39}}{\dfrac{19}{39}}$

15. A plumber needs four sections of pipe $2\dfrac{7}{8}$ feet long. Can this be cut from a 12 foot section? If so, how much pipe will be left over? If not, why not?

16. Heidi's class had 17 A's out of 30 students and Barbara's class had 15 A's out of 27 students. Which class had the higher ratio of A's? Why?

17. Mable read 20 pages of a book in 15 minutes. If she continues to read at the same rate, how many pages will she read in 25 minutes?

18. Valerie can weed the lawn in 3 hours and Jim can weed the lawn in 5 hours. If they work together and continue at these rates, how long would it take to weed the lawn?

Sample Test

1. Reduce each of the following rational numbers to simplest form.

   (a) $\dfrac{6^2}{48}$

   (b) $\dfrac{(xy)^2}{x^{-2}y^2}$

   (c) $\dfrac{xy^{-3}}{x^3y^{-2}}$

   (d) $\dfrac{3x + 9x^2}{x + 3x^2}$

2. Perform each of the following computations.

   (b) $\dfrac{3}{8} + \dfrac{7}{12}$

   (b) $1 - \dfrac{1}{2} + \dfrac{1}{3} - \dfrac{1}{4} + \dfrac{1}{5} - \dfrac{1}{6}$

   (c) $\left(5\dfrac{2}{7} + 2\dfrac{3}{7}\right) \div 2\dfrac{1}{2}$

   (d) $\dfrac{3}{2} \cdot 4\dfrac{1}{3}$

3. If possible, find the additive and multiplicative inverses for each of the following.

   (a) $3\dfrac{7}{8}$

   (b) $\dfrac{^{-}3}{4}$

   (c) $\dfrac{0}{1}$

   (d) $\dfrac{1}{x^2}$

4. Simplify each of the following. Write your answer in the form $\dfrac{a}{b}$ where a and b are integers and $\dfrac{a}{b}$ is reduced to its simplest form.

   (a) $\dfrac{\dfrac{2}{3} - \dfrac{1}{6}}{\dfrac{2}{3} + \dfrac{1}{6}}$

   (b) $\dfrac{\dfrac{2}{9} \cdot \dfrac{3}{4}}{\left(\dfrac{2}{3}\right)^2}$

   (c) $\dfrac{\left(\dfrac{1}{2}\right)^2 + \left(\dfrac{2}{4}\right)^2}{\dfrac{1}{2} + \dfrac{3}{4}}$

5. Solve for x in $\dfrac{3}{4}x \geq \dfrac{1}{5} + \dfrac{x}{2}$.

▶ 6. Is the following statement true or false? (Justify your answer.) For all positive integers a, b such that $b \geq 2, \dfrac{a+1}{b-1} > \dfrac{a}{b}$.

7. Solve each of the following for x:

   (a) $\dfrac{x}{3} \geq x$

   (b) $\dfrac{3}{4}\left(\dfrac{2}{3}x - 1\right) \geq \dfrac{1}{2} - x$

   (c) $\dfrac{3}{20} = \dfrac{3+x}{5}$

8. Write the following in simplest form with nonnegative exponents in the final answer.

(a) $\left(\dfrac{1}{2}\right)^6\left(\dfrac{1}{8}\right)^{-4}$

(b) $\left(\left(\dfrac{2}{3}\right)^4\right)^{-2}$

(c) $\dfrac{\left(\dfrac{2}{3}\right)^{-4}}{\left(\dfrac{3}{2}\right)^6}$

9. A car travels 55 miles per hour and a plane travels 15 miles per minute. How far does the car travel when the plane travels 500 miles?

10. A $46\dfrac{5}{16}$ lb bag of nuts is packaged into $1\dfrac{3}{4}$ lb containers. The remaining nuts are given to the person packing the nuts. How much does the person get? Justify your answer.

11. If the ratio of boys to girls in a class is 3 to 8, will the ratios of boys to girls change, become greater, or become smaller if 2 boys and 2 girls leave the class? Justify your answer.

12. Estimate each of the following, indicating if the actual answer is greater than (+) or less than (-) the estimate.

(a) $\dfrac{29}{15}+\dfrac{198}{199}$

(b) $5\dfrac{12}{13}+2\dfrac{9}{10}+\dfrac{19}{20}$

(c) $10\dfrac{4}{9}-5\dfrac{1}{2}+\dfrac{99}{100}$

13. Estimate each of the following.

(a) $7\dfrac{33}{100}\cdot 3$

(b) $2\dfrac{25}{99}\cdot 8$

(c) $\dfrac{\dfrac{25}{13}}{2\dfrac{1}{100}}$

(d) $\dfrac{4\dfrac{10}{99}}{\dfrac{1}{10}}$

14. Place <, >, or = between each of the following pairs to make true statements.

(a) $\dfrac{11}{23}$ and $\dfrac{33}{65}$

(b) $\dfrac{7}{8}$ and $\dfrac{8}{9}$

(c) $-\dfrac{6}{7}$ and $-\dfrac{11}{13}$

(d) $\left(\dfrac{3}{4}\right)^5$ and $\left(\dfrac{4}{5}\right)^5$

15. The ratio of oranges to apples in the gift basket is 3 to 5. If there are 9 oranges, how many apples are there?

16. If $9\dfrac{1}{8}$ lb of nails cost $4.25, what is the cost of 292 lb?

17. Tom can paint the house in 15 days. Tom and Dick working together can paint the house in 12 days. If both Tom and Dick always work at these rates, how long would it take Dick to paint the house working alone?

18. The ratio of private school students to public school students in Adams City is 3 to 20. If there are 16,020 total students, how many are in private schools?

Sample Test

1. Place >, <, or = between each of the following pairs to make true sentences.

   (a) $4.\overline{9}$ and 5   (b) $0.\overline{44}$ and $\dfrac{1}{25}$ (c) $0.\overline{46}$ and $0.4\overline{6}$ (d) $\sqrt{3}$ and 1.7

2. Perform each of the following computations.

   (a)   3.0001 - 0.998   (b)   0.14 + 2.157 + 36.001 - 0.04
   (c)   0.04 · 3.62   (d)   2.178 ÷ 0.13   (to nearest tenth)

3. Find the additive and multiplicative inverses for each of the following.

   (a)   4.2   (b)   0.36

4. Write each of the following in expanded form:

   (a)   16.47   (b)   0.008

5. Solve each of the following for x, where x is a real number.

   (a) $x\sqrt{3} - 2 = 5x\sqrt{3}$ (b) $0.4x - 0.68 \geq \dfrac{1}{2}(x - 3.8)$

   (c)   16% of x is 3200   (d)   11 is x percent of 55
   (e)   13 is 50% of x   (f) $0.\overline{4} + x = 1$
   (g) $0.\overline{9} - x = 1$ (h) $5.2x - 0.01 < 0.2x + 3.6$

6. Use fractions to justify the algorithm for the subtraction in the following.

   $$\begin{array}{r} 23.6 \\ -\ \ 8.34 \\ \hline \end{array}$$

7. A roll of ribbon three meters long is to be made into 16 bows of equal size. If all of the ribbon is to be used, how long is the piece of ribbon for each bow?

8. Answer each of the following.

   (a)   7 is what percent of 3.5?
   (b)   What is 210% of 50?
   (c)   18 is 40% of what number?

9. Change each of the following to percents.

   (a) $\dfrac{1}{5}$ (b) $\dfrac{3}{80}$ (c)   5.36   (d)   0.013

10. Change each of the following percents to decimals.

    (a)   40%   (b) $\frac{1}{6}$%   (c)   200%

11. Round each of the following numbers as specified.

    (a)   508.576 to the nearest hundredth   (b)   508.576 to the nearest tenth
    (c)   508.576 to the nearest hundred

12. Convert each of the following rational numbers to the form $\frac{a}{b}$ where a and b are integers and b ≠ 0.

    (a)   0.27   (b)   3.104   (c) $0.2\overline{4}$ (d)   0. 24

13. Convert each of the following fractions to decimals that either terminate or repeat.

    (a) $\frac{3}{40}$ (b) $\frac{3}{24}$ (c) $\frac{2}{13}$

▶ 14. Is the set of irrational numbers closed under multiplication? Explain your answer.

15. Find an approximation for $\sqrt{15}$ rounded to the nearest thousandth.

16. Write each of the following in scientific notation.

    (a)   5,268,000   (b)   0.000325

17. Classify each of the following as a rational or irrational number.

    (a)   6.76776777677776...   (b) $\frac{1}{\sqrt{15}}$

    (c) $\frac{8}{3}$ (d)   0.22332233...

18. Judy received an REI dividend of 9.7% of her purchases. If her dividend was $55.05, what was the sum of her purchases during the year?

19. Great Home Realty receives a 7% commission on each piece of property it sells. If it sold a house for $132,000, how much commission did the real estate office receive?

20. The teacher was hired at a salary of $18,200 and was to receive raises of 5.5% after the first year and 4% after the second year. What should her salary be after the two-year period?

21. Tony took an 80-item test and missed 18 questions. What percent did he get correct?

22. For a promotional boost, a store is offering successive discounts of 6%, 9%, and 15% in any order you wish. What order should you choose?

23. What is the number of significant digits in each of the following:

    (a)   3,287,000   (b)   3,028   (c)   0.0328   (d)   2.380

* 24. Find the simplest form for each of the following.

    (a) $\sqrt{363}$ b) $\sqrt{576}$ (c) $\sqrt{480}$ (d) $\sqrt[3]{343}$

* 25. Write each of the following in simplest form with non-negative exponents in the final answer.

    (a) $\left(\dfrac{1}{3}\right)^3 \cdot \left(\dfrac{1}{3}\right)^8$ (b) $5^{-12} \div 5^{-3}$ (c) $\left(\left(\dfrac{1}{4}\right)^{-3}\right)^5$ (d) $5^{19} \cdot 5^7$

26. Charles bought a new car and sold if two years later for 41% less than he paid for it. He sold it for $7,130. How much did he pay for it originally?

* 27. A credit union offered a saving account that paid 8% annual interest compounded quarterly. What is the value, rounded to the nearest cent, of $500 if it is left in the account for exactly 2 years?

Sample Test

1. Place >, <, or = between each of the following pairs to make true sentences.

   (a) $2.\overline{23}$ and $\sqrt{5}$

   (b) $0.\overline{3}$ and $\dfrac{1}{3}$

   (c) $0.\overline{4} + 0.\overline{5}$ and 1

   (d) $3.\overline{78}$ and $3.7\overline{8}$

2. Perform each of the following computations.

   (a) $5.082 - 0.34$

   (b) $(3.2) \cdot (3.4) + .001 - 15.3$

   (c) $\dfrac{(2.4) \cdot (0.03)}{0.6}$

   (d) $2.782 \div 0.23$ (to nearest tenth)

▶ 3. For which values of k can $\dfrac{k}{3840}$ can be written as a terminating decimal. Explain your reasoning.

4. Find the additive and multiplicative inverses for each of the following.

   (a) 0.4

   (b) $2.\overline{6}$

5. Solve each of the following for x, where x is a real number.

   (a) $5x\sqrt{2} - x\sqrt{2} = 7x\sqrt{2} + 5$

   (b) $\dfrac{x}{0.4} + 80 = 0.5x + 0.8$

   (c) 18% of $x = 58.32$

   (d) $0.\overline{3} + x = 0.\overline{7}$

   (e) 36 is x percent of 48

   (f) 6.6 is 30% of x

   (g) $1.\overline{9} - x = 2$

   (h) $x - \dfrac{0.5}{3} = \dfrac{1}{3}(3.7 + 2x)$

6. Use fractions to justify the algorithm for the subtraction in the following.

   $8.07 - 2.3$

7. A board is 9′ $8\dfrac{1}{4}$″ long. How many $7\dfrac{3}{4}$″ blocks can be cut from this board? (Disregard the width of the cuts.)

8. Answer each of the following.

   (a) 8 is what percent of 2?
   (b) What is 25% of 8?
   (c) 12 is 60% of what number?

9. Change each of the following to percents.

   (a) $\dfrac{4}{6}$ (b) $\dfrac{5}{80}$ (c) 2.06   (d) $2.\overline{4}$

10. Change each of the following percents to decimals.

   (a) 45%   (b) $\dfrac{4}{5}\%$ (c) 320%

11. Is the set of irrational numbers closed under addition? Explain your answer.

12. Round each of the following numbers as specified.

   (a) 483.765 to the nearest hundredth
   (b) 483.765 to the nearest unit
   (c) 483.765 to the nearest hundred

13. Convert each of the following rational numbers to the form $\dfrac{a}{b}$ where a and b are integers and $b \neq 0$.

   (a) 0.38   (b) 2.607   (c) $0.4\overline{7}$ (d) $0.\overline{324}$

14. Convert each of the following fractions to decimals that either terminate or repeat.

   (a) $\dfrac{7}{30}$ (b) $\dfrac{11}{40}$ (c) $\dfrac{5}{11}$

15. Find an approximation for $\sqrt{11}$ rounded to the nearest thousandth.

16. Write each of the following in scientific notation.

   (a) 3286
   (b) 0.0000032

17. How many significant digits are there in each part of Problem 16?

18. Eight stereo speakers in a shipment of 185 were found to be defective. What percentage of the speakers were defective?

19. Classify each of the following as a rational or irrational number.

   (a) $\sqrt{2} + 8$ (b) $\dfrac{7}{22}$

   (c) $0.\overline{23}$ (d) 3.14114111411114...

20. Marcy agreed to try to sell her brother's car if he would give her a 5% commission on the selling price. If she sells the car for $3250, how much commission will she receive?

21. Audrey's salary this year is $18,200. She received a 4% raise from last year to this year. What was her last year's salary rounded to the nearest dollar?

22. Justin bought 3 old desks for $243 each. After fixing them up and refinishing them, he sold one for twice what he paid for it, one for 47% more than he paid for it, and one for 81% more than he paid for it. How much profit did he make?

23. Tony got 80% of his test questions correct. If there were 80 questions on the test, how many questions did he miss?

24. Find the simplest form for each of the following.

   (a) $\sqrt{117}$ (b) $\sqrt{700}$
   (c) $\sqrt{588}$ (d) $\sqrt[3]{192}$

* 25. Write each of the following in simplest form with non-negative exponents in the final answer.

   (a) $\left(\dfrac{2}{5}\right)^3 \cdot \left(\dfrac{2}{5}\right)^8$ (b) $\left(3^2 \cdot 3^3\right)^2 \div 3^3$

   (c) $\left(5^{-3} + 5^{-5}\right)^{-1}$ (d) $\left(\left(\dfrac{2}{3}\right)^{-3}\right)^{-4}$

▶ 26. A bank offers a CD (certificate of deposit) which pays $8\frac{1}{2}\%$ simple interest and it offers a CD which pays 8% interest compounded quarterly. You have $1000 to invest.

   (a)   Which should you choose if you want to invest for one year?
   (b)   Which should you choose if you want to invest for three years?

   Explain your answers.

* 27. A credit union offered a saving account that paid 6% annual interest compounded monthly. What is the value, rounded to the nearest cent, of $800 if it is left in the account for exactly 1 year?

Sample Test

1. Suppose the names of the days of the week are placed in a hat and a name is drawn at random.

   (a) List the sample space for this experiment.
   (b) List the event consisting of the outcomes that the month drawn starts with the letter T.
   (c) What is the probability of drawing the name of a month that starts with T?

2. A fair coin was flipped three times and landed heads three times. What is the probability of a head on the next toss?

3. A bag contains five red candies, six white candies, and seven blue candies. Suppose one piece of candy is drawn at random. Find the probability for each of the following.

   (a) A white candy is drawn.
   (b) A red or blue candy is drawn.
   (c) Neither a white nor a blue candy is drawn.
   (d) A red candy is not drawn.

4. One card is selected at random from an ordinary deck of 52 cards. Find the probability of each of the following events.

   (a) A heart is drawn.
   (b) A heart and a king are drawn.
   (c) A heart or a face card is drawn.
   (d) The two of heart is not drawn.

5. A box contains three blue cards and three white cards. If two cards are drawn one at a time, find the probability that both cards are blue if the draws are made as follows:

   (a) With replacement   (b) Without replacement

6. In a NASA rocket firing, the probability of the success of stage 1 is 95%, at stage 2, 97%, and at stage 3, 98%. What is the probability for success for the three-stage rocket?

7. If a letter is drawn from container 1, shown below, and placed in container 2, and then a letter is drawn from container 2, what is the probability that the letter is an S?

8. Use the containers in Problem 7. Select a container at random, and then select a letter from the chosen container. What is the probability that the letter is an S?

9. If a couple plans to have 3 children, what is the probability of having at least 2 girls?

10. If two dice are rolled 360 times, approximately how many times should you expect the sums of 2, 3, or 12?

11. A teacher has prepared a 5-item test with the first three items being true or false and the last two items being multiple choice with 4 choices each. What is the probability that a student will score 100 percent if every answer is chosen at random?

12. Two cards are drawn from an ordinary deck of 52 playing cards. What is the probability that they are both twos given the following?

   (a)   The first card is replaced before the second card is drawn.
   (b)   The first card is not replaced before the second card is drawn.

* 13. A committee of 3 is selected at random from a set consisting of 5 Democrats, 8 Republicans, and 2 Independents.

   (a)   How many choices of committee members are there?
   (b)   What is the probability that the committee consists of all Democrats?
   (c)   What is the probability that the committee consists of no Republicans?

* 14. There were 7 nominees for president and 4 nominees for vice president. In how many ways can the slate be chosen?

* 15. Compute $\dfrac{100!}{99!}$

* 16. How many different 2-person committees can be formed from a group of 6 people?

* 17. If automobile license plates consist of 2 letters followed by 4 digits, how many different possible license plates are possible if letters and numbers can be repeated?

18. Given the spinner below, find each of the following.

   (a)   P(A)   (b)   P(B)

* 19. Find the number of ways to rearrange the letters in the following words.

   (a)   CAROLYN   (b)   MATHEMATICS

20. If the odds in favor of the Rangers winning the game are 7 to 5, what is the probability that they will win?

21. Two standard dice are rolled. What are the odds in favor of rolling a sum of 10?

22. What are the odds against drawing a queen of hearts when one card is drawn from an ordinary deck of playing cards?

23. A sorority sold 132 tickets in a raffle for a $264 television set. What is the expected value of a single ticket if only one ticket wins?

24. A game consists of rolling two dice. Rolling doubles, for example (3, 3), pays $60. Rolling anything but doubles pays $6.00. What is the expected value for the game?

25. How could each of the following be simulated using a random digit table?

    (a) Tossing a fair coin.
    (b) Picking a day of the week at random.
    (c) Picking three dates at random in the month of April.

Sample Test

1. Suppose the natural numbers from 1 to 26 are placed in a hat and a number is drawn at random.

    (a)   List the sample space for this experiment.
    (b)   List the event consisting of the outcomes that the number drawn is even.
    (c)   What is the probability of drawing a number that is even?

2. What is the probability of a fair coin landing heads four times in a row?

3. A box contains 4 red marbles, 7 white marbles, and 5 blue marbles. If one marble is drawn at random, find the probability for each of the following.

    (a)   A blue marble is drawn.
    (b)   A red or a blue marble is drawn.
    (c)   Neither a red nor a blue marble is drawn.
    (d)   A blue marble is not drawn.

4. One card is drawn from an ordinary deck of 52 playing cards. Find the probability of each of the following events.

    (a)   A spade or a heart is drawn.
    (b)   A face card and a club is drawn.
    (c)   A face card or a club is drawn.
    (d)   A king is not drawn.

5. A box contains 4 red marbles, 7 white marbles, and 5 blue marbles. If 2 marbles are drawn one at a time, find the probability that both marbles are white if draws are made as follows.

    (a)   With replacement   b)   Without replacement

6. The probability of Ann passing her math test is 90%. The probability she passes her English test is 80%. The probability she passes her Chemistry test is 70%. What is the probability she passes all 3 tests?

7. If a letter is drawn from container number 1, shown below, and placed in container number 2, then a letter is drawn from container 2, what is the probability that the letter is an H?

BETH   ALVOHEZ

#1   #2

8. Use the containers in problem 7. If a letter is drawn from container number 1 and then a letter is drawn from container number 2, what is the probability of the outcome TO?

9. If a couple plans to have 3 children, what is the probability of having at least 1 boy?

10. If two dice are rolled 360 times, approximately how many times should you expect a sum which is a prime number?

11. A teacher has prepared a 6-item test with the first three items being true or false and the last three items being multiple choice with four choices each. What is the probability that a student will score 0 if every answer is chosen at random?

12. Two cards are drawn from an ordinary deck of 52 playing cards. What is the probability that they are both face cards given the following?

    (a) The first card is replaced before the second card is drawn.
    (b) The first card is not replaced before the second card is drawn.

13. A committee of 2 is selected at random from a set of people consisting of 3 Democrats, 4 Republicans, and 1 Independent.

    (a) What is the probability that the committee has no Republicans?
    (b) What is the probability that the committee has all Republicans?

14. There were 8 nominees for president and 3 nominees for vice president. In how many ways can the slate be chosen?

15. Compute $\dfrac{26!}{24!2!}$.

16. How many different 4-person committees can be formed from a group of 6 people?

17. If automobile license plates consist of 3 letters followed by 3 digits, how many different license plates are possible if letters and numbers can be repeated?

18. Given the spinner below, find each of the following.

    (a) P(A)   (b) P(B)

19. Find the number of ways to rearrange the letters in the following words.

    (a) FACTOR   (b) PROBABILITY

20. A hat contains the letters in the word GEOMETRY. If 4 letters are drawn from the hat one at a time without replacement, what are the odds against spelling the word TRY?

21. If the odds against the Tigers winning their next game are 8 to 4, what is the probability that they will win?

22. Two standard dice are rolled. What are the odds in favor of rolling a sum of 8?

23.   What are the odds against drawing a face card that is a spade when one card is drawn from an ordinary deck of playing cards?

24.   Joe's baseball team sold 200 chances to win a $250 set of golf clubs. What is the expected value of a single chance if only one chance wins?

25.   A game consists of rolling a die. If a number greater than 4 is rolled, you receive the number of dollars showing on the die. If any other number shows, you receive $1.00. What is the expected value of this game?

26.   How could each of the following be simulated using random digit table?

   (a)   Picking a letter of the alphabet at random.
   (b)   Picking one of the five oceans at random.
   (c)   Spinning the spinner shown below.

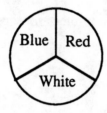

Sample Test

1. Claude paid $38.80 for dinner for himself and two friends. If one friend's meal cost twice as much as Claude's and Claude's meal cost the same as his other friend, answer the following:

   (a)   What is the mean cost of the meals?
   (b)   What is the median cost of the meals?
   (c)   What is the mode cost of the meals?

2. Find the mean, median, mode, and range of the following scores.

98	98	98	98	45
84	84	52	45	37

3. Find the Standard deviation of the scores in problem 2.

4. The budget for the Women's Center is $1,000,000. If $500,000 is spent on advertising, $150,000 is spent on conferences, and the remainder is spent on long-term securities, draw a circle graph to indicate how the money is spent.

5. If the median is higher than the mean on a set of test scores, describe the distribution.

6. The following are the weights in kilograms to the nearest tenth of Miss Brown's class. Construct an ordered stem and leaf plot for the data with the stem defined to be the whole number of kilograms.

28.3	27.3	25.6	29.0	27.4
22.7	21.9	22.4	23.7	20.9
21.5	20.1	24.1	21.2	21.9
26.4	23.5	22.5	26.4	23.6
30.1	28.7	27.5	24.6	28.2

7. Twenty test scores are shown below.

31	30	23	27	19
26	28	38	17	29
26	34	21	32	32
22	12	26	39	25

   (a)   Make a grouped frequency table for these scores, using 10 to start the first class and having interval size 5..
   (b)   Draw a histogram for the grouped data.
   (c)   Draw an ordered standard-leaf for the data.

8. The mean age of members of a class reunion was 71.9. The next year the mean age was 71.5 years. How can the mean age decrease when all the class members are a year older?

9. The mean age of 10 persons in a room is 15 years. A 50-year-old person walks in. How much is the mean increased?

10. The quiz scores for Mr. Brown's and Miss Burke's classes are given below.

   (a) Draw a line plot for each set.
   (b) Draw a back-to-back stem and leaf plot for the two classes.
   (c) Give the interquartile range for each set of scores.
   (d) Are there any outliers for either set of data? If yes, what are they?
   (e) Draw box plots to compare the two sets of data.
   (f) What can you say about the two sets of data.

Mr. Brown	Miss Burke
75	78
82	76
91	79
85	78
90	92
92	86
94	74
90	78
94	80
92	90
90	82
90	80

* 11. An advertisement claims "Four out of five doctors surveyed recommend Tielitnot for their patients with arthritis." State why you would or would not accept this as a valid claim to product superiority.

* 12. A standardized test has a mean of 500 with a standard deviation of 70. If 2000 students took the test and their scores approximated a normal curve, how many scores are between 360 and 640?

13. Explain how to determine if a score is an outlier when constructing a box plot.

* 14. On a final exam the mean was 72 with a standard deviation of 15. Find the grade corresponding to a z score of -1.

Sample Test

1. The weights in pounds of six elementary students are: 80, 92, 71, 63, 76, and 83. Find (a) the mean (b) the median (c) the mode.

2. Find the standard deviation for the weights in problem 1 to the nearest tenth of a pound.

3. The reaction times of an organism to certain stimuli were recorded as follows: 0.53, 0.46, 0.55, 0.44, 0.52, 0.49, and 0.53. What is the mode of this set of data?

4. The mean annual salary paid to the employees at Pay-Less Food Store was $5000. The mean annual salaries paid to female and male employees at the store were $5200 and $4200 respectively. Determine the percentages of females and males employed by the store.

5. The mean average for Joyce's 11 test scores was 62.5. How much will a score of 100 increase her mean average?

6. The ages at inauguration of the Presidents from 1945 to 1987 are given below. What is the mean and standard deviation for the data?

$$60, 62, 43, 55, 56, 61, 52, 69, 64.$$

7. The scores for the winners of the British open from 1981 to 1991 are given below.

Year	Score
1981	276
1982	284
1983	275
1984	276
1985	282
1986	280
1987	279
1988	273
1989	275
1990	270
1991	272

    (a) Construct a line plot for the data.
    (b) Draw a bar graph for the data.

8. The following are the weights in pounds of 30 students at the Summer Math Camp.

    (a) Construct a frequency table for the data above with the first class starting at 115 and interval size 10.
    (b) Draw a histogram depicting the data.

146	163	142	147	135	153	140	135	128	145
146	158	140	147	136	148	152	144	156	150
168	126	138	176	163	119	154	165	142	135

9. A principal remarked that no student from his school should have a mathematics score on a standardized test below the national mean. Comment on this.

10. On an exam two instructors gave the same test and both classes had the same mean. However, the standard deviation of one class was twice the standard deviation of the other class. What can you say about the classes based of this information?

11. The quiz scores for Mr. Read's and Miss Sol's classes are given below.

   (a) Draw a line plot for each set.
   (b) Draw a back-to-back stem and leaf plot for the two classes.
   (c) Give the interquartile range for each set of scores.
   (d) Are there any outliers for either set of data? If yes, what are they?
   (e) Draw box plots to compare the two sets of data.
   (f) What can you say about the two sets of data?

Mr. Read	Miss Sol
72	90
78	88
85	78
92	83
75	96
76	92
89	90
96	84
78	75
92	98
90	93
80	92

* 12. What does if mean to say that there is a positive correlation when viewing a scattergram?

* 13. Two students received z-scores of 0.8 and -0.4 respectively on a test. If their scores on the test were 88 and 64 respectively, what are the mean and standard deviation on the test?

* 14. A standardized test has a mean of 200 with a standard deviation of 50. If 1000 students took the test and their scores approximated a normal curve, how many scores are between 100 and 300?

Sample Test

1. Sketch four lines with exactly four intersection points.

2. Sketch and name two adjacent angles that are supplementary.

3. What is the least number of vertices that a polyhedron may have?

4. (a) Sketch a pentagonal pyramid.
    (b) Count the number of vertices, edges, and faces for the pyramid in part (a) and determine if Euler's Formula holds for this pyramid.

5. Classify the following as true or false. If false, tell why.

    (a) Two distinct lines that do not intersect are parallel.
    (b) No square is a rectangle.
    (c) If a plane contains one point of a line, then it must contain the entire line.
    (d) A line separates space into three distinct sets of points.
    (e) For any two distinct points A and B, $\overleftrightarrow{AB} = \overleftrightarrow{BA}$
    (f) A ray contains has no endpoints.

6. Describe each of the following sets of points with reference to the given figure.

    (a) (plane AFP) ∩ (plane XYE)
    (b) (plane XYE) ∩ $\overleftrightarrow{AE}$
    (c) $\overline{BE} \cap \overline{CE}$
    (d) $\overline{CE} \cap \triangle ADF$
    (e) $\overrightarrow{AE} \cup \overleftrightarrow{DE}$
    (f) $\overrightarrow{EB} \cup \overrightarrow{EC}$
    (g) interior (△ADF) ∩ $\overleftrightarrow{AF}$

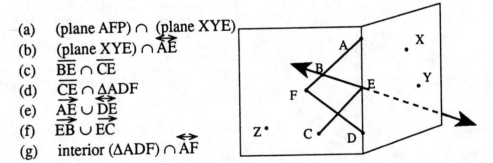

7. If the measure of an angle is 23°17'18", what is the measure of its supplement?

8. If the non-base angle of an isosceles triangle has a measure of 70°, what is the measure of each base angle?

9. How many diagonals does a decagon have?

10. If 9x° and (5x + 8)° are the measures for complementary angles, what is the measure of each angle?

11. Is a rhombus a regular polygon? Explain your answer.

12. Given the figure shown with $\overleftrightarrow{AX} \parallel \overleftrightarrow{DY}$, find the following:

  (a) m($\angle 1$)
  (b) m($\angle 2$)
  (c) m($\angle 3$)
  (d) m($\angle 4$)
  (e) m($\angle 5$)

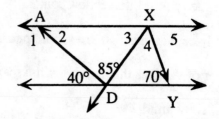

13. Determine if points A, B, and C are inside or outside the given curves. Explain how you arrived at your answer.

  (a)   (b)

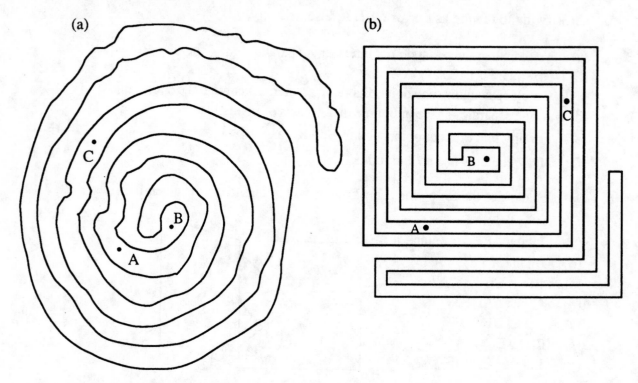

14. In the figure, how is the measure of angle 4 related to the sum of the measures of angle 1 and angle 2. Justify your answer.

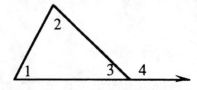

15. Which of the figures are traversable? For those that are traversable, circle all possible starting points.

(a)   (b)   (c)

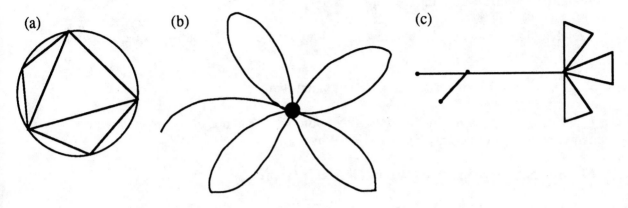

16. Draw each of the following.

    (a) A simple closed curve that is not a polygon.
    (b) A convex quadrilateral.

17. Write a Logo procedure to draw a pair of complementary angles given the measure of one angle, :A.

Sample Test

1. Sketch two angles whose intersection is exactly 3 points.

2. Sketch and name two angles that have a common vertex and a common side, but are not adjacent angles.

3. What is the number of vertices in an octagonal prism?

4. If planes α and β are distinct planes having points X, Y, and Z in common, what conclusion can you make about points X, Y, and Z? Why?

5. Classify the following as true or false. If false, tell why.

    (a) For any line $\overleftrightarrow{AB}$ and point C such that $C \varepsilon \overleftrightarrow{AB}$, there is one and only one plane containing both C and $\overleftrightarrow{AB}$.
    (b) A parallelogram has four acute angles.
    (c) A line segment contains an infinite number of points.
    (d) The union of two half lines is always a line.
    (e) For any two distinct points A and B, $\overrightarrow{AB} = \overrightarrow{BA}$.
    (f) If $\overrightarrow{AB} = \overrightarrow{CB}$, then A must be a different name for C.
    (g) Every equilateral triangle is a scalene triangle.

6. Describe each of the following sets of points with reference to the given figure.

    (a) $\alpha \cap \beta$
    (b) $\triangle ADF \cap \overleftrightarrow{BE}$
    (c) $\overline{AF} \cap \overline{BE}$
    (d) $\angle CAF \cap \overleftrightarrow{CF}$
    (e) $\overline{AE} \cup \overleftrightarrow{FE}$
    (f) $\overrightarrow{BD} \cup \overrightarrow{BA}$
    (g) interior $(\triangle ADF) \cap \overleftrightarrow{AF}$
    (h) $\overline{AE} \cup \overline{EF}$

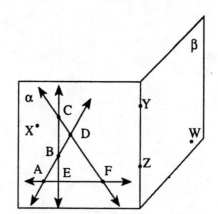

7. (a) What is the measure of each angle in a regular dodecagon?
    (b) How many diagonals does a dodecagon have?

8. Show that Euler's formula holds for an octagonal pyramid.

9. A rectangle has been defined as a parallelogram in which one of the angles is a right angle. Explain why a rectangle must have four right angles.

10. If 5x° and (7x - 12)° are the measures for vertical angles formed by two intersecting lines, what is the measure of each angle?

11. (a) Find 28°29'46" - 16°48'59".
     (b) Express 5.4° in terms of degrees, minutes, and seconds.

12. Given the figure shown with $\overleftrightarrow{AX} \parallel \overleftrightarrow{DY}$, find the following:

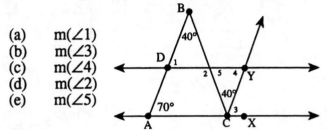

     (a) m(∠1)
     (b) m(∠3)
     (c) m(∠4)
     (d) m(∠2)
     (e) m(∠5)

13 . Determine if points A, B, and C are inside or outside the given curves. Explain how you arrived at your answer

     (a)   (b)

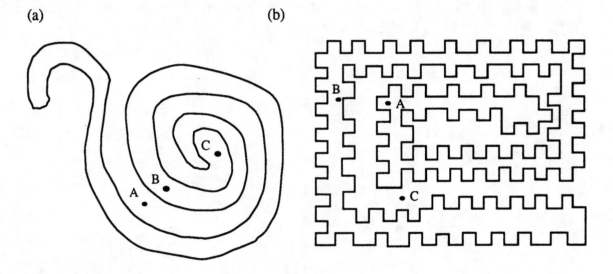

14. If $\overrightarrow{AX}$ bisects ∠DAB and $\overrightarrow{AY}$ bisects ∠BAC, show $\overrightarrow{AX} \perp \overrightarrow{AY}$.

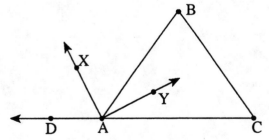

*   15.   Which of the figures are traversable? For those that are traversable, circle all possible starting points.

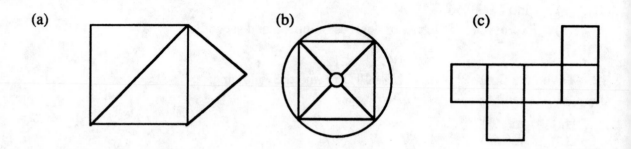

(a)   (b)   (c)

16.   Draw each of the following curves.

(a)   A closed curve that is not simple.

(b)   A concave hexagon.

*   17.   Write a Logo procedure to construct a pair of supplementary angles given the measure of one angle, :A.

Sample Test

1. Given the figures, state whether the triangles are congruent based upon the given conditions. If your answer is yes, name the theorem or postulate abbreviation to justify your answer.

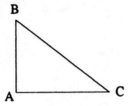 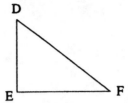

   (a) $\angle A \cong \angle E$, $\angle B \cong \angle D$, $\overline{AB} \cong \overline{ED}$
   (b) $\angle A$ and $\angle E$ are right angles. $\overline{BC} \cong \overline{DF}$; $\angle C \cong \angle F$.
   (c) $\triangle ABC$ and $\triangle EDF$ are right triangles and $\overline{AC} \cong \overline{EF}$. $\angle B \cong \angle D$, and they are not right angles.
   (d) $\overline{AC} \cong \overline{EF}$; $\angle C \cong \angle F$; $\overline{BC} \cong \overline{DF}$
   (e) $\overline{AC} \cong \overline{EF}$; $\overline{BC} \cong \overline{DF}$; $\overline{AB} \cong \overline{ED}$

2. In each of the parts, there is at least one pair of congruent triangles. Identify them and tell why they are congruent.

   (a)

   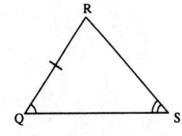 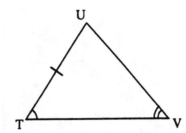

   (b)

   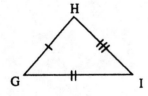 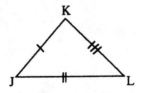

   (c)

   (d)

   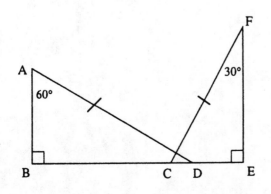 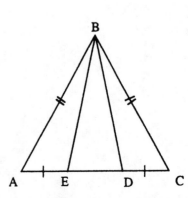

3. Construct each of the following using (i) compass and straightedge, (ii) paper folding.

    (a) Angle bisector of ∠ A

    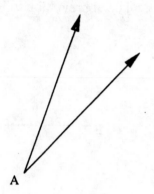

    (b) Perpendicular bisector of $\overline{AB}$

    A   B

    (c) Altitude of ∆ABC from A

    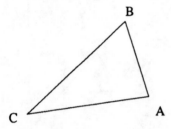

    (d) Parallel to *ℓ* through *M*

    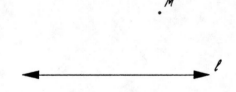

4. For each of the following pairs of similar triangles, find the missing measure.

(a)

(b)

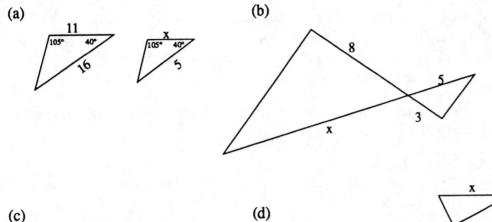

(c)

(d)

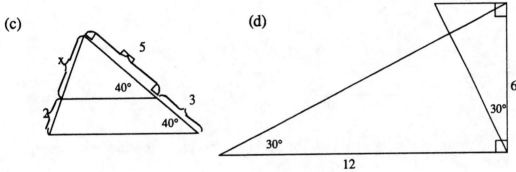

5. Divide the given segment into three congruent parts.

A   B

6. Construct the center of the circle containing $\overset{\frown}{AB}$.

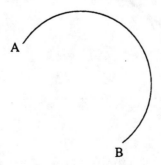

▶ 7. Determine whether each of the following is true or false. If false, explain why.

 (a) A diameter of a circle is a chord of the circle.
 (b) A chord may be a tangent of the circle.
 (c) If a radius is perpendicular to a chord, the radius bisects the chord.
 (d) A sphere may intersect a plane in a circle.

8. A person 122 cm tall casts a 37-cm shadow at the same time a tree casts a 148-cm shadow. How tall is the tree?

9. Find x in the diagram below.

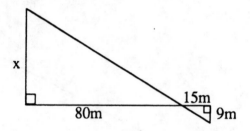

▶ 10. Given any circle, explain how to inscribe a regular octagon in it using only a compass and a straightedge.

11. In each of the following, answer true or false. Justify your answer.

 (a) The center of the circle circumscribing a triangle is always in the interior of the triangle.

 (b) In every triangle the center of the inscribed circle is different from the center of the circumscribing circle.

 (c) If the three circles with centers at O_1, O_2, and O_3 (shown below) are tangent to $\overleftrightarrow{AB}$ and $\overleftrightarrow{AC}$ then A, O_1, O_2, and O_3 are collinear.

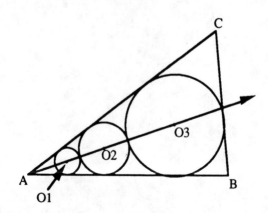

▶ 12. Suppose you have three straight sticks of lengths 5 cm, 12 cm, and 19 cm. Can you arrange these sticks into a triangle? If not, why not?

13. (a) What kind of figure is quadrilateral ABCD?
    (b) Is ∠GFB congruent to ∠FGC? Justify your answer.
    (c) Is ∠GFB congruent to ∠FGD? Justify your answer.

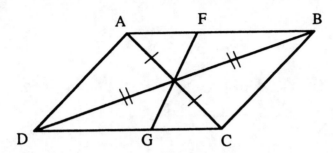

14. Give one example of information that would determine congruency for each of the following.

    (a) Two squares
    (b) Two triangles
    (c) Two spheres

15. $\overline{AD}$ is the perpendicular bisector of $\overline{CB}$

    Construct and label three isosceles triangles that have points B and C as two of their vertices.

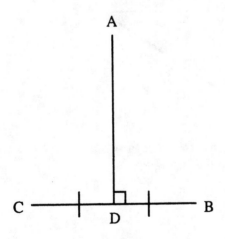

16. Use any method to construct the three altitudes of the following triangle.

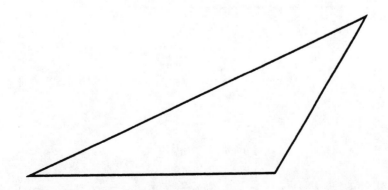

Sample Test

1. Assume that each of the pairs of triangles is congruent and write an appropriate symbolic congruence in each case.

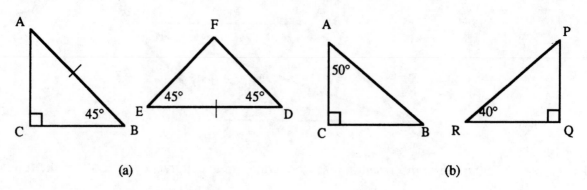

(a)   (b)

2. Using a compass and straightedge construct each of the following:

    (a)   An equilateral triangle.
    (b)   A 30° angle.
    (c)   A 75° angle.

3. Given $\overline{AM} \cong \overline{MC}$ and $\overline{BM} \cong \overline{MD}$ why are the following true? Justify your answer.

    (a) $\overline{AB} \cong \overline{CD}$
    (b) $\overline{AB} \,||\, \overline{CD}$

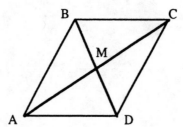

4. Use a straightedge and compass to construct the circle which circumscribes the given triangle and the circle that is inscribed in the triangle.

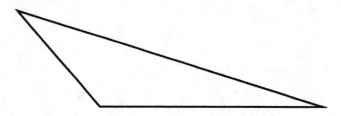

5. In each of the following find x and y if possible.

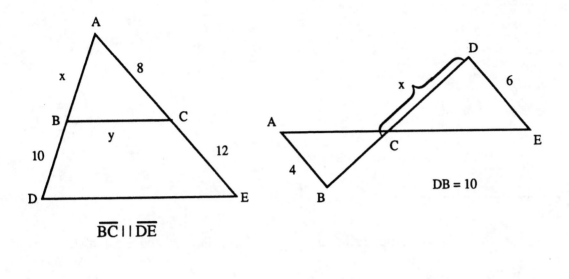

BC || DE

(a)   (b)

6. An Indian girl wants to calculate how tall her family's tepee is. She is 112 cm tall an she finds that when she stands so that her head touches the side, her feet are 64 cm from the edge. If the tepee is a right circular cone with a diameter of 352 cm, what is its height?

7. Use a compass and a straightedge to divide the segment $\overline{AB}$ into 3 congruent parts.

8. Explain how to construct a circle tangent to ℓ and m where ℓ || m that passes through P using only a compass and straightedge.

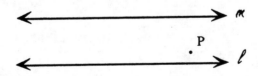

9. In each of the following answer true or false. Justify your answers.

    (a) Congruent triangles are also similar.
    (b) Two similar triangles are also congruent triangles.
    (c) Any two equilateral triangles are similar.
    (d) Two isosceles triangles are similar.
    (e) The diagonals of a trapezoid divide it into four triangles, two of which are similar.
    (f) If three sides of one triangle are parallel, respectively, to three sides of a second triangle, then the triangles are similar.

10. Use a compass and a straightedge to divide the square below into 25 congruent squares.

11. Given △ABC below, construct a similar triangle whose sides are twice as great.

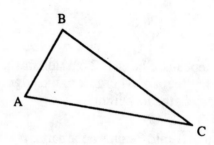

12. Construct a circle that contains points A, B, and C.

B
•

A •

•C

13. Suppose you have three straight sticks of lengths 10 cm, 20 cm, and 31 cm. Can you arrange these sticks into a triangle? If not, why not?

14. Use the figure below to answer the following questions.

    (a) What kind of figure is quadrilateral ABCD?

    (b) Is ∠GFB congruent to ∠FGC? Justify your answer.

    (c) Is ∠GFB congruent to ∠FGD? Justify your answer.

    (d) Is it possible to circumscribe a circle about quadrilateral ABCD? If yes, construct the circle. If no, explain why not.

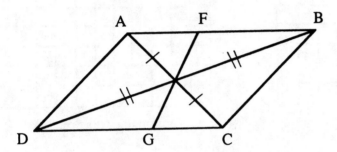

15. Give one example of information that would determine congruency for each of the following.

    (a) Two squares

    (b) Two triangles

    (c) Two rhombuses

    (d) Two parallelograms

Sample Test

1. Complete each of the following motions.

(a)

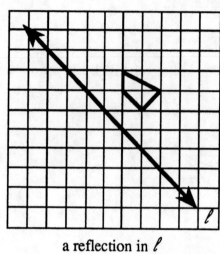

a reflection in ℓ

(b)

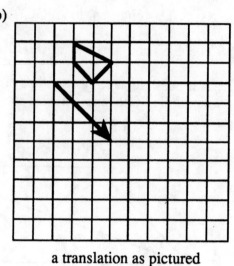

a translation as pictured

(c)

a rotation in O through
the given arc

(d)

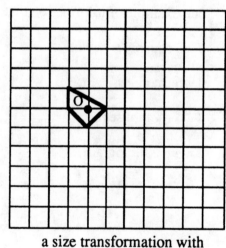

a size transformation with
center O and scale factor 2

2. How many lines of symmetry, if any, does each of the following figures have?

(a)

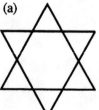

(b)

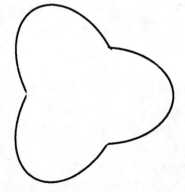

3. The following pairs of figures are congruent. Tell which transformations will take (1) to (2).

(a)

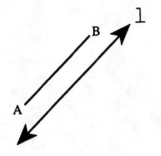

(b)

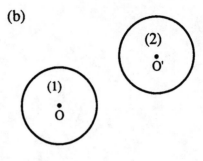

4. For each of the following transformations, construct the image of $\overline{AB}$.

(a)   A reflection in ℓ

(b) A translation which takes M to N

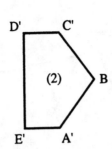

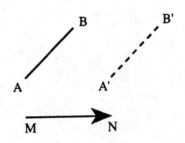

(c)   A rotation in O as indicated

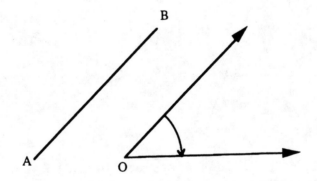

5. Describe objects which have each of the following types of symmetry.

(a)   line
(c)   Plane

(b)   point
(d)   45° rotational

6. For each of the following pairs of figures, determine which transformation might take one figure to the other.

(a)

(b)

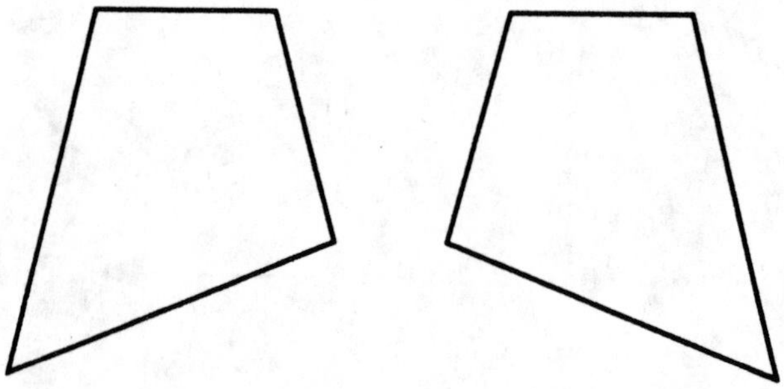

(c)

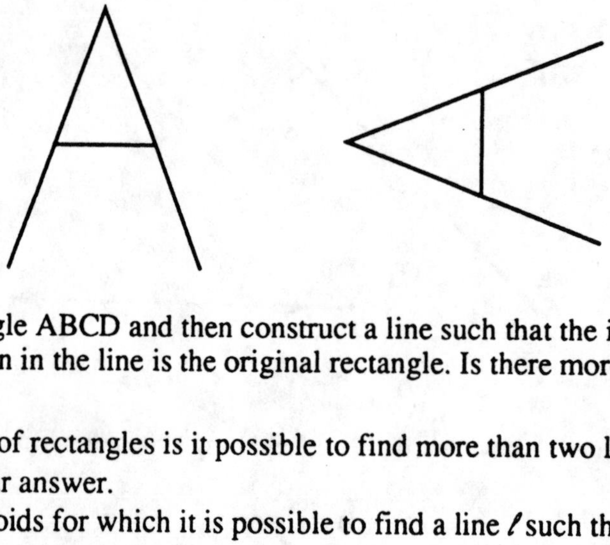

7. (a) Draw a rectangle ABCD and then construct a line such that the image of the rectangle under reflection in the line is the original rectangle. Is there more than one line with this property?

▶ (b) For what kind of rectangles is it possible to find more than two lines with the property in (a). Justify your answer.

(c) Find all trapezoids for which it is possible to find a line ∕ such that when the trapezoid is reflected in ∕ its image is itself.

8. (a) Find the image of the circle with center O under a size transformation with scale factor $\frac{3}{4}$.

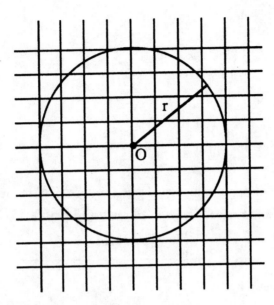

   (b) What kind of figure is the image in (a)? Why?

9. Show that the circle with center O_1 is the image of the circle with center O under a succession of isometries with a size transformation.

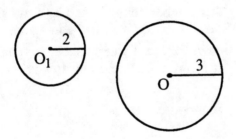

10. If possible, describe a geometric figure that can be transformed into itself by each of the following:

   (a) reflection
   (b) rotation
   (c) translation
   (d) glide reflection

11. Use a reflection to argue that the base angles of an isosceles triangle are congruent.

12. Given points A and B and △DEF below, find point C on △DEF such that △ABC is isosceles.

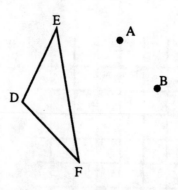

13. Let ℓ ' be the image of ℓ under a half-turn about point O. If A' is the image of A and B' the image of B and $\overline{OB} \perp \ell$ answer each of the following true of false. Justify your answers.

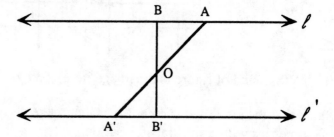

   (a)   △OAB ≅ △OA'B'

   (b)   OB' is the distance from
          O to ℓ '

   (c) $\ell \| \ell$ '

   (d)   The image of $\overline{AA'}$ is $\overline{BB'}$

14. A student claims that anything that can be accomplished by a translation can also be accomplished by a reflection. She claims that if A' is the image of A under a translation then A' can be obtained by a reflection in the line l which is the perpendicular bisector of $\overline{AA'}$. Hence, a translation and a reflection are the same. How do you respond?

▶ 15. Explain why a regular pentagon cannot tessellate the plane.

* 16. Write a Logo procedure called H that will draw a strip of H's similar to the one below.

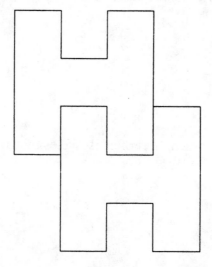

Sample Test

1. Complete each of the following motions.

    (a)

    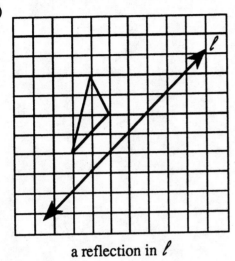

    a reflection in ℓ

    (b)

    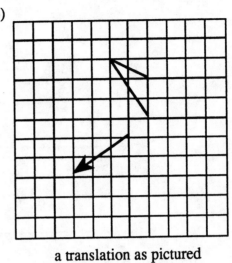

    a translation as pictured

    (c)

    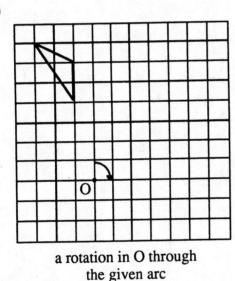

    a rotation in O through
    the given arc

    (d)

    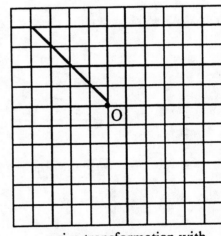

    a size transformation with
    center O and scale factor 1/2

2. For each of the following transformations construct the image of the indicated figure.

    (a)   A reflection of ΔABC in ℓ

    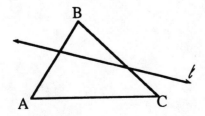

2. (cont.)

(b) A translation of the circle along the arrow from M to N.

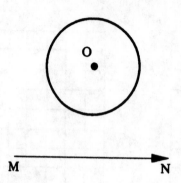

M   N

(c) A half-turn of the line l in O.

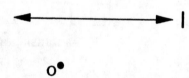

O•

(d) A 60° rotation counterclockwise of △ABC in A.

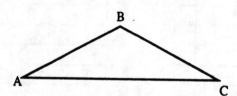

3. Tessellate the plane with the quadrilateral given below.

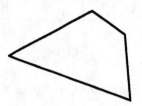

4. How many lines of symmetry, if any, does each of the following figures have?

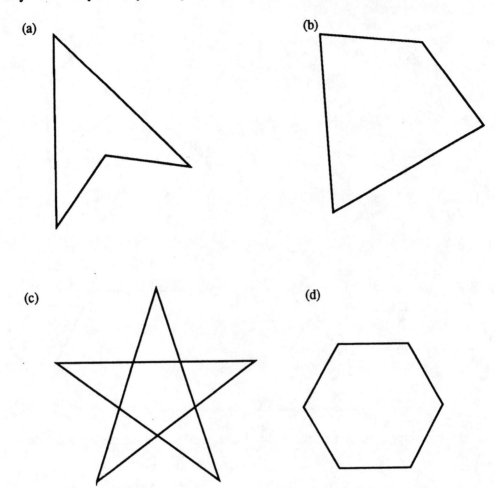

(a)

(b)

(c)

(d)

5. Describe point symmetry and rotational symmetries, if any, of the parts of Problem 4.

6. For each of the following pairs of figures, determine which transformation might take one figure to the other.

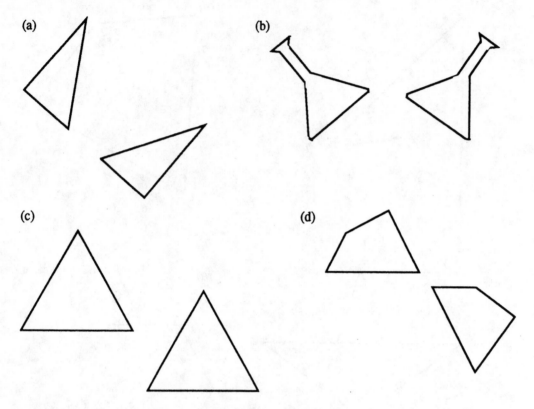

(a)

(b)

(c)

(d)

7. Find the minimum number of reflecting lines needed to accomplish the isometries in Problem 6.

8. Use a reflection to argue that the base angles of an isosceles trapezoid are congruent.

9. Show that △ADE is the image of △ABC under a succession of isometries with a size transformation.

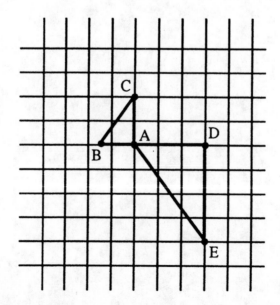

▶ 10. A student claims that anything that can be accomplished by a glide reflection can also be accomplished by a half-turn. He claims that if A' is the image of A under a glide reflection then A' can also be obtained by a half-turn about point O, where O is the intersection of the line of reflection with $\overline{AA'}$. Hence a glide reflection and a half-turn are the same. How do you respond?

▶ 11. A student claims that a succession of two reflections in two ⊥ lines can always be accomplished by a half-turn. Hence a succession of two reflections in two ⊥ lines is a half-turn. How do you respond?

12. What regular figure can be used with a regular octagon to tessellate the plane?

* 13. Write a Logo procedure called HOUSE to draw a strip of houses similar to the ones below.

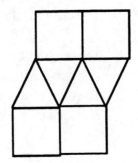

Sample Test

1. Complete the following table converting metric measures.

	mm	cm	m	km
(a)		5200		
(b)			260	
(c)				0.3
(d)	1,300,000			

2. For each of the following choose an appropriate metric unit: millimeter, centimeter, meter or kilometer.

   (a)   The thickness of a dime
   (b)   The length of a straw
   (c)   The diameter of a penny
   (d)   The distance the winner travels at the Talledega 500
   (e)   The height of a desk
   (f)   The length of a football field
   (g)   A section of land
   (h)   The surface area of the Great Salt Lake
   (i)   The surface area of a contact lens
   (j)   The area of a pencil point
   (k)   The area of a football field
   (l)   The area of a television screen

3. Find the area of each of the following.

   (a)

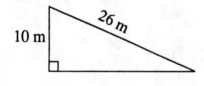

   (b)

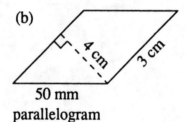

   50 mm
   parallelogram

4. Find the surface area of the square prism whose base has a side of length 5 cm and a height of 6 cm.

5. Find the area of the shaded region on the following geoboard if the unit of measurement is 1 cm².

6. Is it possible to have a square with area 10 cm²? Explain why or why not.

7. Explain how the formula for the area of a triangle can be determined by using the formula for the area of a parallelogram.

8. Answer the following.

   (a)   If the volume of a sphere is $\dfrac{500\pi}{3}$ m³, what is the diameter of the sphere?

   (b)   Find the volume of a cylinder whose height is 2 m and whose base has an area of 9π m².

9. What is the area of the figure below? The arc shown is a semicircle.

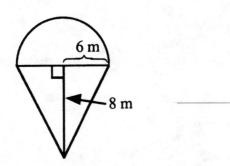

10. For each of the following, can the measures represent sides of a right triangle? Explain your answers.

(a) 3 m, 4 m, 5 m

(b) $\sqrt{2}$ cm, $\sqrt{3}$ cm, $\sqrt{5}$ cm

11. Complete each of the following:

(a) 500 cm^2 = ___ m^2

(b) 18 km = ___ m

(c) 4000 g = ___ kg

(d) 300 mL = ___ L

(e) 17 ha = ___ m^2

(f) 0.027 kL = ___ mL

(g) 0.027 L = ___ cm^3

(h) 4738 kL of water at 4°C has a mass of ___ kg.

12. Complete the following: (Use a calculator whenever convenient.)

(a) 1.7 mi = ___ yd

(b) 40 ft = ___ yd

(c) 1400 ft^2 = ___ yd^2

(d) 1/9 yd^3 = ___ ft^3

(e) 4.5 lb = ___ oz

*(f) 32°C= ___ °F

*(g) 105°F= ___ °C

13. (a) Suppose one edge of a cubic tank is 8 m and the tank is filled with water at 4°C; find the volume of the tank in cubic meters.

(b) Find the capacity of the tank of (a) in liters.

(c) Find the mass of the water of (a) in kilograms.

14. Complete each of the following.

(a) 3 dm^3 of water has a mass of _____ g.

(b) 2 L of water has a mass of _____ g.

(c) 13 cm^3 of water has a mass of _____ g.

(d) 4.2 L of water has a mass of _____ g.

(e) 3.01 L of water has a volume of _____ m^3.

15. Find the volume of a cone whose slant height is 50 cm and whose height is 40 cm.

16.   If the diameter of a circle is 14 cm, find each of the following.

    (a)   The circumference of the circle
    (b)   The area of the circle
    (c)   The area of a sector of the circle that corresponds to a central angle of 18°.

17.   Find the perimeter of the following if all arcs shown are semicircles.

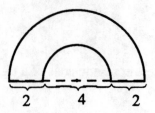

        2   4   2

Sample Test

1. Find the area of △ABC in each of the following.

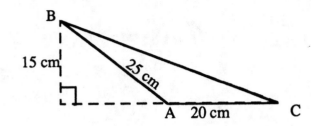
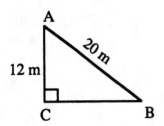

▶ 2. Assume that the only area formula you know is the formula for the area of a triangle. Explain how to derive the formula for the area of a trapezoid.

3. A toy manufacturer wants to design a wooden square pyramid whose volume is 8000 cm³.

 (a) Design such a pyramid. Make a sketch and show the dimensions of the base and the altitude.

 ▶ (b) How many such pyramids are possible? Why?

4. If each dimension of a box is quadrupled, how are the surface area and the volume affected?

5. Complete each of the following:

 (a) 1000 m = ___ km
 (b) 25 m = ___ cm
 (c) 52,000 g = ___ kg
 (d) 26,000 mm = ___ m

6. A rectangular prism has dimensions 60 cm, 40 cm, 200 cm.

 (a) Find the surface area of the prism in square centimeters.
 (b) Find the volume of the prism in cubic meters.
 (c) Find the volume of the prism in liters.

7. A cone has a circular base with radius 50 cm and slant height 90 cm. Find the surface area and the volume.

8. A box shaped container has a 2 m by 3 m rectangular base. It is partially filled with water and the height of the water is 0.5 m.

 (a) How many liters of water are in the container?
 (b) Find the weight of the water in kilograms.
 (c) If 60 liters of water are added into the container, how much will the water rise?

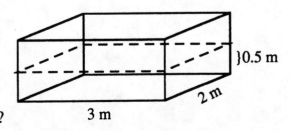

9. The base of a right pyramid is a regular hexagon with the sides of length 12 m. The altitude of the pyramid is 9 m. Find the following:

    (a) The area of the base of the pyramid.
    (b) The surface area of the pyramid.

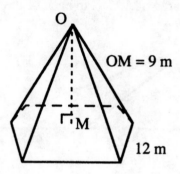

OM = 9 m

12 m

10. Find x in each of the following:

    (a)

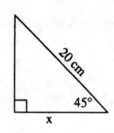

    20 cm
    45°
    x

    (b)

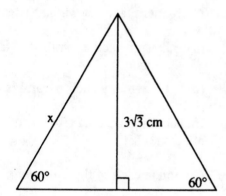

    x
    $3\sqrt{3}$ cm
    60°
    60°

    (c)

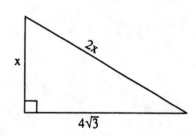

    2x
    x
    $4\sqrt{3}$

11. Complete the following. (Use a calculator whenever convenient.)

    (a) 0.4 mi = _____ ft
    (b) 4.8 yd = _____ ft
    (c) 3 yd^2 = _____ ft^2
    (d) 48,033 ft^3 = _____ yd^3
    (e) 8.6 lb = _____ oz
    (f) $-40°C$ = _____ °F
    (g) 98.6°F = _____ °C

Sample Test

1. Sketch a picture of a line meeting each of the following conditions.

    (a) A positive slope
    (b) A negative slope
    (c) Slope of 0
    (d) A negative slope with y-intercept -2
    (e) No slope

2. For each of the following conditions, write the equation (in slope-intercept form) of the line determined.

    (a) The line through $(4, 7)$ and $(-8, -3)$
    (b) The line through $(4, -7)$ with y-intercept -8
    (c) The line through $(4, -7)$ parallel to $y = 3x + 15$
    (d) The line through $(4, -7)$ perpendicular to the y-axis

3. Sketch the graph of each of the following.

    (a) $x^2 + y^2 = 16$
    (b) $(x + 3)^2 + (y + 4)^2 = 16$
    (c) $x^2 + y^2 \leq 9$
    (d) $3x - 2y = 6$
    (e) $4y = 3x - 12$
    (f) $\dfrac{x}{2} + \dfrac{y}{3} = 1$
    (g) $x \geq y + 4$
    (h) $y \leq 4x + 1$

4. Find the equation of the circle whose center is at $(2, 6)$ and which passes through the point $(7, 8)$.

5. Find the perimeter of the triangle with vertices at A $(0, 0)$, B $(4, 3)$, and C $(-6, 0)$.

6. Solve each of the following systems, if possible. Indicate whether the system has a unique solution, infinitely many solutions, or no solutions.

    (a) $4x + 3y = 8$
         $4x + 3y = 8$
    (b) $3x + 5y = 7$
         $-6x + 10y = -14$
    (c) $14x + 8y = -2$
         $7x + 4y = 13$

7. Graphically show the solution to the following system of inequalities.

    $3x - 7y \leq 14$
    $y \geq x + 3$

8. In each part, determine if the three points are collinear.

    (a) $(0, 7)$, $(0, 3)$, and $(0, 9)$
    (b) $(2, 3)$, $(4, 6)$, and $(6, 9)$
    (c) $(0.1, -3)$, $(0.2, -4)$, and $(0.3, -5)$

9. Find the equation of the line passing through the y-intercept of the line $x = -3y + 1$ and perpendicular to the line $x = -3y + 1$.

Sample Test

1. Use slopes to explain why the following points are the vertices of a parallelogram.

   A(3, 4), B(5, 8), C(8, 3), D (6, ⁻1)

2. Find the coordinates of 3 different points which are on the circle $(x-2)^2 + (y+3)^2 = 9$.

3. The lines $\overset{\leftrightarrow}{AB}$ and $\overset{\leftrightarrow}{BC}$ are the graphs of $y = 1 - 2x$ and $y = x - 3$. The line $\overset{\leftrightarrow}{CD}$ contains the point D whose coordinates are (0,5) and is parallel to the x-axis. Find the coordinates of A, B and C.

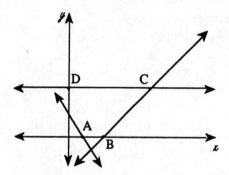

4. The vertices of $\triangle ABC$ are A(⁻1, 5), B(3, 5) and C (5, ⁻7). Find the following:

   (a) The slope of the altitude to side $\overline{BC}$,
   (b) The midpoint of $\overline{BC}$,
   (c) The equation of the line through B and parallel to the x-axis.

5. Solve each of the following systems if possible. Indicate whether the system has a unique solution, infinitely many solutions, or no solution.

   (a) $6x + 5y = 4$
        $3x + 2y = 1$

   (b) $x = 3y + 5$
        $6y = 2x - 10$

   (c) $2x - 3y = 1$
        $\dfrac{3}{4}y + \dfrac{1}{2}x = 13$

6. Find the equation of the circle whose diameter has an endpoint at (3, ⁻5) and midpoint at (5, ⁻2).

7. Graph each of the following.

   (a) $x \le {}^-2$
        $y \ge 1$
        $x \ge {}^-3$

   (b) $x - y > 1$
        $y - x \le 3$

8. Find a system whose graph is shaded below.

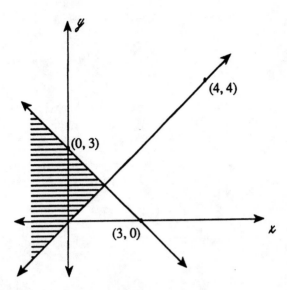

9. David has $50.05 in quarters and dimes. How many coins of each kind does he have if he has a total of 301 coins?

10. Company A produces $\frac{1}{3}$ of the cars that company B produces annually. If it is known that company A produces 24,000,000 fewer cars than B, how many cars does each company produce?

11. The vertices of $\triangle ABC$ are at A(0, 0), B(4, 0) and C(2, 6). Find the coordinates of the point where the median through A intersects the altitude from C.

Answers to Sample Test

1. (a) 16, 18, 20 (b) 13, 8, 3
   (c) 40, 20, 10 (d) 61, 99, 160
   (e) 128, 256, 512 (f) 215, 342, 511
   (g) 4, 9, 16

2. (a) arithmetic (b) arithmetic
   (c) geometric (d) neither
   (e) geometric (f) neither
   (g) neither

3. (a) $4n + 3$ (b) $n^3 + 1$ (c) 5^n

4. (a) 9, 14, 19, 24, 29 (b) 0, 2, 6, 12, 20
   (c) 10, 13, 16, 19, 22 (d) 2, 6, 12, 20, 30

5. (a) 2544 (b) 1520

6. (a) $(n + 1)$th term = nth term + 111 (b) 11090

7. 1415.

There are 9 pages with a one-digit number, 90 pages with a two-digit number, 900 pages with a three-digit number, and so on. Since $9 \cdot 1 + 90 \cdot 2 + 900 \cdot 3 = 2889$ digits, she must be past page 999. (Check that she hasn't yet reached page 9999.) She is now numbering pages with four-digit page numbers, so the number of digits she has written is:
$9 \cdot 1 + 90 \cdot 2 + 900 \cdot 3 + p \cdot 4$, or $2889 + 4 \cdot p$, where p is the number of pages past 999. Because she has written 4553 digits, $4553 = 2889 + 4 \cdot p$. Consequently:

$$4553 - 2889 = 4p$$
$$1664 = 4p$$
$$p = 416.$$

Therefore, she has numbered 416 pages past 999 and therefore a total of 1415 pages.

8. 93 x 74

9. (a) No. The five tables in the middle of this arrangement can seat only two people. The two end tables can seat four people. Consequently, John will only be able to seat $5 \cdot 2 + 2 \cdot 4$ or 18 people with this arrangement.
   (b) Yes. The five tables in the middle of this arrangement can seat four people. The two end tables can seat five people. Consequently, John can seat $5 \cdot 4 + 2 \cdot 5$ or 30 people with this arrangement.

10. (a) 2·4·5·7·8·9, or 3·4·5·6·7·8
    (b) Two. The product of all eight numbers is 362,880. This product divided by 20,160 yields 18. So the product of the two excluded numbers must be 18. Only two pairs have a product of 18;

    3 and 6,
    2 and 9.

11. 81 rabbits.

12. (a) 17 cm.   (b) 46 cm.

13. 49 ways if not all must be used at any given time.

14. 100 rectangles.

15. 5

Answers to Sample Test

1. (a) 17, 23, 30
   (b) 127, 107, 147
   (c) 24300, 72900, 218700
   (d) 6250, 31250, 156250
   (e) 43, 50, 57
   (f) 32, 0, 64
   (g) 25, 29, 33.
   (h) 1295, 2400, 4095

2. (a) neither
   (b) neither
   (c) geometric
   (d) geometric
   (e) arithmetic
   (f) neither
   (g) arithmetic
   (h) neither

3. (a) $5n - 1$
   (b) $6 \cdot 2^{(n-1)}$

4. (a) 11, 15, 19, 23, 27
   (b) 3, 8, 15, 24, 35
   (c) 2, 5, 8, 11, 14

5. (a) 1218
   (b) 16700

6. 9

7. Answers may vary.

```
A B C D
D C B A
B A D C
C D A B
```

8. The test tube will overflow on the 12th night. At the end of the first night the test tube contains 25 ml, but by the end of the first day it contains only 16 ml. The net gain after one night and one day is 16 ml. If the test tube has more than 175 ml at nightfall, it will overflow during the night. After the 11th night and day the test tube contains 11·16 or 176 ml. Therefore, it will overflow the following night.

9. 47 posts. To solve this problem, count the number of posts in each side of the rectangle, but make sure that you count each corner post only once. One of the 120' sides has a post every 10'. That means there are 13 posts on that side.

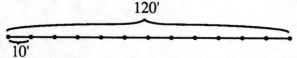

Note that two of the thirteen posts are corner posts. Similarly, the other 120' side has 16 posts and the two 80' sides have 11 posts each. Each corner post is in two sides, so we have counted the corner posts twice. So, we need to subtract 4. 13 + 16 + 11 + 11 - 4 = 47.

10. Caterina had 5 of each coin.

11. The bell will ring 528 times.

12. B. There are six letters that repeat. So the seventh letter in the sequence is one complete repetition plus one letter, so it is an 'A.' The 16th letter in the sequence is two complete repetitions plus 4 letters, so it is a 'D.' Similarly, the 200th letter in the sequence is 33 complete repetitions plus 2 letters, so it is a 'B.'

13. They ran 35 blocks on the 11th day.

14.
$$\begin{array}{r} 465 \\ \times\ 23 \\ \hline 10695 \end{array}$$

15. 606

Answers to Sample Test

1. V = {x | x is a vowel in the name "Georg Cantor"}

2. Ø, {2}, {o}, (2, o}, {t}, (2, t}, (o, t}, (2, o, t}

3. (a) x is a female who does not own a pickup.
    (b) x is a female who either owns a pickup or a dog or both.
    (c) x is a female mathematician who does not own a dog.
    (d) x is a female nonmathematician who does not own a dog.
    (e) x is a female who owns a pickup but is not a mathematician.
    (f) x is a female nonmathematician.

4. (a) {n}   (b) {u, n, i, t, e} or C or U
    (c) (n, i, t} or A   (d) Ø
    (e) Ø   (f) {e}
    (g) (n, i, t, e}   (h) Ø
    (i) 5   (j) 5

5. (a)   (b)

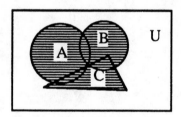   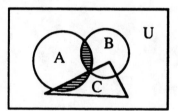

6. 15

7. 6   8. 9

9.

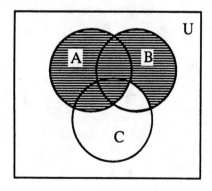   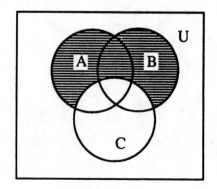

A ∪ (B − C)   ≠   (B ∪ A) − C

10. Answers may vary.

    (a) [(A ∩ B) ∪ (A ∩ C) ∪ (B ∩ C)]
    (b) (A ∩ C) ∪ (D ∩ C) ∪ B

11. $A \times (B \cup C) = \{(o, t), (o, w), (o, o), (o, z), (o, e), (o, r), (n, t), (n, w), (n, o), (n, z), (n, e), (n, r),$
$(e, t), (e, w), (e, o), (e, z), (e, e), (e, r)\}$

$(A \times B) \cup (A \times C) = \{(o, t), (o, w), (o, o), (n, t), (n, w), (n, o), (e, t), (e, w), (e, o), (o, z), (o, e),$
$(o, r), (n, z), (n, e), (n, r), (e, z), (e, e), (e, r)\}$

12.   (a)   False; Let $A = \{1, 2\}$ and $B = \{1\}$
      (b)   True
      (c)   True
      (d)   True
      (e)   False; The empty set is equivalent to itself.

13.   7

14.   (a)   Yes   (b)   No   (c)   No

15.   (a) $\{3, 8, 13, 18, 23\}$
      (b) $\{0, 80, 15\}$
      (c) $\{3, 0, 8\}$

16.   (a)   4   (b)   6

17.   (a)   Reflexive, symmetric, and transitive
      (b)   Transitive
      (c)   None
      (d)   None

18.   (a)   15   (b) $1200   (c)   32

19.   (a)   Yes   (b)   No   (c)   Yes   (d)   No

20.   (a)   There exists a butterfly that is not an animal.
      (b)   Sometimes Whitney Houston does not say "How de do Boo Boo."
      (c)   All umpire calls are incorrect.
      (d) $7 + 3 \neq 10$

21.   (a)

p	q	$p \wedge q$	$[p \wedge q] \to p$
T	T	T	T
T	F	F	T
F	T	F	T
F	F	F	T

21. (cont.)

(b)

q	~q	q ∨ (~q)	[q ∨ (~q)] → q
T	F	T	T
F	T	T	F

(c)

p	q	~q	p → (~q)	(~q) → q	[p → (~q)] ↔ [(~q) → q]
T	T	F	F	T	F
T	F	T	T	F	F
F	T	F	T	T	T
F	F	T	T	F	F

(d)

p	p → p
T	T
F	T

22. (a) No   (b) No

23. Converse: If the Director was Doc Severinson, then the host was Jay Leno.
    Inverse: If the host was not Jay Leno, then the director was not Doc Severinson.
    Contrapositive: If the Director was not Doc Severinson, then the host was not Jay Leno.

24. (a) I get an increase in salary.
    (b) The map is not in the plane.
    (c) Gloria Hewitt is well known.

25. Let p be the statement: A nail is lost;
        q be the statement: A shoe is lost;
        r be the statement: A horse is lost;
        s be the statement: A rider is lost;
        t be the statement: A battle is lost;
        u be the statement: A kingdom is lost.

$$[(p \to q) \wedge (q \to r) \wedge (r \to s) \wedge (s \to t) \wedge (t \to u)] \to (p \to u)$$

The argument is valid using the Chain Rule several times.

26. (a) Valid   (b) Invalid
    (c) Valid   (d) Invalid

Answers to Sample Test

1. $D = \{\text{August}\}$

2. $M = \{x | x$ is an odd natural number less than $11\}$

3. $\{a\}, \{b\}, \{c\}, \{a, b\}, \{a, c\}, \{b, c\}$

4. (i) (a) A nonsmoking American
        (b) A healthy nonsmoking American
        (c) An American smoker with a health problem
        (d) An American nonsmoker with a health problem
        (e) An American who is either a smoker or unhealthy or both

    (ii) (a) $\overline{D} \cap E$
         (b) $D \cap E \cap C$
         (c) $\overline{C} \cap \overline{D} \cap \overline{E}$
         (d) $\overline{E} \cup \overline{C}$

5. (a) T
    (b) T
    (c) T
    (d) T
    (e) F. $A \cup \overline{A} = U$
    (f) F. $A - \overline{A} = A$
    (g) F. Let $A = \{1\}$, and $U = \{1, 2\}$. Then $\overline{A} = \{2\}$ and $A \times \overline{A} = \{(1, 2)\}$.
    (h) F. $\emptyset \subseteq \emptyset$

6. (a) $\{s, u, e, t\}$
    (b) $\{s, e, t\}$ or A
    (c) $\{q, e, s, t\}$
    (d) $\{q\}$
    (e) $\{t\}$
    (f) $\{s, u, e, t\}$
    (g) U
    (h) 1

7. (a) 2
    (b) 2
    (c) $B \times B = \{(a,\ a)\}$
    (d $A \times A = \{(1,\ 1),(1,\ 2),(2,\ 1),(2,\ 2)\}$
    (e) ∅
    (f) No
    (g) Yes
    (h) 0

8. (a)
{1,	2,	3,	4,	...,	n,	...}
↕	↕	↕	↕	↕	↕	
{4,	9,	14,	19,	...,	5n - 1, ...}	

    (b) 284, because 5 (57) - 1 = 284
    (c) 5n - 1

9. (a) {5, 7, 3}   (b)   {0}

10.

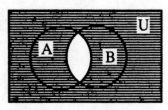

$\overline{A} \cup \overline{B}$

11. $(A \cap B) \cup [C - (A \cup B)]$

12. Use a Venn Diagram as shown below, where C represents card catalog users, R represents Reader's Guide users and I represents the users of the information booth.

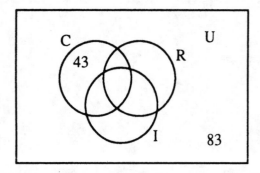

If there was no overlap between the users of the information booth and the Reader's Guide, we would have the following: n (R) + n (I) + 43 + 83 = 200. Thus, n (R) + n (I) = 74, but n (R) = 60 and n (I) = 68. Since 60 + 68 ≠ 74, there must be an overlap.

13. 72

14. $4 \cdot 3 \cdot 2 \cdot 1 = 24$

15. (a) Yes
     (b) It is a function.

16. (a) Reflexive, symmetric, and transitive
     (b) Transitive
     (c) None
     (d) None

17. (a) 30   (b) $2000 loss
     (c) 70 units

18. (a) Yes   (b) No
     (c) Yes   (d) Yes

19. (a) *Valley of the Horses* was not written by Jean Auel.
     (b) There exists a realtor who does not get a commission on a house the realtor sold.
     (c) All used car salesmen are honest.
     (d) $5 - 2 = 3$

20. (a)

p	q	~q	p ∨ q	p → (~ q)	(p ∨ q) ↔ (p → ~ q)
T	T	F	T	F	F
T	F	T	T	T	T
F	T	F	T	T	T
F	F	T	F	T	F

(b)

p	q	~q	p → q	(p ∧ ~ q)	~ (p ∧ ~ q)	(p → q) → (p ∧ ~ q)
T	T	F	T	F	T	T
T	F	T	F	T	F	T
F	T	F	T	F	T	T
F	F	T	T	F	T	T

(c)

p	q	r	p ∨ q	(p ∨ q) ∧ r
T	T	T	T	T
T	T	F	T	F
T	F	T	T	T
T	F	F	T	F
F	T	T	T	T
F	T	F	T	F
F	F	T	F	F
F	F	F	F	F

21. (a) No   (b) No

22. Converse: If Michelle Pfeiffer came from Gotham City, then she is Catwoman.

      Inverse: If Michelle Pfeiffer is not Catwoman, then she did not come from Gotham City.

      Contrapositive: If Michelle did not come from Gotham City, then she is not Catwoman.

23. (a) You understand the problem.
     (b) You are not a student.
     (c) I will get cold.

24. Let p be the statement: I pay attention to my job;
          q be the statement: I will get a salary increase;
          r be the statement:: I shirk my job.

Symbolically, we have $\left[(p \rightarrow q) \wedge (r \rightarrow \sim q) \wedge r\right] \rightarrow \sim p$

It is valid.

25. (a) Valid   (b) Not valid   (c) Not valid

Answers to Sample Test

1. (a) 1045   (b) 37   (c) 1464
   (d) 5   (e) 78   (f) 902

2. (a) CXXVIII   (b) 2341_{five} (c) 670_{eight}
   (d) $T7_{twelve}$

3. (a) 3^{13} (b) 3^{26} (c) 4^4

4. (a) Commutative Property of Addition
   (b) Commutative Property for Addition
   (c) Multiplicative Identity
   (d) Distributive Property of Multiplication over Addition
   (e) Associative Property of Addition
   (f) Associative Property for Multiplication

5. (a) Let $k = 2$. Since $2 + 5 = 7$, then $5 < 7$.
   (b) Let $k = 4$. Since $18 = 4 + 14$, then $18 > 14$.

6. Because $12 \cdot 100 = (1 \cdot 10 + 2) \cdot 10^2 = 1 \cdot 10^3 + 2 \cdot 10^2 = 1 \cdot 10^3 + 2 \cdot 10^2 + 0 \cdot 10 + 0$, the tens digit and the units digit are 0.

7. (a)

$$
\begin{array}{r}
{}^{1}5\ {}^{1}4\ 2 \\
\cancel{8}_4\ \cancel{8}_3\ \cancel{9}_1 \\
\cancel{6}_0\ 1\ 1 \\
\hline
2\ 0\ 4\ 2
\end{array}
\qquad
\begin{array}{r}
{}^{1}5\ {}^{1}4\ 2 \\
8\ 8\ 9 \\
6\ 1\ 1 \\
\hline
2\ 0\ 4\ 2
\end{array}
$$

(b)

$$
\begin{array}{r}
{}^{1}3\ {}^{1}1\ 2_{five} \\
\cancel{4}_3\ \cancel{3}_0\ \cancel{4}_1{}_{five} \\
\cancel{3}_1\ 1\ 1_{five} \\
\hline
2\ 1\ 1\ 2_{five}
\end{array}
\qquad
\begin{array}{r}
{}^{1}3\ {}^{1}1\ 2_{five} \\
4\ 3\ 4_{five} \\
3\ 1\ 1_{five} \\
\hline
2\ 1\ 1\ 2_{five}
\end{array}
$$

8. (a)

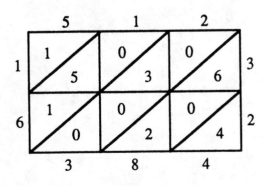

$$
\begin{array}{r}
5\ 1\ 2 \\
\times\ \ 3\ 2 \\
\hline
1\ 0\ 2\ 4 \\
1\ 5\ 3\ 6 \\
\hline
1\ 6\ 3\ 8\ 4
\end{array}
$$

Answer: 16384

8. (cont.)

(b)

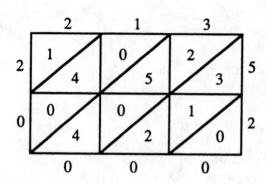

$$\begin{array}{r} 213_{six} \\ \times\ 52_{six} \\ \hline 430 \\ 1513\ \\ \hline 20000_{six} \end{array}$$

Answer: 20000_{six}

9. (a)

$$\begin{array}{r|ll} 312 & & \\ -240 & 20 & 12's \\ \hline 72 & & \\ -72 & \underline{6} & 12's \\ \hline 0\,R & 26 & \text{Quotient} \end{array}$$

OR

$$\begin{array}{r} 26 \\ 12\overline{)312} \\ -24\ \ \\ \hline 72 \\ -72 \\ \hline 0 \end{array}$$

(b)

$$\begin{array}{r|ll} 10011_{two} & & \\ -1010 & 10 & 101's \\ \hline 1001 & & \\ -101 & \underline{1} & 101 \\ \hline 100\,R & 11 & \text{Quotient} \end{array}$$

OR

$$\begin{array}{r} 11 \\ 101_{two}\overline{)10011_{two}} \\ -101\ \ \\ \hline 1001 \\ -101 \\ \hline 100 \end{array}$$

10. (a) $12 \cdot 26 + 0 = 312$ (b) $(101 \cdot 11 + 100 = 10011)_{two}$

11. (a)   Hundreds   (b)   Thousands   (c)   Tens

12. (a) $\{0, 1, 2, 3, 4\}$ (b) $\{19\}$
     (c)   W   (d) $\{0, 1, 2, \ldots, 14\}$

13. (a)

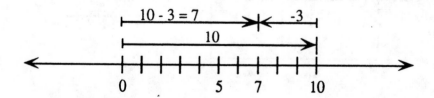

13.   (cont.)

(b)

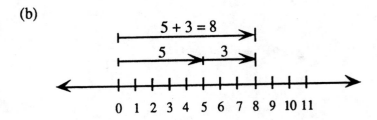

(c)

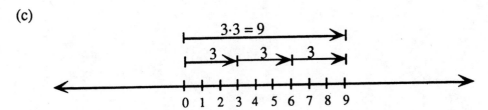

(d)

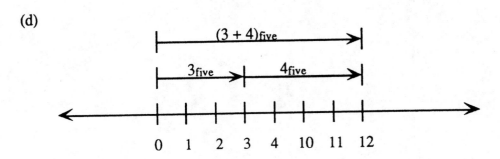

14.   (a)   18x   (b) $13x^3$ (c) $ab + ac + ad$

15. $29

16.   (a) $T10_{twelve}$ (b)   XXX

17. $106

18.   Answers may vary. For example:

(a) $(2 + 3) + 4 = 2 + (3 + 4)$
(b) $2(3 + 4) = 2 \cdot 3 + 2 \cdot 4$
(c) $3 \cdot 1 = 3 = 1 \cdot 3$

19.   Dick should pay Tom $1 and Mary should pay Tom $6.

20. $30/month

21. $10,020

22. $0 \div 0$ is equal to some unique number x such that $0 = 0 \cdot x$. Because no unique whole number exists, $0 \div 0$ is undefined.

23. (a)   1456
        + 2572
          4028

        (b)   5382
             - 2191
            3191

24. 2^{20}, because $2^{10} + 2^{10} = 2^{10}(1 + 1) = 2^{10} \cdot 2 = 2^{11}$ and $2^{20} > 2^{11}$

25. 7

Answers to Sample Test

1. (a) 1,000,400 (b) 233 (c) 1452
   (d) 11 (e) 10 (f) 224

2. (a) CDLIV (b) 1300_{five} (c) 412_{twelve}
   (d) 10_{nine}

3. (a) 3^{15} (b) 4^{93} (c) 5^7

4. (a) Commutative Property for Addition
   (b) Associative Property for Multiplication
   (c) Distributive Property for Multiplication over Addition
   (d) Identity Property for Multiplication
   (e) Closure Property for Addition
   (f) Commutative Property for Multiplication

5. (a) Let $k = 4$. Since $18 + 4 = 22$, then $18 < 22$.
   (b) Let $k = 1$. Since $0 + 1 = 1$, then $1 > 0$.

6. $1 \div 0$ is equal to some unique whole number x, such that $1 = 0 \cdot x$. Because $0 \cdot x$ is always 0, no such number exists, and the solution is undefined. If $1 \div 0$ were equal to 1, then this implies $1 = 0 \cdot 1$ which is false.

7. (a)

$$
\begin{array}{cccc}
{}^2 3 & {}^2 6 & 2 \\
7 & 8 & 0 \\
8 & 3 & 4 \\
7 & 9 & 3 \\
\hline
1\ 0 & 5 & 3
\end{array}
\qquad
\begin{array}{cccc}
{}^2 3 & {}^2 6 & 2 \\
& 7 & 8 \\
5 & 3 & 4 \\
+ & 7 & 9 \\
\hline
1\ 0 & 5 & 3
\end{array}
$$

(b)

$$
\begin{array}{cccc}
{}^1 2 & {}^1 1 & 4_{\text{five}} \\
2 & 3 & 2_{\text{five}} \\
2 & 2 & 3_{\text{five}} \\
\hline
1\ 2 & 2 & 4_{\text{five}}
\end{array}
\qquad
\begin{array}{cccc}
{}^1 2 & {}^1 1 & 4_{\text{five}} \\
2 & 3 & 2_{\text{five}} \\
2 & 2 & 3_{\text{five}} \\
\hline
1\ 2 & 2 & 4_{\text{five}}
\end{array}
$$

8. (a)

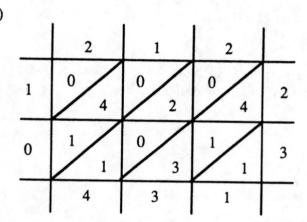

```
      5     1     8
  1 │ 1 ╱ │ 0 ╱ │ 2 ╱ │
    │ ╱ 5 │ ╱ 3 │ ╱ 4 │ 3
  7 │ 2 ╱ │ 0 ╱ │ 3 ╱ │
    │ ╱ 0 │ ╱ 4 │ ╱ 2 │ 4
  7 │ 1 ╱ │ 0 ╱ │ 1 ╱ │
    │ ╱ 0 │ ╱ 2 │ ╱ 6 │ 2
        1     5     6
```

$$\begin{array}{r} 518 \\ \times\ 342 \\ \hline 1036 \\ 2072\ \ \\ 1554\ \ \ \\ \hline 177{,}156 \end{array}$$

Answer: 177,156

(b)

```
      2     1     2
  1 │ 0 ╱ │ 0 ╱ │ 0 ╱ │
    │ ╱ 4 │ ╱ 2 │ ╱ 4 │ 2
  0 │ 1 ╱ │ 0 ╱ │ 1 ╱ │
    │ ╱ 1 │ ╱ 3 │ ╱ 1 │ 3
        4     3     1
```

$$\begin{array}{r} 212_{\text{five}} \\ \times\ 23_{\text{five}} \\ \hline 1141 \\ 424\ \ \\ \hline 10431_{\text{five}} \end{array}$$

9. (a)

```
8 │ 3648
   -3200        400   8's
    448
   - 400         50   8's
     48
   -  48          6   8's
      0 R        456  Quotient
```

```
          4 5 6
    8 ) 3 6 4 8
        3 2
        4 4
       -4 0
         4 8
        -4 8
          0  R
```

(b)

```
12_three │ 2021_three
          1200          100   12's
           121
           120           10   12's
             1 R        110_three
```

```
                 110_three
   12_three ) 2021_three
              12
              12
              12
              01
               0
               1  R
```

10. (a) $8 \cdot 456 + 0 = 3648$
    (b) $(12 \cdot 110 + 1 = 2021)_{three}$

11. (a)   Tens
    (b)   Thousands
    (c)   Units

12. (a)   W
    (b)   4
    (c) $\{0, 1, 2, 3, 4, 5\}$
    (d) $\{0, 1, 2, 3, 4, 5\}$

13. (a)

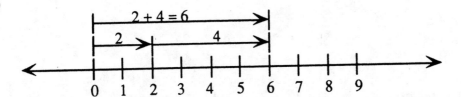

    (b)

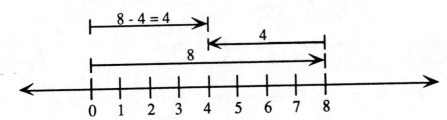

    (c)

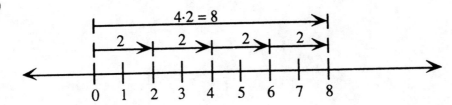

    (d)

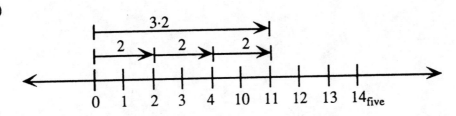

14. (a) $14x^2$ (b) $37x$
    (c) $ac + ad + bc + bd$

15. (a)   DCLXIV   (b) $E0T_{twelve}$

16. Answers may vary.

    (a) $3 + 0 = 3 = 0 + 3$
    (b) $2 \cdot (3 \cdot 4) = (2 \cdot 3) \cdot 4$
    (c) $2 + 3 = 3 + 2$

17. $430

18. 6 points

19. $71

20. 1260

21. (a)   2365   (b)   8654
         + 4824   - 3282
           7189   5372

22. $3 \cdot 2^{20}$ is the greatest because $2^{20} + 2^{20} = 2 \cdot 2^{20}$ which is equal to 2^{21} and $3 \cdot 2^{20} > 2 \cdot 2^{20}$.

23. 12

24. The front-end estimate is based only on the leftmost digits that are significant. Because the remainder of the numbers are not used in the first estimate, it is less than the actual answer.

25. No, because $2 \in W$, $5 \in W$ and $2 \cdot 5$ does not have an answer in the set of whole numbers with 10 removed.

Answers to Sample Test

1. (a) 7 (b) ^-x (c) ^-2-x (d) ^-x+y

2. (a) 10 (b) 4 (c) $^-16$ (d) 12
   (e) $^-60$ (f) $^-40$

3. (a) 2 (b) 3, $^-3$
   (c) 7, $^-7$ (d) 5, $^-5$
   (e) $x > {}^-16, x \in I$ (f) 5, $^-9$
   (g) $x \le {}^-2, x \in I$ (h) 11, $^-5$

4. $2 \cdot 4 = 8$ The first three products 8, 4, 0 are terms of an arithmetic
   $1 \cdot 4 = 4$ sequence with fixed difference $^-4$. If the pattern continues
   $0 \cdot 4 = 0$ the next three terms are $^-4$, $^-8$ and $^-12$.
   $^-1 \cdot 4 = {}^-4$
   $^-2 \cdot 4 = {}^-8$
   $^-3 \cdot 4 = {}^-12$

5. (a) $x(5 - 3x)$ (b) $(5 - x)(5 + x)$
   (c) $(a+1)(a-b+1)$ (d) $5(1 + x)$

6. Answers may vary.

7. The additive inverse of a is ^-a. Also, the additive inverse of ^-a is $^-(^-a)$. Since additive inverses are unique and both a and $^-(^-a)$ are additive inverses of ^-a, then $a = {}^-(^-a)$.

8. (a) 3 (b) 3 (c) $^-27$
   (d) 27 (e) 27 (f) $^-3$

9. (a) $b^2 - 9d^2$ (b) $16j^2 - 4k^2$

10. (a) F. Counterexample: $2(^-1) > 7(^-1)$ and $2 < 7$.
    (b) F. If $^-x > {}^-7$, then $(^-1)(^-x) < (^-1)(^-7)$, or $x < 7$.
    (c) T
    (d) F. Counterexample: $x = {}^-2$.
    (e) F. $^-3x + 72x + 14 = 69x + 4$ while $^-3x + 7 + {}^-72x + {}^-7 = {}^-75x$.
    (f) F. $(a + b)(a + b) = a^2 + 2ab + b^2$
    (g) T

11. (a) $x = 9$ (b) $x = 10, {}^-16$ (c) $x > 5$

12. (a) T
    (b) F. For example, $5 - 3 \ne 3 - 5$.
    (c) T
    (d) F. For example, $5 \div 3 \notin I$

13. They must be nonzero integers with like signs, that is, they must both be positive or both be negative.

14.
    (a) The multiplicative inverse of 2 is 1/2: 2 x 1/2 = 1 but 1/2 is not an integer
    (b) 10 - 6 ≠ 6 - 10 since 4 ≠ ⁻4

15. 17 yards gained

16. 9°C

17. 16 gallon tank

18. A drop of 40°

19. Fifteen pounds of rose food and 5 pounds of enriched compost

20. Fifteen quarters, 81 pennies

21. 11 and 3

22.   (a)

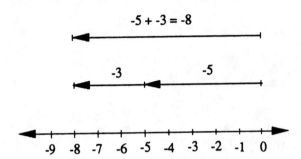

(b)

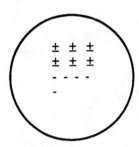

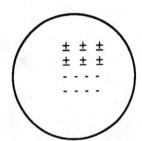

-5 charge on
field

Add three negative charges;
net result is -8 charge on
field

(c)

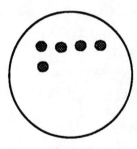

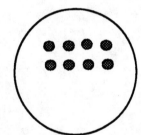

5 shaded
chips

Add three shaded chips for a
total of 8 shaded chips

Answers to Sample Test

1. (a) $^-13$ (b) x (c) $3 - x$ (d) $x - y$

2. (a) 21   (b) $^-53$ (c) $^-30$
   (d) 406,250   (e) 0   (f) 28

3. (a) 5   (b) $^-3$
   (c) 16, $^-16$ (d) 9, $^-9$
   (e) $x > 4, x \in I$ (f) $^-3, 13$
   (g) $x \geq 3, x \in I$ (h) 0, 4

4. (a) $3x (3x - 1)$ (b) $(2x - 3) (2x + 3)$
   (c) $(a + 1) (x + 1)$ (d) $11 (x - 1)$

5. (a) 21, $^-19$ (b) $x > 0$, or $x \geq 1$
   (c) $x < {}^-8$ or $x \leq {}^-9$

6. From the definition of the additive inverse, we know that $ab + {}^-(ab) = 0$. Also $ab + ({}^-a) (b) = (a + ({}^-a)) \cdot b = 0 \cdot b = 0$. Because $^-(ab)$ and $({}^-a) (b)$ are both additive inverses of ab and because the additive inverse must be unique, then $^-(ab) = ({}^-a) (b)$.

7. (a) $(x + y)(x + y) = x(x + y) + y(x + y) = x^2 + xy + yx + y^2 = x^2 + 2xy + y^2$
   (b) $(^-5 + 2a)(^-5 + 2a) = (^-5)^2 + 2(^-5)(2a) + (2a)^2 = 25 - 20a + 4a^2$

8. (a) $^-4$ (b) 2   (c) $^-2$
   (d) $^-8$ (e) 8   (f) $^-16$

9. (a) T   (b) F. $x < {}^-2$
   (c) F. $x = 2$ (d) F. $|^-x| = {}^-x$ if $x < 0$
   (e) F. $^-5 - 8 \cdot 3 = {}^-29$ (f) T
   (g) F. $a^2 - b^2 = (a - b) (a + b)$

10. (a) F. For example, $^-2$ is an integer but not a whole number.
    (b) F. For example, $5 - (3 - 2) \neq (5 - 3) - 2$
    (c) T
    (d) T

11. (a) $(24 \div 6) \div 2 = 4 \div 2 = 2$; $24 \div (6 \div 2) = 24 \div 3 = 8$
    (b) $(24 \div 6) + (24 \div 2) = 4 + 12 = 16$; $24 \div (6 + 2) = 24 \div 8 = 3$

12. They must be nonzero integers with unlike signs.

13. $2(^-4) = {^-8}$ The first three products $^-8$, $^-4$, 0 are terms of an arithmetic
     $1(^-4) = {^-4}$ sequence with fixed difference 4. If the pattern continues
     $0(^-4) = 0$ the next two terms are 4 and 8.
     $^-1(^-4) = 4$
     $^-2(^-4) = 8$

14. $^-\$62$

15. $^-19°$ C

16. 29°C

17. Let x = the number of 3 oz envelopes, y = the number of 5 oz envelopes.
     x + y = 86 (the total number of envelopes)
     3x + 5y = 19 lbs, 12 oz = 316 oz (the total weight of the envelopes)
     2y + 258 = 316
     y = 29
     x = 57

18. 51¢/pound

19. juniors = 2(freshmen)
     seniors = 8 + freshmen
     sophomores = freshmen + seniors = 2(freshmen) + 8
     freshmen + sophomores + juniors + seniors = 6 freshmen + 16 = 178
     freshmen =162/6 = 27
     sophomores = 62
     juniors = 54
     seniors = 35

20. 7 and 29

21. (a)

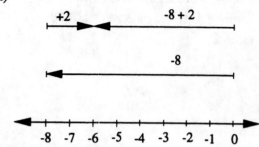

(b)

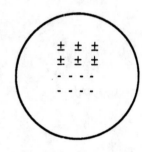 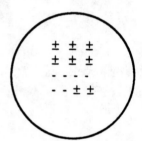

-8 charge on
field

Add two positive charges;
net result is -6 charge on
field

(c)

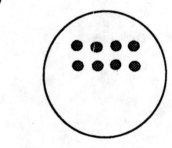 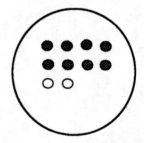

8 shaded
chips

Add two white chips for a
net excess of 6 shaded chips

Answers to Sample Test

1. (a)   0, 7
    (d)   None
    (b)   4
    (e)   2 or 6
    (c)   8
    (f)   0 or 8

2. $3 \mid (a+b+c)$; $3 \mid 9$ implies the following: $3 \mid 9b$ and $3 \mid 9 \cdot 11a$, or $3 \mid 99a$. Thus

$$3 \mid [(a+b+c)+9b+99a]$$
$$3 \mid (100a+10b+c)$$
$$3 \mid N$$

3. (a)   F. Let $a = 4$ and $b = 8$.
    (b)   F. Let $a = 4$ and $b = 8$.
    (c)   F. Let $a = 4$ and $b = 8$.
    (d)   F. Let $a = 6$.
    (e)   F. 0 does not divide any number except 0.
    (f)   T

4. 2, 3, 4, 6, 7, 8, 11, 12, 22

5. Sixty-four is the least whole number with exactly seven divisors because of the following:

$64 = 2^6$;
2^6 has exactly 7 divisors: 1, 2, 4, 8, 16, 32, and 64.
Every other positive number with 7 divisors must have some prime other than 2 in its prime factorization, and if it has a number greater than 2 in its prime factorization, then the number must be greater than 64.

6. (a)   Composite
    (c)   Composite
    (b)   Composite
    (d)   Composite

7. (a)   19
    (c)   1
    (b)   114
    (d) $2^2 \cdot 3 \cdot 5 \cdot 13$ or 780

8. 4

9. (a) $2^2 \cdot 3^5 \cdot 11$
    (b) $2^3 \cdot 3^7 \cdot 5^3 \cdot 7^2 \cdot 11^4 \cdot 13$

10. (a)   31
    (b)   13

11. 1, 2, 4, 8, 5, 10, 20, 40, 7, 14, 28, 56, 35, 70, 140, 280

12. For a number to be divisible by 35, it must be divisible by both 5 and 7.

13. 24 pieces

14. 53

15. Wednesday

16. (a)   7
    (b)   5
    (c)   19

Answers to Sample Test

1. (a) 0, 3, 6, 9   (b) 0, 9   (c) 2
   (d) 1, 4, 7   (e) 0, 1, 2, 3, 4, 5, 6, 7, 8, 9   (f) 0, 5

2. $n = a \cdot 10^2 + b \cdot 10 + c$. Because $4 \mid 10^2$, then $4 \mid a \cdot 10^2$. Therefore if $4 \mid (b \cdot 10 + c)$ then $4 \mid (a \cdot 10^2 + b \cdot 10 + c)$ or $4 \mid n$.

3. (a) F. If $a = 0$, then there is no GCD.
   (b) F. LCM $(a, a) = 0$ for all $a \in W$.
   (c) T
   (d) T
   (e) F. Let $a = 6$.
   (f) T

4. 2, 3, 5, 6, 10, 15

5. 30

6. (a) Composite   (b) Composite
   (c) Composite   (d) Prime

7. (a) 1   (b) 5025
   (c) 4   (d) $2^2 \cdot 3 \cdot 7 \cdot 13 \cdot 73$ or 79,716

8. 12

9. (a) $5^2 \cdot 7$ (b) $2^3 \cdot 5^2 \cdot 7^3 \cdot 11 \cdot 13 \cdot 17$

10. (a) 13   (b) 41

11. 1, 2, 4, 61, 122, 244

12. For a number to be divisible by 33, it must be divisible by both 3 and 11.

13. 96

14. 2:45 P.M.

15. 3 years

16. (a) 1
    (b) 0
    (c) 0

Answers to Sample Test

1. (a)

   (b)

2. $\dfrac{8}{10}, \dfrac{12}{15}, \dfrac{16}{20}$, and so on.

3. (a) $\dfrac{3}{4}$ (b) $\dfrac{c^2 y^4}{d}$ (c) $\dfrac{0}{1}$

   (d) $\dfrac{4}{1}$ (e) $\dfrac{1}{b}$ (f) $\dfrac{29}{57}$

4. (a) $=$ (b) $<$ (c) $<$

   (d) $=$ (e) $=$ (f) $<$

5. (a) $\dfrac{22}{15}$ (b) $\dfrac{1}{12}$ (c) $\dfrac{9}{8}$

   (d) $\dfrac{21}{5}$ (e) $\dfrac{83}{68}$

6. (a) $^-8$ and $\dfrac{1}{8}$ (b) $-3\dfrac{1}{2}$ and $\dfrac{2}{7}$

   (c) $\dfrac{1}{4}$ and $\dfrac{^-4}{1}$ (d) $\dfrac{^-8}{3}$ and $\dfrac{3}{8}$

7. (a) $\dfrac{85}{2}$

   (b) $\dfrac{2}{1}$

8. (a) $x = \dfrac{3}{2}$

   (b) $x \le \dfrac{21}{26}$

9. 36

10. (a) $\dfrac{1}{3^{10}}$ (b) 5^8 c) 2^2 or 4 (d) $\dfrac{a^2 b^2}{a^2 + b^2}$

11. 76 packages, and $\dfrac{4}{13}$ oz. will be left over.

12. The student is wrong He considers $\dfrac{9+\frac{1}{4}}{3+\frac{3}{4}}$ and $\dfrac{9}{3}+\dfrac{\frac{1}{4}}{\frac{3}{4}}$ to be equal, and they are not. In general,

$$\frac{a+b}{c+d} \neq \frac{a}{c}+\frac{b}{d}.$$

13. (a)   3+
    (b)   10-
    (c)   4+

14. (a)   40   (b)   14
    (c)   7   (d)   29

15. Yes, 1/2 ft will be left.

16. Heidi's class because $\dfrac{17}{30} > \dfrac{15}{27}$.

17. $33\dfrac{1}{3}$ pages.

18. $1\dfrac{7}{8}$ hours.

Answers to Sample Test

1. (a) $\dfrac{3}{4}$ (b) x^4 (c) $\dfrac{1}{x^2 y}$ (d) 3

2. (a) $\dfrac{23}{24}$ (b) $\dfrac{37}{60}$ (c) $3\dfrac{3}{35}$ (d) $\dfrac{13}{2}$ or $6\dfrac{1}{2}$

3. (a) $-3\dfrac{7}{8}$ and $\dfrac{8}{31}$ (b) $\dfrac{3}{4}$ and $-\dfrac{4}{3}$

    (c) 0 and no multiplicative inverse   (d) $-\dfrac{1}{x^2}$ and x^2

4. (a) $\dfrac{3}{5}$ (b) $\dfrac{3}{8}$ (c) $\dfrac{2}{5}$

5. $x \ge \dfrac{4}{5}$

6. True. When the denominator of a fraction (whose numerator and denominator are positive) decreases, the fraction increases. When the numerator increases the fraction increases as well. A more formal approach follows: $\dfrac{a+1}{b-1} > \dfrac{a}{b}$ if and only if $ab + b > ab - a$ or $b > \bar{}a$. The last inequality is true because $a > 0$ and $b \ge 2$.

7. (a) $x \le 0$ (b) $x \ge \dfrac{5}{6}$ (c) $x = -2\dfrac{1}{4}$

8. (a) 2^6 (b) $\dfrac{3^8}{2^8}$ or $\left(\dfrac{3}{2}\right)^8$ (c) $\dfrac{4}{9}$

9. $30\dfrac{5}{9}$ miles

10. The person gets approximately $\dfrac{13}{16}$ of a pound of nuts.

11. It will become smaller because $\dfrac{3x}{8x} > \dfrac{3x - 2}{8x - 2}$

12. (a) 3^- (b) 10^- (c) 6^-

13. (a) 22   (b) 18   (c) 1   (d) 41

14. (a) $<$ (b) $<$ (c) $<$ (d) $<$

15.   15 apples

16. $136

17.   60 days

18.   Approximately 2090 students

Answers to Sample Test

1. (a) $4.\overline{9} = 5$

    (b) $0.\overline{44} > \dfrac{1}{25}$

    (c) $0.\overline{46} < 0.4\overline{6}$

    (d) $\sqrt{3} > 1.7$

2. (a) 2.0021

    (b) 38.258

    (c) 0.1448

    (d) 16.8

3. (a) $^{-}4.2$ and $\dfrac{1}{4.2}$, or $\dfrac{10}{42}$ or $\dfrac{5}{21}$

    (b) $^{-}0.36$ and $\dfrac{100}{36}$, or $\dfrac{25}{9}$

4. (a) $1 \cdot 10^{1} + 6 \cdot 10^{0} + 4 \cdot 10^{-1} + 7 \cdot 10^{-2}$

    (b) $0 \cdot 10^{0} + 0 \cdot 10^{-1} + 0 \cdot 10^{-2} + 8 \cdot 10^{-3}$

5. (a) $\dfrac{^{-}1}{2\sqrt{3}}$ or $\dfrac{^{-}\sqrt{3}}{6}$

    (b) $x \le 12.2$

    (c) 20,000

    (d) 20%

    (e) 26

    (f) $\dfrac{5}{9}$ or $0.\overline{5}$

    (g) $x = 0$

    (h) $x < 0.722$

6. $23.6 - 8.34 = 23.60 - 8.34$
    $$= \frac{2360}{100} - \frac{834}{100}$$
    $$= \frac{1526}{100}$$
    $$= 15.26$$

7. 18.75 cm

8. (a) 200%

    (b) 105

    (c) 45

9. (a) 20%

    (b) $3\dfrac{3}{4}$% or 3.75%

    (c) 536%

    (d) 1.3%

10. (a) 0.40

    (b) $0.001\overline{6}$

    (c) 2

11. (a) 508.58

    (b) 508.6

    (c) 500

12. (a) $\dfrac{27}{100}$ (b) $\dfrac{3104}{1000}$ or $\dfrac{388}{125}$ (c) $\dfrac{22}{90}$ or $\dfrac{11}{45}$ (d) $\dfrac{24}{100}$ or $\dfrac{6}{25}$

13. (a) 0.075
    (b) 0.125
    (c) $0.\overline{153846}$

14. No, for example, $\sqrt{2}\cdot\sqrt{2}=2$, which is not irrational.

15. 3.873

16. (a) 5.268×10^6 (b) 3.25×10^{-4}

17. (a) Irrational if pattern continues
    (b) Irrational
    (c) Rational
    (d) Rational if pattern continues repeating

18. $567.53

19. $9240

20. $19,969.04

21. 77.5 %

22. The order makes no difference, the final discount will be 27.291%.

23. (a) 4   (b) 4   (c) 3   (d) 3

24. (a) $11\sqrt{3}$ (b) 24   (c) $4\sqrt{30}$ (d) 7

25. (a) $\left(\dfrac{1}{3}\right)^{11}$, or $\dfrac{1}{3^{11}}$ (b) $\dfrac{1}{5^9}$

    (c) 2^{15} (d) 5^{26}

26. $12,084.75

27. $585.83

Answers to Sample Test

1. (a) <   (b) =   (c) >   (d) <

2. (a) 4.742   (b) -4.419   (c) 0.12   (d) 12.1

3. Because $3840 = 2^8 \cdot 3 \cdot 5$ the prime factorization of the denominator of this fraction will contain only powers of 2 and 5 if and only if k is a multiple of 3.

4. (a) $^-0.4$ and $\dfrac{10}{4}$ or $\dfrac{5}{2}$ or 2.5

    (b) $^-2.\overline{6}$ and $\dfrac{3}{8}$ or 0.375.

5. (a) $\dfrac{^-5}{3\sqrt{2}}$ or $\dfrac{^-5\sqrt{2}}{6}$ (b) $^-39.6$

    (c) 324   (d) $0.\overline{4}$ or $\dfrac{4}{9}$

    (e) 75   (f) 22
    (g) 0   (h) 4.2

6. $8.07 - 2.3 = \dfrac{807}{100} - \dfrac{23}{10}$

    $= \dfrac{807}{100} - \dfrac{230}{100}$

    $= \dfrac{807 - 230}{100}$

    $= \dfrac{577}{100}$

    $= 5.77$

7. 15

8. (a) 400%   (b) 2   (c) 20

9. (a) $66.\overline{6}\%$ or $66\dfrac{2}{3}\%$ (b) 6.25%

    (c) 206%   (d) $244.\overline{4}\%$ or $244\dfrac{4}{9}\%$

10. (a) 0.45   (b) 0.008   (c) 3.2

11. No, for example, $^-\sqrt{2} + \sqrt{2} = 0$ which is not an irrational number.

12. (a) 483.77   (b) 484   (c) 500

13.   (a) $\dfrac{38}{100}$ or $\dfrac{19}{50}$ (b) $\dfrac{2607}{1000}$

(c) $\dfrac{43}{90}$ (d) $\dfrac{324}{999}$ or $\dfrac{36}{111}$

14.   (a) $0.2\overline{3}$ (b) 0.275
(c) $0.\overline{45}$

15.   3.317

16.   (a) 3.286×10^3 (b) $3.2 \cdot 10^{-6}$

17.   (a)   4   (b)   2

18.   Approximately 4.3%

19.   (a)   Irrational
(b)   Rational
(c)   Rational
(d)   Irrational (if pattern continues)

20. $162.50

21. $17,500

22. $554.04

23.   16

24.   (a) $3\sqrt{13}$ (b) $10\sqrt{7}$ (c) $14\sqrt{3}$ (d) $4\sqrt[3]{3}$

25.   (a) $\left(\dfrac{2}{5}\right)^{11}$ or $\dfrac{2^{11}}{5^{11}}$ (b) 3^7

(c) $\dfrac{5^5}{26}$ (d) $\left(\dfrac{2}{3}\right)^{12}$ or $\dfrac{2^{12}}{3^{12}}$

26.   (a)   For one year, choose 8.5% simple interest:
$1000(0.085)(1) = \$85.00 > \$1000(1.02)^4 - \$1000 = \$82.43$
(b)   For three years, choose 8% compounded quarterly:
$1000(0.085)(3) = \$255.00 < \$1000(1.02)^{12} - \$1000 = \$268.24$

27. $849.34

Answers to Sample Test

1. (a) {Sunday, Monday, Tuesday, Wednesday, Thursday, Friday, Saturday}

    (b) {Tuesday, Thursday}

    (c) $\dfrac{2}{7}$

2. $\dfrac{1}{2}$

3. (a) $\dfrac{6}{18}$ or $\dfrac{1}{3}$ (b) $\dfrac{12}{18}$ or $\dfrac{2}{3}$

    (c) $\dfrac{5}{18}$ (d) $\dfrac{13}{18}$

4. (a) $\dfrac{13}{52}$ or $\dfrac{1}{4}$ (b) $\dfrac{1}{52}$

    (c) $\dfrac{22}{52}$ or $\dfrac{11}{26}$ (d) $\dfrac{51}{52}$

5. (a) $\dfrac{9}{36}$ or $\dfrac{1}{4}$ (b) $\dfrac{3}{6} \cdot \dfrac{2}{5}$ or $\dfrac{1}{5}$

6. 0.90307 or approximately 0.9   7. $\dfrac{9}{20}$

8. $\dfrac{3}{8}$ 9. $\dfrac{1}{2}$

10. 40   11. $\dfrac{1}{128}$

12. (a) $\dfrac{1}{169}$ (b) $\dfrac{1}{221}$

13. (a) 455   (b) $\dfrac{10}{455}$ or $\dfrac{2}{91}$ (c) $\dfrac{35}{455}$ or $\dfrac{1}{13}$

14. 28 ways   15. 100

16. 15   17. 6,760,000

18. (a) P(A) = $\dfrac{3}{8}$ (b) P(B) = $\dfrac{5}{8}$

19. (a) 7! or 5040

(b) $\dfrac{11!}{2! \cdot 2! \cdot 2!}$ or 4,989,600

20. $\dfrac{7}{12}$

21. $\dfrac{3}{33}$ or $\dfrac{1}{11}$

22. 51 to 1

23. $2.00

24. $15

25. Answers vary, for example,

(a) Let an even number represent a head and an odd number represent a tail.

(b) Let the days of the week be represented by the digits 0 through 6 and choose one digit at random. If the digit is not in this range, continue until a number in this range is found.

(c) Let the numbers 01, 02, 03, 04, 05, ..., 29, 30 represent the dates of the month. Pick a starting place and mark off blocks of 2 until three of the digits are obtained.

Answers to Sample Test

1. (a) $\{1, 2, 3, ..., 26\}$
    (b) $\{2, 4, 6, ..., 26\}$

    (c) $\dfrac{1}{2}$

2. $\dfrac{1}{16}$

3. (a) $\dfrac{5}{16}$ (b) $\dfrac{9}{16}$ (c) $\dfrac{7}{16}$ (d) $\dfrac{11}{16}$

4. (a) $\dfrac{26}{52}$ or $\dfrac{1}{2}$ (b) $\dfrac{3}{52}$

    (c) $\dfrac{22}{52}$ or $\dfrac{11}{26}$ (d) $\dfrac{48}{52}$ or $\dfrac{12}{13}$

5. (a) $\dfrac{49}{256}$ (b) $\dfrac{42}{240}$ or $\dfrac{7}{40}$

6. 0.504   7. $\dfrac{5}{32}$

8. $\dfrac{1}{28}$ 9. $\dfrac{7}{8}$

10 150   11. $\dfrac{27}{512}$

12. (a) $\dfrac{144}{2704}$ or $\dfrac{9}{169}$ (b) $\dfrac{132}{2652}$ or $\dfrac{33}{663}$

13. (a) $\dfrac{6}{28}$ or $\dfrac{3}{14}$ (b) $\dfrac{6}{28}$ or $\dfrac{3}{14}$

14. 24 ways   15. 325

16. 15   17. $26^3 \cdot 10^3$ or 17,576,000

18. (a) $P(A) = \dfrac{1}{2}$ (b) $P(B) = \dfrac{1}{2}$

19. (a) 6! or 720   (b) $\dfrac{11!}{2! \cdot 2!}$ or 9,979,200

20.   335 to 1

21. $\dfrac{4}{12}$ or $\dfrac{1}{3}$

22.   5 to 31

23   49 to 3

24. $1.25

25. $2.50

26.   Answers may vary, for example,

(a)   Mark off the digits in blocks of two. Let the numbers 01, 02, 03, 04, 05, …, 25, 26 represent the consecutive letters of the alphabet. Disregard blocks of two not in this range.

(b)   Let each of the oceans be represented by one of the numerals 1, 2, 3, 4, or 5. Disregard the rest of the digits.

(c)   Let Red be represented by the digits 1, 2, and 3; let Blue be represented by the digits 4, 5, 6; and let White be represented by the digits 7, 8, 9. Disregard the digit 0.

Answers to Sample Test

1. (a)   Approximately $12.93
   (b) $9.70
   (c) $9.70

2. Mean, 73.9;
   median, 84;
   mode, 98;
   range, 61

3. Approximately 24.57

4.

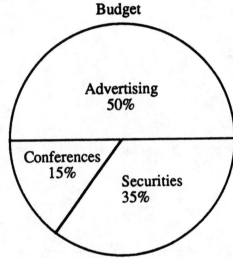

Budget

5. There are more high scores than low ones, but the low ones lower the mean.

6. Weights of Miss Brown's Students

20	19
21	2599
22	457
23	567
24	16
25	6
26	44
27	345
28	237
29	0
30	1

25 | 6 represents 25.6 kg

7. (a)

Class	Frequency
10-14	1
15-19	2
20-24	3
25-29	7
30-34	5
35-39	2
Total	20

7.   (cont.)

(b)

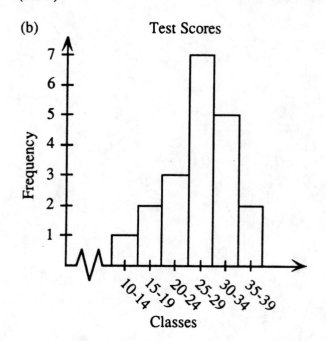

(c)

Test Scores	
1	279
2	1235666789
3	0122489

2 | 1 represents a score of 21

8.   More of the older members have died or did not attend or a greater number of younger members attended.

9.   Approximately 3.18 years.

10.   (a)

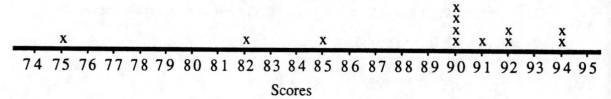

(b)

TEST SCORES

Miss Burke's Class		Mr. Brown's Class	
988864	7	5	
6200	8	25	9	4 = 94
20	9	000012244	

10. (cont.)

   (c) Brown's IQR = 4.5
        Burke's IQR = 6
   (d) Yes, the score of 75 in Mr. Brown's class is an outlier.
   (e)

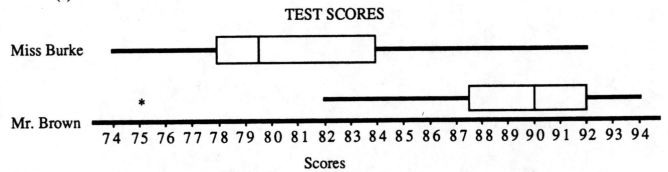

TEST SCORES

Miss Burke

Mr. Brown

74 75 76 77 78 79 80 81 82 83 84 85 86 87 88 89 90 91 92 93 94

Scores

   (f) Mr. Brown's class scored considerably higher than Miss Burke's class. All of Mr.
        Brown's class, except the outlier of 75, scored above the median for Miss Burke's
        class.

11. You do not know who was surveyed, how many were surveyed, or what types of questions
     were asked. The claim should not be taken at face value without more information.

12. 1900 students

13. An outlier is any score that is more than 1.5 interquartile ranges above the upper quartile
     or more than 1.5 interquartile ranges below the lower quartile.

14. 57

Answers to Sample Test

1. (a)   77.5   (b)   78   (c)   no mode

2.   Approximately 9.14

3.   0.53

4.   80% females and 20% males

5.   3.125

6. $\bar{x} = 58$, $s \doteq 7.15$

7.   (a)

British Open Scores - 1981-1991

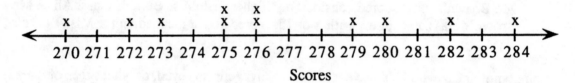

Scores

(b)

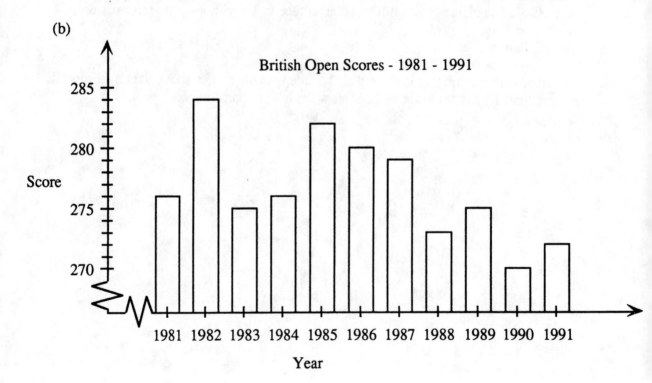

8. (a)   <u>Class of Weights</u>   <u>Frequency</u>

Class of Weights	Frequency
115-124	1
125-134	2
135-144	10
145-154	10
155-164	4
165-174	2
175-184	1
Total	30

(b)   Class Weights of Huntsville Space Camp

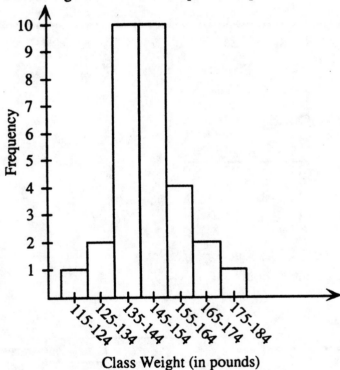

Class Weight (in pounds)

9. On a standardized test, or on any test, there should be students that score below the mean. Without more information, there is no reason to believe that every student in any given school should score above the national mean on a test. Although possible, this is highly unlikely.

10. The class in which the standard deviation was twice the standard deviation of the other is much more heterogeneous than the other class.

11. (a)

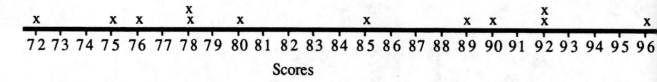

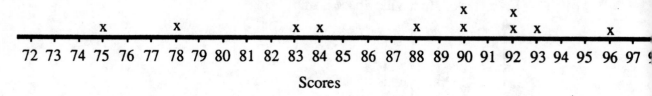

(b)

TEST SCORES

Miss Sol's Class		Mr. Read's Class
85	7	25688
843	8	059
8632200	9	0226

$9 \mid 8 = 98$

(c) The IQR for Mr. Read is 14. The IQR for Miss Sol is 9.

(d) There are no outliers for either set of data.

(e)

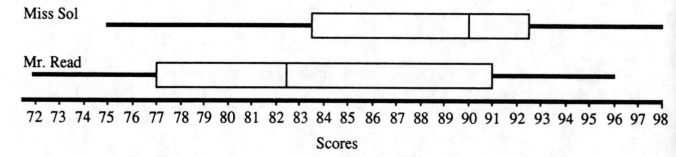

(f) Miss Sol's class did better on the quiz than Mr. Read's class. 75% of Miss Sol's class scored above the median for Mr. Read's class.

* 12. A positive correlation means that the points fell near a trend line and the trend line slopes up from left to right. This implies that the data on the two axes are related and given one value we can make predictions about the other.

* 13. Mean, 72. Standard deviation, 20.

* 14. 950

Answers to Sample Test

1. Answers may vary. For example,

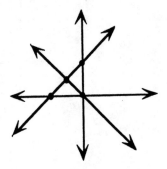

2. Answers may vary. For example,

∠ABC and ∠CBD are supplementary.

3. 4

4. (a)

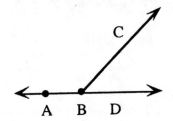

    (b) There are 6 vertices, 6 faces and 10 edges. Euler's Formula holds because 6 + 6 - 10 = 2.

5. (a) False, they could be skew.
    (b) False, all squares are rectangles.
    (c) False, the line can pass through the plane and intersect in 1 point.
    (d) False, it takes a plane to separate space.
    (e) True.
    (f) False, it has one end point.

6. (a) $\overset{\leftrightarrow}{AD}$

    (b) $\overset{\leftrightarrow}{AE}$

    (c)   Point E

    (d)   Points P and E

    (e) $\overset{\leftrightarrow}{AE}$

    (f) $\angle BEC$

    (g) $\varnothing$

7. 156° 42' 42"

8. 55°

9. 35

10 63° and 27°

11. No, to be a regular polygon all sides and all angles must be congruent. The angles of a rhombus are not necessarily congruent.

12. (a) 140°   (b) 40°   (c) 55°

     (d) 55°   (e) 70°

13. In parts (a) and (b), you could choose a point that you know is in the exterior and draw a segment to the indicated points. An odd number of intersection points indicates the point is an interior point, otherwise it is an exterior point.

     (a) Points A and C are interior points and B is an exterior point.

     (b) Points B and C are interior points and point A is an exterior point.

14. The measure of angle 4 is equal to the sum of the measures of angles 1 and 2. A justification follows.

    $m(\angle 3) + m(\angle 4) = 180°$

    $m(\angle 1) + m(\angle 2) + m(\angle 3) = 180°$

    Therefore $m(\angle 3) + m(\angle 4) = m(\angle 1) + m(\angle 2) + m(\angle 3)$ which implies $m(\angle 4) = m(\angle 1) + m(\angle 2)$.

15. (a)   Traversable

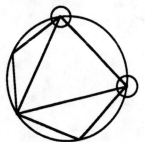

(b)   Traversable

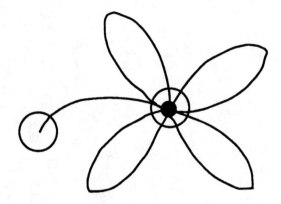

(c)   Not traversable

16.   (a)   For example,

(b)

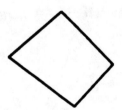

17.   TO COMP. ANGLES :A
          FD 100
          BK 100
          RT :A
          FD 100
          BK 100
          RT 90-:A
          FD 100
          BK 100
          LT 90
       END

Answers to Sample Test

1.

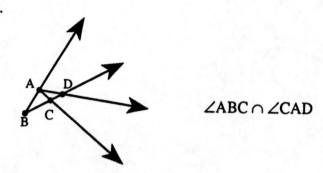

$\angle ABC \cap \angle CAD$

2.

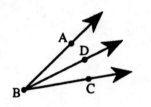

$\angle ABC$ and $\angle DBC$

3.   16

4.   X, Y, and Z are collinear because if two distinct planes intersect, they intersect in a line.

5.   (a)   F, there are an infinite number of planes containing a line.
   (b)   F, the sum of the four interior angles in a parallelogram must be 360°, with four acute angles this cannot happen.
   (c)   T
   (d)   F, for example in the figure below $\overset{\leftrightarrow}{BA} \cup \overset{\leftrightarrow}{CD}$ is not a line.

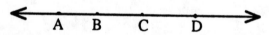

   (e)   F, one ray starts at A and goes in the B direction and one ray starts at B and goes in the A direction.
   (f)   T
   (g)   F, in an equilateral triangle at least 2 sides are congruent.

6.   (a) $\overset{\leftrightarrow}{YZ}$
   (b)   points B and E
   (c)   point E
   (d)   points B and E
   (e) $\overset{\leftrightarrow}{FE}$
   (f) $\overset{\leftrightarrow}{AB}$
   (g) $\varnothing$
   (h) $\overline{AF}$

7. (a)   150°
    (b)   54

8. $V + F - E = 9 + 9 - 16 = 2$

9.   Let ABCD be the rectangle shown, with $\angle A$ as a right angle.

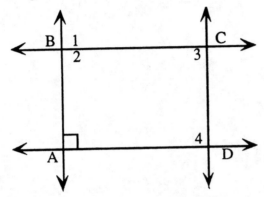

Because rectangle ABCD is a parallelogram, $\overleftrightarrow{BC} \parallel \overleftrightarrow{AD}$ and $\overleftrightarrow{AB} \parallel \overleftrightarrow{DC}$. Corresponding angles, $\angle BAD$ and $\angle 1$ are congruent, and thus $\angle 1$ is a right angle. Because $\angle 1$ and $\angle 2$ are supplementary, $\angle 2$ is a right angle. Similarly, it can be proved that $\angle 3$ and $\angle 4$ are right angles.

10.   30°

11.   (a)   11° 40' 47"
      (b)   5° 24' 0"

12.   (a)   70°
      (b)   70°
      (c)   70°
      (d)   110°
      (e)   70°

13.   (a)   Points A and C are outside, but point B is inside.
      (b)   Points A and B are inside, and point C is outside.
      In parts (a) and (b) you could choose a point that is on the outside and draw a segment to the indicated points. An odd number of intersection points indicates an interior point.

14.

$\overrightarrow{AX}$ bisects $\angle DAB$, so $\angle DAX \cong \angle XAB$. $\overrightarrow{AY}$ bisects $\angle BAC$, so $\angle BAY \cong \angle YAC$.

$m(\angle DAX) + m(\angle XAB) + m(\angle BAY) + m(\angle YAC) = 180°$.

Hence, $2m(\angle XAB) + 2m(\angle BAY) = 180°$ and $m(\angle XAB) + m(\angle BAY) = 90°$.

Therefore, $\angle XAY$ is a right angle. Hence $\overrightarrow{AX} \perp \overrightarrow{AY}$.

15. (a) Traversable,

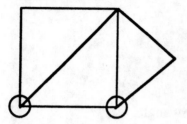

(b) Not traversable.
(c) Not traversable.

16. (a) For example,

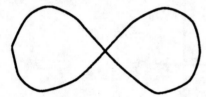

(b) For example,

17. TO SUPP.ANGLES :A
    FD 100
    BK 50
    RT :A
    FD 50
    BK 50
    RT 180-:A
    LT 180
    BK 50
    END

Answers to Sample Test

1. (a)   Yes. ASA   (b)   Yes. AAS   (c)   Yes. AAS
    (b)   Yes. SAS   (e)   Yes. SSS

2. (a) $\triangle QRS \cong \triangle TUV$ by AAS.
    (b) $\triangle GHI \cong \triangle JKL$ by SSS.
    (c) $\triangle ABD \cong \triangle CEF$ by ASA. (It must first be determined that m($\angle FCE$) is 60°.)
    (d) $\triangle ABE \cong \triangle CBD$ by SAS. (It must first be determined that $\angle A \cong \angle C$, because they are base angles of an isosceles triangle.)

3. Constructions.

4. (a) $\dfrac{55}{16}$ (b) $\dfrac{40}{3}$ (c) $\dfrac{10}{3}$ (d)   3

5. Construction.

6. Draw two nonparallel chords. Construct the perpendicular bisectors of each chord and extend them until they intersect. They intersect at the center of the circle.

7. (a)   T   (b)   F. A chord intersects a circle in two points.
    (c)   T   (d)   T

8. 488 cm

9. 48 m

10. Draw any diameter. Construct a diameter perpendicular to it. Bisect the right angles formed. The points of intersection of the diameters with the circle, and the angle bisectors with the circle are the vertices of the octagon.

11. (a)   False. In case of an obtuse triangle the center is in the exterior.
    (b)   False. In an equilateral triangle the two centers are the same. (This is because in an equilateral triangle the angle bisectors and the perpendicular bisectors of the sides are the same.)
    (c)   True. Each center is the same distance from line AB as from line AC and hence each center is on the angle bisector of $\angle A$.

12. No, the length of any side of a triangle must be less than the sum of the lengths of the other two sides. Note that $19 > 5 + 12$.

13. (a)   ABCD is a parallelogram.
    (b)   No, these two angles are supplementary, but not necessarily congruent.
    (c)   Yes, these two angles are congruent because they are alternate interior angles of parallel lines.

14. Answers may vary.

    (a) A side on one square is congruent to a side on the other square.
    (b) SAS
    (c) Equal radii

15. Any triangle with its third vertex on line AD is isosceles.

Answers to Sample Test

1. (a) $\triangle ABC \cong \triangle EDF$ (b) $\triangle ABC \cong \triangle PRQ$

2. Constructions.

3. (a)   Follows from $\triangle AMB \cong \triangle CMD$ which are congruent by SAS.
    (b)   From $\triangle AMB \cong \triangle CMB$ it follows that $\angle BAM \cong \angle DCM$ and hence that $\overline{AB} \parallel \overline{CD}$.

4. Construction.

5. (a) $x = \dfrac{20}{3}$; y cannot be determined from the given data.
    (b) $x = 6$

6. 308 cm

8. If the distance between the lines is d, the radius of the required circle is d/2. The center of the circle is on the line ℓ parallel to m and at the distance d/2 from m and from l. To locate the center, draw an arc with center at P and radius d/2; the points of intersection of the arc width ℓ are the possible centers of the required circle. There are two such circles.

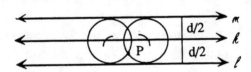

9. (a)   True by AA.
    (b)   False. In similar triangles the ratio between corresponding sides does not have to be 1.
    (c)   True by AA since all the angles are 60° angles.
    (d)   False. Two isosceles triangles may have non-congruent base angles.
    (e)   True. $\triangle BCE \sim \triangle DAE$ by AA; $\angle CBE \cong \angle EDA$ as they are alternate interior angles between the parallels $\overleftrightarrow{BC}$ and $\overleftrightarrow{AD}$ and the transversal $\overleftrightarrow{BD}$, and the angles at E are congruent as vertical angles.

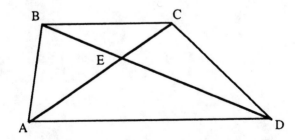

    (f)   True. If two sides of one angle are parallel respectively to two sides of a second angle, the angles must be congruent. (If a proof is desired extend two non-parallel sides of the angles and use corresponding angles to show that the angles are congruent.) Consequently the statement follows by AA.

10. Divide each of two adjacent sides of the square into five congruent segments and then construct lines parallel to the sides of the square.

11. Construction.

12. Construction.

13. No, the length of any side of a triangle must be less than the sum of the lengths of the other two sides. Note that $31 > 10 + 20$.

14. (a) ABCD is a parallelogram.
    (b) No, these two angles are supplementary, but not necessarily congruent.
    (c) Yes, these two angles are congruent because they are alternate interior angles of parallel lines.
    (d) No, because $\overline{AC}$ is not necessarily congruent to $\overline{BD}$. So there is no point to center our circle that is equidistant to points A, B, C, and D.

15. Answers may vary.

    (a) A side on one square is congruent to a side on the other square.
    (b) SAS
    (c) A side and an angle on one rhombus are congruent to a side and an angle on the other rhombus.
    (d) Two sides and the included angle on one parallelogram are congruent to two sides and the included angle on the other parallelogram.

Answers to Sample Test

1.
(a)

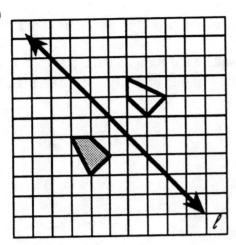

(b)

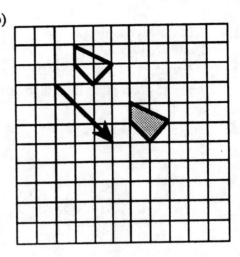

(c)

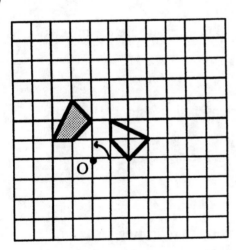

(d)

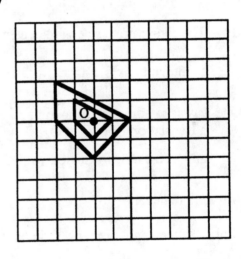

2. (a) 6   (b) 3

3. (a) Reflection or half turn
    (b) Slide, reflection, or half turn

4. (a)   (b)   (c)

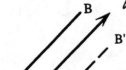

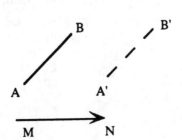

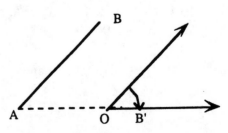

5.   Answers may vary.

6.   (a)   Rotation   (b)   Reflection   (c)   Rotation

7.   (a)   A line which is the perpendicular bisector of any pair of opposite sides has the property. There are two such lines.

   (b)   For squares. Because the diagonals of a square are perpendicular bisectors of each other, the lines containing the diagonals have the required property. Hence a square has four such lines.

   (c)   Isosceles trapezoids.

8.   (a)

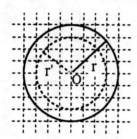

   (b)   The figure is a circle with center O and radius $\frac{3}{4}$ r because the image of every point is a point which is $\frac{3}{4}$ r away from O.

9.   One way is to apply the following transformations in succession; a translation from O to O_1,

   and a size transformation with center O_1 and scale factor $\frac{2}{3}$.

10.   Answers may vary.

11.   Hint: Use the angle bisector of the non-base angle as a reflecting line.

12.   Hint: Use the perpendicular bisector of $\overline{AB}$.

13.   (a)   True. $\triangle OAB \cong \triangle OA'B'$ by SAS since $\overline{OA} \cong \overline{OA'}$, $\overline{OB} \cong \overline{OB'}$ and the angles at O are vertical angles.

   (b)   True. From (a) by CPCTC $\angle B' \cong \angle B$ and hence $\angle B'$ is a right angle. Because $\overline{OB} \cong \overline{OB'}$ and $\overline{OB'} \perp \ell\,'$, OB' is the distance from O to $\ell\,'$.

   (c)   True. The angles at B are alternate interior angles between ℓ and $\ell\,'$ and the transversal $\overleftrightarrow{BB'}$.

   (d)   False. The image of $\overleftrightarrow{AA'}$ is $\overleftrightarrow{AA'}$.

14. What the student says is true for a single point, but not for the entire plane. For example, if B is on ℓ, then B', the image of B under the translation, is not the reflection of B in ℓ.

15. The measure of each interior angle in a regular pentagon is $\dfrac{3 \cdot 180°}{5}$ or 108°. Because 360 is not divisible by 108 a regular pentagon cannot tessellate the plane.

16.
```
TO H :S
    IF YCOR > 80 TOPLEVEL
    HE :S
    FORWARD 2*:S
    LEFT 90
    FORWARD :S
    RIGHT 90
    H :S
END
TO HE :S
    FORWARD 3*:S
    RIGHT 90
    FORWARD :S
    RIGHT 90
    FORWARD :S
    LEFT 90 FORWARD :S
    LEFT 90 FORWARD :S
    RIGHT 90 FORWARD S RIGHT 90
    FORWARD 3*:S
    RIGHT 90 FORWARD :S
    RIGHT 90 FORWARD :S
    LEFT 90 FORWARD :S
    LEFT 90 FORWARD :S
    RIGHT 90 FORWARD :S RIGHT 90
END
```

Answers to Sample Test

1.
(a)

(b)

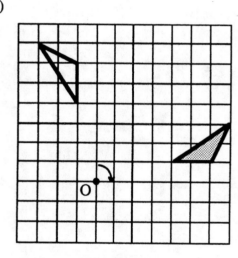

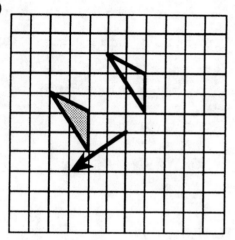

(c)

(d)

2.   (a)

(b)

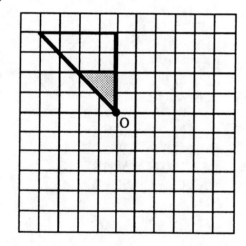

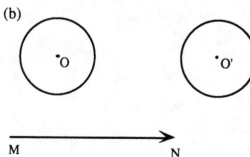

2. (cont.)

(c)

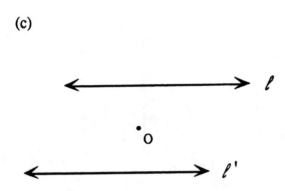

(d)

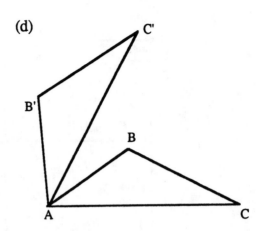

3. Hint: Try half-turns of the figure about midpoints of the sides.

4. (a) 1   (b) 1   (c) 5   (d) 6

5. (a) Neither
    (b) Neither
    (c) Rotational symmetries of 72°, 144°, 216°, 288°
    (d) Rotational symmetries of 60°, 120°,180°, 240°, 300°; Also has point symmetry

6. (a) Reflection   (b) Reflection
    (c) Translation   (d) Rotation

7. (a) 1   (b) 1   (c) 2   (d) 2

8. Hint: Use the line through the midpoints of parallel sides.

9. Find the image of ΔABC under a translation from B to A. Then apply to this image a reflection in the line BA. Finally apply a size transformation with center A and a scale factor of 2.

10. What the student says is true for a single point, but not for the entire plane, or even two points. If B' is the image of B (B ≠ A) under the same glide reflection, then the intersection of the line of reflection with $\overline{BB'}$ is different than O.

11. The student is correct. The half-turn is about the point of intersection of the ⊥ lines. If the ⊥ lines ℓ and m intersect at O, then A' is the reflection of A in ℓ, A'' is the reflection of A' in m, and A''' is the reflection of A'' in ℓ. Then A, A', A'' and A''' are vertices of a rectangle. Because the bisectors of a rectangle bisect each other at O, A'' is the image of A under a half-turn in O.

11.   (cont.)

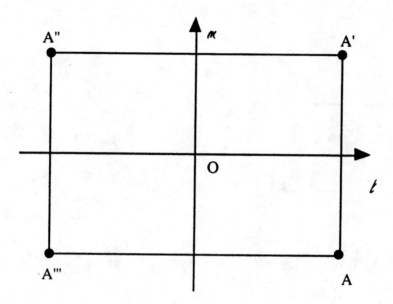

12.   A square with side the same length as a side of the octagon.

13.   TO HOUSE :S
      IF XCOR > 80 TOPLEVEL
      HOUS :S
      SETUP1 :S
      HOUS :S
      SETUP2 :S
      HOUSE :S
  END

  TO HOUSE :S
    SQUARE :S
    FORWARD :S
    TRIANGLE :S
  END

  TO SQUARE :S
    REPEAT 4[FORWARD :S RIGHT 90]
  END

  TO TRIANGLE :S
    REPEAT 3[FORWARD :S RIGHT 120]
  END

  TO SETUP1 :S
    FORWARD :S LEFT 30
    REPEAT 2[FORWARD :S RIGHT 90]
  END

  TO SETUP2 :S
    FORWARD :S LEFT 30
    FORWARD :S RIGHT 180
  END

Answers to Sample Test

1.

	mm	cm	m	km
(a)	52,000	5200	52	0.052
(b)	260,000	26,000	260	0.260
(c)	300,000	30,000	300	0.3
(d)	1,300,000	130,000	1300	1.3

2. (a) millimeter
   (b) centimeter
   (c) centimeter or millimeter
   (d) kilometer
   (e) meter or centimeter
   (f) meter
   (g) square kilometer
   (h) square kilometer
   (i) square centimeter
   (j) square millimeter
   (k) square meter
   (l) square centimeter

3. (a) 170 m^2
   (b) 12 cm^2

4. 170 cm^2

5. 8 cm^2

6. Yes. The sides must be of length $\sqrt{10}$ cm.

7. Given any triangle ABC as shown, another triangle A'B'C' can be constructed and placed to form parallelogram ABA'C. The area of parallelogram ABA'C is bh. Thus, the area of $\triangle ABC$ is $\frac{1}{2}$bh.

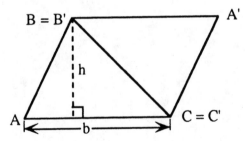

8. (a) 10 m
   (b) $18\pi \text{ m}^3$

9. $(48 + 18\pi) \text{ m}^2$

10. (a) Yes. $3^2 + 4^2 = 5^2$
    (b) Yes. $\left(\sqrt{2}\right)^2 + \left(\sqrt{3}\right)^2 = \left(\sqrt{5}\right)^2$

11. (a) 0.05
    (b) 18.000
    (c) 4
    (d) 0.3
    (e) 170,000
    (f) 27,000
    (g) 27
    (h) 4,738,000

12. (a) 2992   (b) 13.3   (c) 155.6
    (d) 3   (e) 72   (f) 89.6
    (g) 40.6

13. (a) 512   (b) 512,000 L   (c) 512,000 kg

14. (a) 3000   (b) 2000 L   (c) 13
    (d) 4200   (e) 0.00301

15. $12,000\pi$ cm^3

16. (a) 14π cm   (b) 49π cm^2 (c) $(49/20)\pi$ cm^2

17. $6\pi + 4$

Answers to Sample Test

1. (a)   150 cm^2 (b)   96 m^2

2. Hint: Use a diagonal of a trapezoid to divide it into two triangles.

3. (a)

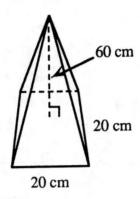

60 cm

20 cm

20 cm

    (b)   There are infinitely many possible pyramids. If a is the length of the side of the base
          and h the height of the pyramid, then the volume of the pyramid if (1/3)a^{2}h. We have
          (1/3)a^{2}h = 8000 or h = 24,000/a^2. Thus we may assign an arbitrary value for a and
          obtain a corresponding value for h.

4. The surface area is 16 times as great; the volume is 64 times as great.

5. (a)   1 km   (b)   2500 cm
    (c)   52 kg   (d)   26 m

6. (a)   44,800 cm^2 (b)   0.48 m^3 (c)   480 L

7. S.A. $= 7000\pi$ cm^2; V $= 50{,}000\sqrt{14}\,/\,3\pi$ cm^3

8. (a)   3000 L   (b)   3000 kg   (c)   1 cm

9. (a) $216\left(\sqrt{3}\right)$ m^2 (b) $\left(108\sqrt{21} + 216\sqrt{3}\right)$ m^2

10. (a) $10\sqrt{2}$ cm   (b)   6 cm   (c)   4

11. (a)   2112   (b)   14.4   (c)   27
    (d)   1779   (e)   137.6   (f)   -40
    (g)   37

Answers to Sample Test

1. Answers may vary.

2. (a) $y = \dfrac{5}{6}x + \dfrac{11}{3}$

    (b) $y = \dfrac{1}{4}x - 8$

    (c) $y = 3x - 19$

    (d) $y = {}^-7$

3. (a)

    (b)

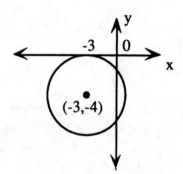

    (c)

    (d)

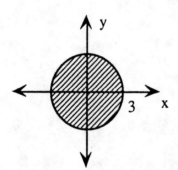

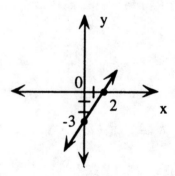

    (e)

    (f)

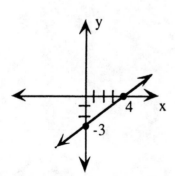

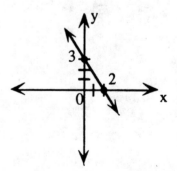

3. (cont.)

(g)

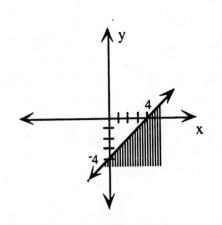

(h)

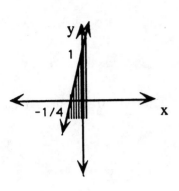

4. $(x-2)^2 + (y-6)^2 = 29$

5. $11 + \sqrt{109}$

6. (a) Infinitely many solutions.

(b) One solution $\left(\dfrac{7}{3}, 0\right)$.

(c) No solution.

7.

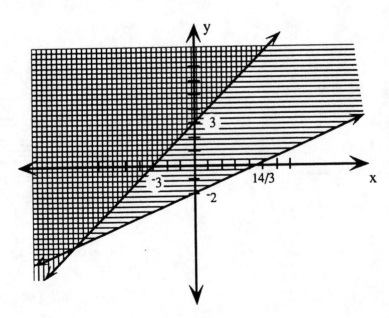

8. (a) Yes   (b) Yes   (c) Yes

9. $y = {}^-3x + 1$

Answers to Sample Test

1. The slope of $\overleftrightarrow{AB}$ is $\dfrac{8-4}{5-3}$ or 2. The slope of $\overleftrightarrow{CD}$ is $\dfrac{3-(^-1)}{8-6}$ or 2. Because the lines have the same slope they are parallel. Similarly the slopes of $\overleftrightarrow{BC}$ and $\overleftrightarrow{AD}$ are equal (each equals $\dfrac{^-5}{3}$).

    Thus $\overleftrightarrow{BC} \parallel \overleftrightarrow{AD}$ and ABCD is a parallelogram.

2. Answers vary.

3. A(0, 1/2), B(4/3, ⁻5/3), C(8,5)

4. (a)   1/6
    (b)   (4,⁻1)
    (c)   y = 5

5. (a)   x = ⁻1, y = 2
    (b)   The system has infinitely many solutions.
    (c)   No solutions.

6. $(x-5)^2 + (y+2)^2 = 13$

7. (a)   (b)

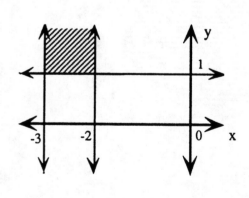

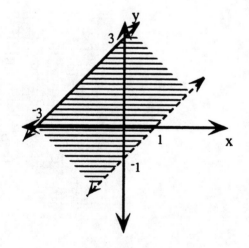

8. $y \le 3 - x$ 9.   133 quarters and 168 dimes
    $y \ge x$

10. Company A produces 12,000,000 cars while company B produces 36,000,000 cars.

11. (2,2)

1. $n^{50} > 2^n$ is not true for n = 1 because $1^{50} = 1$ and $2^1 = 2$, but $1 \not> 2$. Hence, the statement is not true for all values of n. Even though the statement is true for n = 2, 3, ..., 50 we could not conclude that it is true for all values of n greater than 1 because inductive reasoning does not assure the truth of a general statement. In fact, it can be shown that for n ≥ 439 the statement is false.

2.   A geometric sequence has been defined as one in which each successive term is obtained from the previous term by multiplying by a fixed number. The definition does not depend on any geometric interpretation. An arithmetic sequence does not fit that definition and hence is not geometric. (The only sequences that are both arithmetic and geometric are sequences in which all the terms are the same, e.g., the sequence 2, 2, 2, ...)

3.   Since the population is increasing, the ratio of the geometric sequence is greater than 1. Because the terms of such a geometric sequence increase faster than the terms of any arithmetic sequence, it is possible to show that given any increasing geometric sequence and any arithmetic sequence, for some n the nth term of the geometric sequence will exceed the nth term of the arithmetic sequence. From that n on, the terms of the geometric sequence will be greater than the corresponding terms of the arithmetic sequence.

4.   Look at the special cases:

$$1+2 = 3 = 2^2 - 1,$$
$$1+2+2^2 = \left(2^2 - 1\right) + 2^2 = 2 \cdot 2^2 - 1 = 2^3 - 1,$$
$$1+2+2^2+2^3 = \left(2^3 - 1\right) + 2^3 = 2 \cdot 2^3 - 1 = 2^4 - 1.$$

We can conjecture the expression

$$1 + 2 + 2^2 + 2^3 + ... + 2^{n-1} = 2^n - 1$$

for the sum of the first n terms of the sequence. This conjecture can be justified using material in later chapters. On the other hand, the (n+1)st term of the sequence is 2^{n+1-1} or 2^n. Thus, the sum of the first n terms of the sequence is one less than the (n+1)st term. Hence for large n the sum is very close to the (n+1)st term.

5.   In the first case, the calculator multiplies the terminating decimal 0.3333333 by 3 to yield the answer 0.9999999 which is also a terminating decimal. In the second case, $1 \div 3 = 0.\overline{3}$. The calculator stores more than the 8 digits which appear in the display and when it multiplies by 3 it rounds the answer to 1.

1. One way to designate the empty set is { }. Anything we enclose in the braces is an element of the set. Thus, $\{\emptyset\}$ is a set having one element, so it is not empty. The difficulty usually arises from the reluctance to consider the empty set as an element.

2. In fact it is true that $A \cup B = \{a,b,c,d,c,d\}$; however, because the agreement is not to list any element in a set more than once, $\{a, b, c, d, c, d\} = \{a, b, c, d\}$.

3. The student is right. To show that the hypothesis implies $B = C$ we show that $B \subseteq C$ and $C \subseteq B$. To show that $B \subseteq C$ let $x \in B$, then $x \in A \cup B$ and because $A \cup B = A \cup C$, $x \in A \cup C$. Consequently $x \in A$ or $x \in C$. If $x \in C$ then $B \subseteq C$. If $x \in A$ then since we started with $x \in B$ it follows that $x \in A \cap B$. Because $A \cap B = A \cap C$ we conclude that $x \in A \cap C$ and therefore $x \in C$. Thus $B \subseteq C$. Similarly starting with $x \in C$ it can be shown that $x \in B$ and hence that $C \subseteq B$.

4. No. For example, the set of all rational numbers greater than or equal to 0 and less than or equal to 1 is an infinite set whose greatest element is 1.

5. The student is incorrect The student is distributing the complement bar over A and B. The student should be encouraged to check the assertion $\overline{A \cap B} = \overline{A} \cap \overline{B}$ with an example and with a Venn diagram.

6. What the student said is true if $B \subseteq A$ or $B = \emptyset$. However, in general, $\overline{A} \cap \overline{B} \neq \overline{A}$. Consider $U = \{1,2,3,4\}$, $A = \{1\}$, and $B = \{2\}$. Here $\overline{A} = \{2,3,4\}$ and $\overline{A} \cap \overline{B} = \{3,4\} \neq \overline{A}$.

7. Since "formula" is not defined, it is really impossible to answer the question. Most likely, students view a formula as a single equation. If this is the case, the concepts are not the same. Students are usually misled by the fact that many functions which appear in mathematical applications are given by equations. However, not every equation represents a function; for example, let $x = y^2$. For every $x \neq 0$, there are two corresponding values of y, and hence the equation does not define a function.

8. The student is wrong. If, for example, $A = \{1, 2, 3\}$ and $B = \{2, 3, 4\}$, then neither $A \subseteq B$ or $B \subseteq A$.

9. Even though the Cartesian product of sets includes all pairings in which each element of the first set is the first component in a pair with each element of the second set, this is not necessarily a one-to-one correspondence. A one-to-one correspondence implies that there must be the same number of elements in each set. This is not the case in Cartesian product. For example, consider sets $A = \{1\}$ and $B = \{a, b\}$.

11. Addition is not an operation defined for sets. Neither is union an operation defined for numbers. Possibly the confusion arises from addition being defined in terms of union. If two sets, A and B, are not disjoint, then the number of elements in the union of A and B is not the same as the sum of the cardinal numbers of elements of each of the sets.

1. The expressions are not equal because $2 \cdot (3 \cdot 4) = 2 \cdot 12 = 24$ and $(2 \cdot 3) \cdot (2 \cdot 4) = 6 \cdot 8 = 48$. There is no distributive property of multiplication over multiplication.

2. No. The first equation is true because $39 + 41 = 39 + (1 + 40) = (39 + 1) + 40 = 40 + 40$. Now, $39 \cdot 41 = (40 - 1) \cdot (40 + 1) = (40 - 1) \cdot 40 + (40 - 1) \cdot 1 = 40^2 - 40 + 40 - 1 = 40^2 - 1$, and $40^2 - 1 \neq 40^2$.

3. Yes. If $a < b$, we can write $a = bq + r$, where $q = 0$ and $r = a$. Notice that in this case, we still have $0 \leq r < b$. For example, if $a = 3$ and $b = 5$, then $3 = 0 \cdot 5 + 3$.

4. They are equal in value because multiplication is commutative; 5 times 4 means $5 \cdot 4$; 5 multiplied by 4 is $4 \cdot 5$; and $5 \cdot 4 = 4 \cdot 5$.

5. $0 + 0 = x$ if and only if $0 = 0 \cdot x$. Any number x solves the last equation, and consequently $0 \div 0$ does not have a unique value. Suppose $0 \div 0 = 1$. Because $0 = 0 \cdot 2$, if we divide both sides of the equation by 0, then $1 = 1 \cdot 2$ or $1 = 2$. Thus, $0 \div 0 = 1$ leads to a contradiction, and consequently it cannot be defined as 1.

6. Evidently the student does not understand the process of long division. The repeated subtraction method should help in understanding the above mistake.

$$
\begin{array}{r|l}
6\, \lceil\overline{\,36\,} & \\
\underline{6} & 1\ \text{six} \\
30 & \\
\underline{30} & \underline{5\ \text{sixes}} \\
 & 6\ \text{sixes}
\end{array}
$$

Instead of adding 1 and 5, the student wrote 15.

7. It is correct. Because M is a special symbol for 1000, it is preferable to write MI for 1001 rather than $\overline{\text{I}}\text{I}$. Romans usually reserved the bar for numbers greater than 4000.

8. The student probably incorrectly generalized the associative property as follows: $(x + 7) \div 7 = x + (7 \div 7) = x + 1$. The teacher should emphasize that the associative property holds only when all the operations performed are additions or all are multiplications. When other operations are performed, the associative property does not generally hold. Another possibility is that the student ignored the parentheses yet used the correct order of operations. If this was the case the role of parentheses should be discussed.

9. No, $x \div x = 1$ if and only if $x \neq 0$. If $x = 0$, then $x \div x = 0 \div 0$, which is not defined. (See Question 5.)

10. The following should be discussed. $\left(2^3\right)^2 = 2^3 \cdot 2^3 = 2^6$. On the other hand $2^{\left(3^2\right)} = 2^9$.

11. In general, $a \div (b - c) \neq (a \div b) - (a \div c)$. For example, $100 \div (25 - 5) \neq (100 \div 25) - (100 \div 5)$. In fact the right-hand side is $4 - 20$, which is not defined in the set of whole numbers. However, the right distributive property of division over subtraction does hold provided each expression is defined in the set of whole numbers; that is $(b - c) \div a = (b \div a) - (c \div a)$.

12.   The student probably has in mind the fact that if a ∈ W, a − 0 = a. It should be pointed out that 0 would be the identity for subtraction if 0 - a = a was also true. Since 0 - a is not defined in the set of whole numbers, 0 - a ≠ a and therefore 0 is not the identity for subtraction.

13.   Any number can be represented by a directed arrow of a given length. In this case the directed arrow represents 3 units. Any arrow 3 units in length can be used to represent 3, regardless of its starting point.

1. The algorithm is correct, and the student should be congratulated for finding it. One way to encourage such creative behavior is to name and refer to the procedure after the student who invented it - for example, "David's subtraction method." In fourth grade the technique can be explained by using a money model. Suppose you have $4 in one checking account and $80 in another, for a total of $84. You spent $27 by withdrawing $7 from the first account and $20 from the second. The first checking account is overdrawn by $3; that is, the balance is -$3. The balance in the second account is $60. After transferring $3 from the second account to the first, the balance in the first account is $0 and in the second $57; that is, the total balance is $57.

2. The student is correct that a debt of $5 is greater than a debt of $2. However, what this means is that on a number line $^-5$ is farther to the left than is $^-2$. The fact that $^-5$ is farther to the left than $^-2$ on a number line implies that $^-5 < {}^-2$.

3. The student does not complete the argument in details. Indeed a - b = a + $^-$b. However, b - a = b + $^-$a. In general, a + $^-$b $\neq$ b + -a. For example, 5 + $^-2 \neq 2 + {}^-5$.

4. The student is using an analogy in thinking that multiplication and addition behave in the same way. If such arguments were always correct, it would follow that since a·1 = a, then a + 1 = a. An example such as $(2+3)^2 \neq 2^2 + 3^2$ shows that the general case cannot be true. The proofs for the general case can be given to show the difference in the two expressions. By the associative and commutative properties of multiplication, $(ab)^2 = (ab)(ab) = (aa)(aa) = a^2b^2$. A complete expansion of $(a + b)^2$ using the distributive property gives the following:
$$(a + b)^2 = (a + b)(a + b) = (a + b)a + (a + b)b = a^2 + ba + ab + b^2 = a^2 + 2ab + b^2$$

5. The solution set of the given inequality has infinitely many elements, and it would be impossible to substitute all the solutions into the original inequality. However, it is possible to check and see if a particular element of the solution set satisfies the original inequality. For example, x = 1 is indeed a solution since 1 < 2. To see if x = 1 is a solution, we substitute x = 1 in the original inequality and obtain $1 - 2 \cdot 1 > 1 - 5$, or -1 > -4. Since the inequality is true, x = 1 is a solution.
    There is a method of showing that all x such that x < 2 satisfies the original inequality. By reversing the process by which the original inequality was solved, we have: x < 2 implies 3x < 6 and hence 3x - 5 < 6 - 5, or 3x - 5 < 1. Adding -2x to both sides of the last inequality, the original inequality 1 - 2x > x - 5 is obtained.

6. This student does not fully understand the order of operations. The teacher should emphasize that in order to avoid ambiguity, mathematicians agree that multiplication is performed before addition or subtraction. A few simpler examples like $10 - 2 \cdot 3$ should be helpful.

7. The procedure can be justified as follows. Since for all integers c, $-c = (-1)c$, the effect of performing the opposite of an algebraic expression is the same as multiplying the expression by $^-$1. However, in the expression x - (2x - 3), the - is used to denote subtraction not simply finding the opposite. If the expression is first rewritten as x + $^-$(2x + $^-$3), then it is the case that $^-$(2x + $^-$3) = $^-$1(2x + $^-$3) or $^-$2x + 3. Now the expression can be rewritten as x + $^-$2x + 3 which a student might obtain from the father's rule.

8.   No. The check only shows that the equations are correctly solved. It is possible that the equations were not set up correctly; that is, that they do not represent the information given in the word problem. In such a case, without following the written information, it would be impossible to detect the error.

9.   It is quite possible that the student has used a circular argument in this proof. The teacher would need to know how the cancellation property of multiplication involving integers was proved. Most likely, the proof used the fact that $(-1)(-1) = 1$. If so, then there is an error in the reasoning.

10.   The picture is suppose to illustrate the fact that an integer and its opposite are mirror images of each other. Because a could be negative, the picture is correct. For example, possible values for a and $^-$a are: a = $^-$1, $^-$a = 1 and a = $^-$7, $^-$a = 7. At this point the teacher could remind the students that the "-" sign in $^-$a does not mean that $^-$a is negative; if a is positive $^-$a is negative, but if a is negative $^-$a is positive.

1. Yes. The student's conclusion is that $a \mid 0$ and this is true because $a \cdot 0 = 0$.

2. The student is generalizing the statement "if $d \mid a$ and $d \mid b$, then $d \mid (a + b)$" to the corresponding statement for "does not divide." (Generalizations have to be checked carefully.) The statement the student wrote is false, since—for example—$3 \mid 7$ and $3 \mid 2$, but $3 \mid (7 + 2)$.

3. It has been shown that any four-digit number n can be written in the form
$n = a \cdot 10^3 + b \cdot 10^2 + c \cdot 10 + d = (a \cdot 999 + b \cdot 99 + c \cdot 9) + (a + b + c)$. The test for divisibility by some number g will depend on the sum of the digits $a + b + c + d$ if and only if $g \mid (a \cdot 999 + b \cdot 99 + c \cdot 9)$ regardless of the values of a, b, and c. Since the only numbers greater than 1 that divide 9, 99, and 999 are 3 and 9, the test for divisibility by dividing the sum of the digits by the number works only for 3 and 9. A similar argument works for any n-digit number.

4. The student is wrong. For example, 1029 is divisible by 7, but neither 29 or 10 is divisible by 7. However, it is true that a number with an even number of digits is divisible by 7 if each of the numbers formed by pairing the digits into groups of two is divisible by 7. The proof for any six-digit number follows. (The proof for any number with an even number of digits is similar.) Let $a \cdot 10^5 + b \cdot 10^4 + c \cdot 10^3 + d \cdot 10^2 + e \cdot 10 + f$ be any six digit number such that 7 divides each of the two-digit numbers $a \cdot 10 + b, c \cdot 10 + d$, and $e \cdot 10 + f$. The number, n, can be written as follows: $n = a \cdot 10^5 + b \cdot 10^4 + c \cdot 10^3 + d \cdot 10^2 + e \cdot 10 + f = (a \cdot 10 + b)10^4 + (c \cdot 10 + d)10^2 + (e \cdot 10 + f)$. Since 7 divides $(e \cdot 10 + f)$, $(c \cdot 10 + d)$, and $(a \cdot 10 + b)$ it follows from the basic properties of divisibility that $7 \mid \left[(a \cdot 10 + b)10^4 + (c \cdot 10 + d)10^2 + (e \cdot 10 + f) \right]$.

5. It is very hard to refute the student's claim, since there are infinitely many primes. We can say that unlike finding successive counting numbers, where it is possible to produce the next number by adding one, there is no known way to produce the next prime from a given prime number.

6. It is true that a number is divisible by 21 if and only if it is divisible by 3 and by 7. However, the general statement is false. For example, 12 is divisible by 4 and by 6 but not by 4·6, or 24. One part of the statement is true—that is, "if a number is divisible by a·b, then it is divisible by a and by b." The statement "if a number is divisible by a and by b, it is divisible by ab" is true if a and b are relatively prime. To see why this is true, suppose that $GCD(a, b) = 1$ and m is an integer such that $a \mid m$ and $b \mid m$. Since $a \mid m$, $m = ka$ for some integer k. Now $b \mid m$ implies that $b \mid ka$. Since a and b are relatively prime, it follows from the Fundamental Theorem of Arithmetic and the fact that $b \mid ka$ that $b \mid k$ (Why?), and therefore $k = jb$, for some integer j. Substituting $k = jb$ in $m = ka$, we obtain $m = jba$, and consequently $ab \mid m$.

7. The student is partially correct. If a and b are distinct natural numbers, then the student is correct. By definition, $a \leq LCM(a, b)$; $b \leq LCM(a, b)$. Also $GCD(a, b) \leq a$ and $GCD(a, b) \leq b$. Hence, $GCD(a, b) \leq LCM(a, b)$. However, the equality holds if $a = b$.

8. $x = 3k, y = 4k, z = 5k$ satisfies the equation for any integer k, Hence the student is right.

9. The number 1 is not a prime because it does not have exactly two divisors; it has only one.

10. In finding the least common denominator of fractions, one must find the least common multiple of the denominators. Thus, the least common multiple of a set of denominators is the least common denominator.

1. Since nothing has been said about the domain of x, the student's answer is correct if the student assumes and states the assumption that x is an integer. If the domain is the set of rational numbers or the set of real numbers, then the answer is not correct.

2. The student is wrong unless n = 0 or p = m. For example, $\frac{5}{6} = \frac{3+2}{4+2} \neq \frac{3}{4}$. Notice that

    $\frac{m+n}{p+n} = \frac{m}{p}$ is equivalent to each of the following:

    $$(m+n) \cdot p = (p+n) \cdot m$$
    $$mp + np = pm + nm$$
    $$mp + np = mp + nm$$
    $$np = nm$$

    This last equation is equivalent if n = 0 or m = p. Therefore $\frac{m+n}{p+n} = \frac{m}{p}$ if and only if

    n = 0 or m = p.

3. The student was probably thinking that more pieces meant more pizza. A pizza (or circle) could be cut into 6 pieces, then each piece could be cut into 2 pieces. This shows the amount of pizza did not change from these last cuts, only the number of pieces changed.

4. The student is generalizing the distributive property of multiplication over addition into the distributive property of multiplication over multiplication, which does not hold. For example,

    $\frac{1}{2}\left(\frac{1}{3} \cdot \frac{1}{4}\right) = \frac{1}{2} \cdot \frac{1}{12} = \frac{1}{24}$, but $\left(\frac{1}{2} \cdot \frac{1}{3}\right)\left(\frac{1}{2} \cdot \frac{1}{4}\right) = \frac{1}{6} \cdot \frac{1}{8} = \frac{1}{48}$.

5. It is true that the new ratio in the class is $\frac{2+4}{3+6}$, or $\frac{6}{9}$; however, this ratio does not equal $\frac{2}{3} + \frac{4}{6}$.

    Also, $\frac{2}{3} + \frac{4}{6} = \frac{4}{3}$; however, $\frac{2+4}{3+6} = \frac{6}{9} = \frac{2}{3}$. Hence $\frac{2}{3} + \frac{4}{6} \neq \frac{2}{3}$. The student's definition of

    addition of fractions contradicts many properties of addition. For example, $\frac{1}{2} + \frac{2}{2}$ is greater than

    1; however, using the student's definition of addition, we obtain $\frac{1}{2} + \frac{2}{2} = \frac{1+2}{2+2} = \frac{3}{4}$, which is less

    than 1.

6. The teacher was right; Nat obtained the correct answer by using an incorrect method because in general $a + b(x + c) \neq (a + b)(x + c)$. Some advanced student could be encouraged to find other equations for which a similar mistake will produce a correct answer. This will happen if the equations $a + b(x + c) = x + d$ and $(a + b)(x + c) = x + d$ have the same solution. This can be shown to happen if and only if d = a + b + c - 1 Consequently a, b and c can be chosen at will but d is determined by the above equation.

7. $\frac{0}{6}$ is not in simplest form. A fraction $\frac{a}{b}$ is in simplest form if and only if GCD(a, b) = 1; however

GCD(0, 6) = 6. The simplest form of $\frac{0}{6}$ is $\frac{0}{1}$.

8. Let the number be a. One half of a is $\frac{1}{2} \cdot a = \frac{a}{2}$. Dividing a by $\frac{1}{2}$ is $a \div \frac{1}{2} = a \cdot \frac{2}{1} = 2a$.

Consequently, the student is wrong

9. The first student's approach is correct. What the second student has done is to treat the problem

as if had been $\frac{1}{5} \cdot \frac{5}{3} = \frac{1}{3}$, when in reality, the problem is $\frac{15}{53}$. Writing the problem as $\frac{10+5}{50+3}$ may

help him or her understand the problem.

10. The student has incorrectly applied the property which says that multiplying both sides of an

inequality by a negative number reverses the inequality. When both sides of the inequality $\frac{x}{7} < {}^-1$

are multiplied by 7, a positive number, we obtain, $x < {}^-7$, and not $x > {}^-7$. Probably the student

seeing $^-1$ in $\frac{x}{7} < {}^-1$ thinks that the inequality is multiplied by $^-1$ and consequently reverses the

inequality.

11. (a) No. Because $\frac{2}{3} - \frac{1}{2} = \frac{1}{6}$ and $\frac{3}{4} - \frac{2}{3} = \frac{1}{12}$ there is no fixed number that can be added to each

    term in order to obtain the next term.

    (b) No. The difference between each term and the preceding one is not fixed. In fact, this is a

    geometric sequence because each term can be multiplied by $\left(\frac{1}{2}\right)^{-3}$ to obtain the next term.

12. Yes, the student is correct. Suppose that the fractions are positive and $\frac{a}{b} < \frac{c}{d}$ This inequality is

equivalent to ad < bc. The student claims that $\frac{a}{b} < \frac{a+c}{b+d} < \frac{c}{d}$. This is equivalent to

a(b + d) < b(a + c) and (a + c)d < c(b + d). However, each of the last inequalities is equivalent to

ad < bc.

13. Yes, the student is correct. Let $\frac{a}{b} = \frac{c}{d} = r$. Then a = br, c = dr, and therefore

$\frac{a+c}{b+d} = \frac{br+dr}{b+d} = \frac{r(b+d)}{b+d} = r = \frac{a}{b} = \frac{c}{d}$.

14. No. For example, $\frac{1}{{}^-3} < \frac{1}{2}$, but $^-3$ is not greater than 2. However, if x and y are both positive or

both negative, the conclusion is true. (To prove this, multiply both sides of $\frac{1}{x} < \frac{1}{y}$ by xy.)

15. The student is wrong. For example, if x < 2, $\frac{1}{2} < 2$, but if x = $\frac{1}{4}$, then $\frac{1}{1/4} = 4 \not< \frac{1}{4}$.

1. $3\ 1/4\% = 3\% + 1/4\% = 3/100 + (1/4)/100 = 0.03 + 0.0025 = 0.0325$. Knowing that $1/4 = 0.25$, the student incorrectly wrote $1/4\% = 0.25$.

2. The principal square root of 25, written, $\sqrt{25}$ is defined to be the nonnegative number whose square is 25. Consequently, $\sqrt{25} = 5$.

3. The principal square root of a^2 is always nonnegative. Hence, $\sqrt{a^2} = a$ if $a > 0$. If $a < 0$, then $-a$ is positive, and hence $\sqrt{a^2} = -a$. For example, if $a = -5$, then $\sqrt{(-5)^2} = -(-5) = 5$. Consequently the student is wrong.

4. All properties of integral exponents do not automatically extend to rational exponents. The corresponding properties for rational exponents have to be justified. The property $\left(a^m\right)^n = a^{mn}$ is true when a is nonnegative and m and n are rational numbers. For $a < 0$, m is an even integer and $n = 1/m$, the property is false. For example, $\left((-5)^2\right)^{1/2} \neq -5$.

5. Most likely, the student thinks that $-x$ is a negative number. This is wrong. Depending upon the value of x, $-x$ can be positive, negative, or 0. If $x < 0$, then $-x > 0$. In fact, $x = -9$ is the solution of the given equation.

6. The student assumed that $\sqrt{-7}$ is not a real number. That is correct, but does not answer the question. Every real number squared is greater than or equal to -7.

7. It is possible to mark up the price of a product 150%. For example, if a product sells for $10, then a 150% markup is $1.5(\$10) = \$15$. Thus, the product would sell for $25.

8. Scientific notation is typically used for very large numbers or very small numbers (numbers close to 0). In scientific notation, a number N is written in the form $N = A \cdot 10^n$ where $1 \leq A < 10$. Thus, negative numbers are not considered in this definition. If this notation is to be used with negative numbers, we can work with the number as if it were a positive number and then annex a negative sign at the end, for example, $-2,390,000$ could be written as $-2.39 \cdot 10^6$.

9. In the second method, the student did not use the distributive property correctly. Notice that $(8 + 1/2)\ (6 + 1/2) = (8 + 1/2)6 + (8 + 1/2)(1/2)$. Because $(8 + 1/2)6 = 8 \cdot 6 + (1/2)6 = 48 + 3$, the 3 is missing in the student's example. Adding 3 to the student's answer results in the correct answer of $55\ 1/4$.

10. 0.36 can be written as 36/100 and 0.9 can be written as 9/10. Comparing the numerators of the fractions will not determine which fraction is larger because the denominators are different. To compare the fractions, they need to have the same denominator. Because $0.9 = 0.90 = 90/100$ and 90 is greater than 36, $0.9 > 0.36$.

11. (a)   The calculator does not carry the decimals out far enough to compare the two numbers.

(b) $\dfrac{9444}{9445} > \dfrac{9443}{9444}$ is equivalent to each of the following:

$$\frac{9444}{9445} - \frac{9443}{9444} > 0,$$

$$\frac{9444^2 - 9443 \cdot 9445}{9444} > 0$$

The last inequality is true if and only if the numerator of the fraction is positive. Using a calculator we find that $9444^2 - 9443 \cdot 9445 = 1$ and hence that

$$\frac{9444}{9445} > \frac{9443}{9444}$$

It is possible to determine which fraction is greater with fewer calculations as follows.

$$\frac{9443}{9444} = \frac{9444 - 1}{9444} = 1 - \frac{1}{9444} \quad \text{and} \quad \frac{9444}{9445} = \frac{9445 - 1}{9445} = 1 - \frac{1}{9445}.$$

Because $\dfrac{1}{9445} < \dfrac{1}{9444}, \ \dfrac{^-1}{9445} > \dfrac{^-1}{9444}$ and hence, $1 - \dfrac{1}{9445} > 1 - \dfrac{1}{9444}$

Yet another approach is to multiply each decimal equivalent by 10. Because $\dfrac{9444}{9445} \cdot 10$ is displayed as 9.998412 and $\dfrac{9443}{9444} \cdot 10$ as 9.89411, the first fraction is the greater one. However this approach will not work to show that $\dfrac{94444}{94445} > \dfrac{94443}{94444}$.

12. By definition, $\sqrt{5}$ is the principal square root of 5, and has one value, the nonnegative number b such that $b^2 = 5$. The solutions of $x^2 = 5$ are $\sqrt{5}$ and its opposite $^-\sqrt{5}$. Both solutions are written as $\pm\sqrt{5}$.

13. Let s denote the amount of salary. After p% increase, the new salary is s(1 + p/100). When this amount is decreased by q%, the result is s(1 + p/100)(1 - q/100). Similarly if the initial salary is first decreased by q% and then the new amount is raised by p%, the final salary is s(1 - q/100)(1 + p/100). Because the two expressions are equal, the student is right.

14. By definition p% = p/100 where p is any real number. Hence 0.01% = 0.01/100. Because 0.01/100 ≠ 0.01, the student is wrong.

1. Each toss of a fair coin is independent of the previous one. Hence the probability of a tail on each toss is $\frac{1}{2}$ regardless of how many tails appeared in previous tosses.

2. If the four areas corresponding to the colors were equal in size, the events of the spinner landing on each of the colors would be equally likely, and the student would be correct. However, since the four areas are different in size, the events are not equally likely, and the student is wrong.

3. Tossing 3 heads on the first 3 tosses of a coin does not imply the coin is unfair. Only when a fair coin is tossed a much greater number of times can we expect to get approximately equal numbers of tails and heads. The probability of 3 heads in 3 tosses is $\frac{1}{8}$.

4. The student is wrong. The sample space for this event is not {HH, HT, TT}, but rather {HH, HT, TH, TT}. Consequently the probability of HH is $\frac{1}{4}$.

5. The student is not correct. The confusion probably lies in the fact that the student thinks that probabilities are additive. The student does not understand the Multiplication Rule for Probabilities. A tree diagram for the experiment could possibly help. A partial tree diagram is given below

$$\xrightarrow{\frac{1}{6}} 5 \xrightarrow{\frac{1}{6}} 5$$

$$\text{Thus } P(5,5) = \frac{1}{6} \cdot \frac{1}{6} = \frac{1}{36}$$

6. For an experiment with sample space S with equally likely outcomes, the probability of an event A is given by $P(A) = \frac{n(A)}{n(S)}$. Because an event A must be a subset of S, the smallest that n(A) could be is 0. This occurs when A = ∅. Because n(S) is never negative and n(A) is never negative, then the P(A) can never be negative.

7. The probability of an event is a ratio and does not necessarily reflect the number of elements in the event or in the sample space. For example, if n(S) = 20 and n(A) = 12, then $P(A) = \frac{12}{20}$ which could also be reported as $P(A) = \frac{3}{5}$.

8. The student is confused about choosing four objects none at a time. In any set of choices, there is always the option of choosing nothing, and there is one way to choose nothing. Therefore, we say $4P_0 = 1$.

9. We define 0! as 1 because it fits the formula for combinations. It is also not inconsistent with the rest of mathematics. To define 1/0 as 1 would cause many inconsistencies. If 1/0 = 1 and 1/1 = 1, then 1/0 = 1/1 which should imply that 0 = 1. This is not true.

1. The new mean is $\dfrac{9 \cdot (10000) + 20000}{10} = 11{,}000$. Consequently the new mean has increased by $1000. The median and mode may be changed in special cases, for example, if the scores were 2000, 8000, 8000, 8000, 9000, 10,000, 12,000, 12,000, 13,000, and 18,000, then the median and mode change.

2. A first discussion might include asking what the student means by the "best average." If the student is thinking of choosing from the mean, median, or mode, then we need to discuss which is the most appropriate. The mode is used if it is desirable to know which value occurs most often in a distribution. For example, if a store wants to know which size pants is most frequently sold, the mode is the most appropriate average to use.

3. The student is not correct. The stem and leaf plot is very useful when trying to organize information that will later be used to make a bar graph or a frequency polygon. It is not the most useful plot when trying to depict information that will be organized into a circle graph for example.

4. Since the median is 90, at least half of the class had grades of 90 or more. Since Tom scored 80, he did not do better than half of the class.

5. A graph displays the data in a way that is possible to see at a glance how parts of the data compare to each other. One of the disadvantages of graphical representation is that it is not always possible to obtain accurate readings from graphs.

6. In a grouped frequency table, the precise value of the raw data is not displayed, and hence it is impossible to conclude from the table which value occurs most often. Consequently it is impossible to find the exact mode from the information given in a grouped frequency table. In this situation the mode is usually given as a class interval.

7. If the mean is less than the median, then one can be certain that there were more scores above the mean than below it. The low scores tend to be further from the mean than the high scores.

8. No, it is not possible to have a standard deviation of $^-5$ By definition, the standard deviation is the positive square root of the variance.

9. Mel did not really miss the cut-off by a single point. He would have had to increase his score on each of the 10 tests by a single point to reach an average of 90 or increase his total score for the 10 tests by 10 points to reach an average of 90.

10. Bar graphs are typically used to display data that is not continuous, for example, the number of students in each sixth grade class at Washington School. They are used when data falls into distinct categories and we want to compare the totals. The line graph is more appropriate when we want to emphasize trends in data that change continuously over time.

1.   The distinct lines are parallel if they do not intersect and are contained in a single plane. Lines which do not intersect and are not contained in any single plane are called skew lines. Many of the properties of parallel lines depend upon the fact that they are contained in a single plane and therefore do not share these properties with skew lines.

2.   The measure of an angle has nothing to do with the fact that rays cannot be measured. The measure of an angle in degrees is based on constructing a circle with center at the vertex of the angle and dividing the circle into 360 congruent parts. The number of parts in the arc that the angle intercepts is the measure of the given angle in degrees. The number of parts in the intercepted arc is the same regardless of the size of the circle (or protractor).

3.   A regular polygon is a polygon in which all the angles are congruent and all the sides are congruent. In general neither condition implies the other, and hence neither is sufficient to describe a regular polygon. For example, a rhombus that is not a square has all sides congruent, but all its angles are not congruent. A rectangle that is not a square has all its angles congruent, but not all its sides are congruent.

4.   Let n be the number of sides of a regular polygon, all of whose angles measure 90 degrees. The sum of the measures of all the interior angles is $n \cdot 90$ and also $(n - 2)180$. Consequently, $n \cdot 90 = (n - 2)180$. This equation has the solution $n = 4$. Thus, the polygon must have 4 sides, and therefore it is necessarily a square.

5.   If two parallel lines are defined as lines which are in the same plane and do not intersect, then two identical lines cannot be parallel, because their intersection is nonempty. It is possible to define two identical lines as parallel or nonparallel. Some books define it one way; other books the other way.

6.   The student is wrong. Some pairs of such lines are indeed skew lines; others, however, are parallel. For example, consider the line determined by the intersection of the same wall and the floor. These two lines are in the planes of the classroom ceiling and classroom floor and are parallel. They are contained in the plane of the wall.

7.   The answer is no. If lines were great circles, then all lines would intersect in two points.

8.   Since an angle is a set of points determined by two rays with the same endpoint, to say that two angles are equal implies that the two sets of points determining the angles are equal. The only way this can happen is if the two angles are actually the same angle. To say that two angles are congruent is to say that the angles have the same size or measure.

9.   The student is incorrect. While the degree is the basic unit of angle measure, it can be further subdivided. This in itself would prove that the student is incorrect. However, many geometry books also consider a Protractor Postulate which puts all the rays in a half-line emanating from a point in a one-to-one correspondence with the real numbers greater than or equal to 0 and less than 180. This would allow infinitely many rays emanating from one point.

1. The symbol ≅ is used only for congruent parts. Because AB and CD designate length of segments and not the segments themselves, it is not true that AB ≅ CD. Notice that if segments are congruent, then they are of the same length; hence it is correct to write AB = CD.

2. Some of the constructions that cannot be done using a compass and straightedge are angle trisection, duplication of a cube, and squaring the circle. Given any angle, it is impossible with only a compass and straightedge to find two rays which divide the angle into three congruent angles. Some angles, but not all, can be trisected with straightedge and compass. For example, a right angle can be trisected. The duplication of a cube involves constructing the edge of a cube whose volume is twice the volume of a given cube. Squaring a circle involves constructing a square which has the same area as a given circle. For over 2000 years mathematicians tried to perform these three constructions. In the nineteenth century it was finally proved that these constructions cannot be done with straightedge and compass alone. A clear exposition of these proofs can be found in the book by Courant and Robbins, What Is Mathematics? (London: Oxford University Press, 1941 and 1969, pp. 117-140).

3. Perhaps the "best" definition relies on transformational geometry discussed in Chapter 12. Two figures can be defined to be congruent if and only if one figure can be mapped onto the other by successively applying a translation, reflection, rotation, or glide reflection. For similarity add a size transformation.

4. For a detailed discussion of the trisection problem, see The Trisection Problem. by Robert Yates (Washington, D. C.: NCTM Publications, 1971).

5. The student is wrong. ∠1 ≅ ∠2 implies that $\overline{AD}$ and $\overline{BC}$ are parallel, but does not imply that the other two sides are parallel.

6. This is false. Consider, for example, a rectangle which is not a square. The polygon resulting from connecting the midpoints of the sides of the rectangle is a rhombus with no right angles. Such a rhombus is not similar to the rectangle.

7. The symbol = is used for identical objects. Two triangles are equal if they represent the same set of points. Congruent triangles are not necessarily identical because their positions may be different.

8. The student is wrong. The student is forgetting that when we say ΔABC is congruent to ΔBCA, this means that there is a one-to-one correspondence set up among the vertices so that corresponding sides are congruent. If ΔABC is congruent to ΔBCA, then $\overline{AB} \cong \overline{BC}$, $\overline{AC} \cong \overline{BA}$, $\overline{BC} \cong \overline{CA}$. This is not true in a general triangle.

9. This is incorrect. For example, a circle cannot be inscribed in a general rectangle.

10. We will show that no three points A, B, C on a circle can be collinear by showing that ∠ABC is not a straight angle. If O is the center of the circle then ΔBOC is isosceles (why?) and hence each of its base angles is acute (why?) The same is true about ΔABO. Consequently m(∠ABO) + m(∠CBO) < 90 + 90 = 180. Hence ∠CBA cannot be a straight angle.

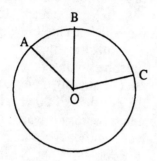

1.   The answer is no. If you are given only a single point and its image, then either a translation, rotation, reflection, or glide reflection could be used. It takes three noncollinear points to determine the isometry.

2.   Again, having only a segment and its image is not enough to determine the transformation. It requires three non-collinear points. For a further examination of this problem, see <u>Transformational Geometry,</u> by Richard Brown (Palo Alto, CA: Dale Seymour Publications, 1989).

3.   A kite always has one line of symmetry. This line of symmetry contains one of the diagonals. It is the diagonal through the vertices of the angles of the kite which are not necessarily congruent.

4.   The student is wrong. One counterexample is a right triangular prism whose bases are scalene triangles.

5.   The student is incorrect when one considers the entire plane or even a triangle. A reflection reverses orientation while a rotation does not. The orientation must be considered any time three non-collinear points are used.

6.   We do have a function that is sometimes called a point transformation. Since it is not a one-to-one mapping of the plane to the plane, it is not a true transformation. The student is correct.

7.   Let the translation on the grid be a translation from A to B. Let C be the vertex of a right $\triangle ABC$ where $\overline{AC}$ is in the horizontal direction. Then the translation from A to B can be accomplished by a translation from A to C followed by a translation from C to B.

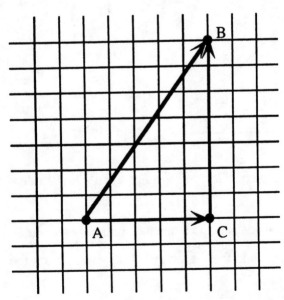

1. The units have to be the same because volume is measured in cubic units. A cubic unit is the volume of a cube having all its dimensions measured in the same units.

2. Yes, the same type of relationship does hold. For a proof and discussion, see G. Polya, Mathematics and Plausible Reasoning, Vol. 1 (Princeton, N.J.: Princeton University Press, 1954, pp. 15-17).

3. No. An angle is a union of two rays. The student probably means the area of the interior of an angle. However, because the interior of an angle occupies an infinite part of a plane, it does not have a measurable area.

4. The area of the interior of any simple closed curve can be described as the sum of the areas of the finitely many nonoverlapping parts into which it can be divided. In the student's case, the square is divided into infinitely many parts, and hence the above property does not apply.

5. Consider a cube with side 6 cm. The volume is 216 cm^3 and its surface area is 216 cm^2.

6. The metric system is much simpler than the English system of measurement. For example, converting from one unit to another within the metric system requires only multiplication or division by a power of 10. Almost all the countries in the world are using the metric system. In order for the United States to be able to trade effectively with other countries, it is essential that it uses the same system as everybody else.

7. Using the student's reasoning, in a right isosceles triangle, the side opposite the 90° angle should be twice as long as the side opposite the 45° angle. We know that the hypotenuse, c, is $\sqrt{2}$ times the length of a leg.

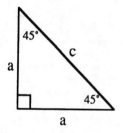

8. The given box has a volume of 125 cm^3 and not 5 cm^3. The student most likely thinks of 5 cm^3 as (5 cm)^3.

9. The ratio will not change because it is a number without any dimensions. Suppose the circumference is a cm long and the diameter is b cm long. Then the ratio is $\dfrac{a \text{ cm}}{b \text{ cm}} = \dfrac{a}{b}$. Now suppose that 1 cm = x in., then $\dfrac{a \text{ cm}}{b \text{ cm}} = \dfrac{ax \text{ in.}}{bx \text{ in.}} = \dfrac{a}{b}$.

10. We use square centimeters or square inches to indicate the area of a square 1 cm or 1 in. on a side. However, we cannot have a square with 1 are or 1 hectare on a side because are and hectare are not linear measures. The area of a square 10 m on a side is 1 a, and 1 ha is the area of a square 100 m on a side.

11. The measurements are only approximations and are reported as rational numbers. Because the quotient of two rational numbers is a rational number, then the student thinks π must be rational. The measurements can never be totally accurate--only approximations.

12. Many areas cannot be found by the use of formulas, but that does not keep the area from existing. The argument is analogous to saying electricity does not exist because it cannot be seen.

1. If the vertical line intersects the x-axis at $x = a$, any two points on the line can be written as (a, y_1) and (a, y_2), where $y_1 \neq y_2$. Using the formula for slope, we obtain $\frac{y_2 - y_1}{0}$. Since division by zero is not defined, $\frac{y_2 - y_1}{0}$ is meaningless, and hence the slope cannot be defined. The teacher may also want to give the following explanations. If a vertical line has a slope m, the equation of the y-axis would have to be $y = mx$ for some m, $m \neq 0$. (Why?) However, none of the points on the y-axis, except (0, 0), satisfy the equation. For example, the point (0, 1) cannot satisfy the equation $y = mx$ because $y = m \cdot 0 = 0$ no matter what the value of m is. Consequently, it is impossible to assign a slope to a vertical line.

2. It is difficult to refute this argument since it is based on a faulty assumption. "Zero is nothing" is a false statement. The student has a problem in understanding zero. Until this is cleared up, any further discussion is futile.

3. The following figure illustrates the values of $x_2 - x_1$ and $\frac{x_2 - x_1}{2}$

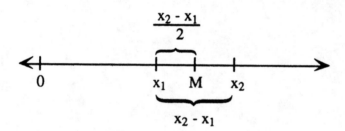

Notice that the x-coordinate of M is $x_1 + \frac{x_2 - x_1}{2}$ rather than $\frac{x_2 - x_1}{2}$. Also,

$$x_1 + \frac{x_2 - x_1}{2} = \frac{2x_1 + x_2 - x_1}{2} = \frac{x_1 + x_2}{2}$$ Since the midpoint of a segment is half the way between the endpoints of a segment, the student has confused the concept of half the distance between the points with that of the midpoint.

4. If a mistake was made in the steps of obtaining the simpler equivalent equations from the original equations and no mistakes were made thereafter, the mistake will not be detected when the answer is checked in the simpler equivalent equations.

5. The student's claim is false whenever $b < 0$. For example, $x - y + 3 > 0$ represents the half-plane below the line $x - y + 3 = 0$. On the other hand, $x - y + 3 < 0$ represents the half-plane above the line. Notice that $ax + by + c > 0$ is equivalent to $by > -ax - c$. If $b > 0$, this inequality is equivalent to $y > \frac{-a}{b}x - \frac{c}{a}$ representing a half-plane below the line. Consequently, the student's claim is true if and only if $b > 0$.

6. The student is making a mistake because in general $\sqrt{a + b} \neq \sqrt{a} + \sqrt{b}$. The student should be encouraged to exhibit counterexamples, such as $\sqrt{4 + 9} \neq \sqrt{4} + \sqrt{9}$.

7. If line k has slope m_1, then the line k', its reflection in the x-axis, has slope -m_1. Consequently, the product of the slopes of lines k' and l is $(^-m_1)m_2$. Because $m_1m_2 = 1$, it follows that $(^-m_1)m_2 = ^-(m_1m_2) = ^-1$. Consequently, the lines k' and l are perpendicular.

8. The RECTANGLE1 procedure used the command SETXY 0 0 as the last line. Because of this command, the turtle automatically returns home at the end of the execution. This procedure will not draw a rectangle unless the turtle starts at home.

Answers to Problems

CHAPTER 1

Problem Set 1-1

1.

(a)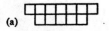

(b)

(c)

(d) △△△△△△

(e) ▧

2. (a) 5x6, 6x7, 7x8 (b) 45, 41, 37 (c) 15, 20, 26
(d) 26, 37, 50 (e) X, Y, X (f) 1, 18, 1 (g) 34, 55, 89
(h) 111111, 1111111, 11111111 (i) 123456, 1234567,
12345678 (j) 6×2^6, 7×2^7, 8×2^8 (k) 2^{32}, 2^{64}, 2^{128}
(l) 5, 10, _15_, 20, _25_, 30, 35, _40_ (m) 0, 7, 14, _21_, 28, _35_,
42, _49_ (n) 0, 1/2, 1, _3/2_, 2, _5/2_, 3, _7/2_ (o) 0, 22, _44_, 66,
_88_, _110_
3. (a) 11, 13, 15 arithmetic (b) 250, 300, 350 arithmetic
(c) 96, 192, 384 geometric (d) $10^6, 10^7, 10^8$ geometric
(e) $5^7, 5^8, 5^9$ geometric (f) 66, 77, 88 arithmetic
(g) $2^{11}, 2^{13}, 2^{15}$ geometric (h) 33, 37, 41 arithmetic
(i) $6^3, 7^3, 8^3$ neither
4. (a) 12, 14 (b) 18, 21
5. (a) 30, 42, 56 (b) 10, 100 (c) n(n+1) or n^2+n
6. (a) 51 (b) 6 + (n-1)5 or 5n + 1
7. (a) 41 (b) 4n+ 1
8. 1200 students
9. 15 liters
10. $1225
11. (a) $1660 (b) $7500 (c) 103 months
12. 19
13. 23rd year

14. (a) 100th figure is 604 (b) 496 matchsticks (c) 165
squares
15. (a) 10,000 (b) n^2
16. (a) 42 (b) 4n + 2
17. (a) 3, 5, 9, 15, 23, 33 (b) 4, 6, 10, 16, 24, 34
(c) 15, 17, 21, 27, 35, 45
18. (a) 299, 447, 644 (b) 56, 72, 90 (c) 108, 190, 304
19. (a) 101 (b) 61 (c) 200 (d) 87 (e) 11 (f) 2 1
(g) 9 8
20. (a) Yes. The difference between terms in the new
sequence is the same as in the old sequence. (b) Yes. If the
fixed number is k, the difference between terms of the second
sequence is k times the difference between terms of the first
sequence.
21. (a) No. (b) Yes, the resulting sequence will be a
geometric sequence. The ratio between each term (starting from
the second term) and the preceding term of the resulting
sequence is the same as the ratio of the corresponding terms in
the original sequence.
22. The resulting sequence is always an arithmetic sequence
because its difference is the sum of the corresponding
differences of the original sequences.
23. If the sequences have the same ratio the resulting
sequence is geometric. If the sequences are

a, ar, ar^2, ar^3, ...

and

b, br, br^2, br^3, ...

then the resulting sequence is

a+b, (a+b)r, $(a + b)r^2$, $(a + b)r^3$, ...

This is a geometric sequence with ratio r and first term a + b.
24. The resulting sequence is geometric. The following term
by term multiplication explains why.

1st sequence:	a, ar, ar^2, ar^3, ...
2nd sequence:	b, bs, bs^2, bs^3, ...
Resulting sequence:	ab, ab(rs), $ab(rs)^2$, $ab(rs)^3$, ...

25. 48, 72, 108
26. (a) 6, 12 (b) ¯3
27. (a) 3, 6, 11, 18, 27 (b) 4, 9, 14, 19, 24 (c) 9, 99,
999, 9999, 99999 (d) 5, 8, 11, 14, 17
28. (a) 1, 1, 2, 3, 5, 8, 13, 21, 34, 55, 89, 144, ...
(b) Yes; the sum of the first 4 terms equals the 6th term - 1.

The sum of the first 5 terms equals the 7th term - 1. The sum of the first 6 terms equals the 8th term - 1 equals 20. **(c)** 143 **(d)** The sum of the 1st n terms equals the (n+2)th term - 1.

29. (a) 2, 4, 6, 10, 16, 26, 42, 68, 110, 178, 288, 466, ... **(b)** The sum of the 1st 3 terms is 4 less than the 5th term . The sum of the 1st 4 terms is 4 less than the 6th term The sum of the 1st 5 terms is 4 less than the 7th term . The sum of the 1st 6 terms is 4 less than the 8th term. **(c)** 462 **(d)** The sum of the 1st n terms equals the (n+2)th term - 4.

30. (a) 199, 2n-1 **(b)** 4950, 50(n- 1) **(c)** 3×2^{99}, $3 \times 2^{n-1}$ **(d)** 10^{100}, 10^n **(e)** 5^{101}, 5^{n+1} **(f)** 1100, 11n **(g)** 2^{199}, 2^{2n-1} **(h)** 405, 5 + 4n or 9 + 4(n- 1) **(i)** $100^3 = 1,000,000$, n^3

31. (a) 1, 5, 12, 22, 35, 51 **(b)** 14,950

32. (a) 300, 500, 700, 900, 1100, 1300, ..., (2n+1)·100

(b) 2, 4, 8, 16, 32, 64, . . ., 2^n The sequence in (b) becomes greater than the sequence in (a) on the 12th term.

33. (a) 1, 5, 9, 13, 17, 21, ... **(b)** 4n- 3

34. (a)

| 1 8 28 56 70 56 28 8 1 | (8) |
| 1 9 36 84 126 126 84 36 9 1 | (9) |

(b)

SUM	ROW	
1	(0)	The sum of row (0) is 2^0
2	(1)	The sum of row (1) is 2^1
4	(2)	The sum of row (2) is 2^2
8	(3)	The sum of row (3) is 2^3
16	(4)	The sum of row (4) is 2^4

The sum of row (10) will be $2^{10} = 1024$

The sum of row (n) will be 2^n

(c)

Alternate Sum	ROW
0	(1)
0	(2)
0	(3)
0	(4)
0	(5)

(d) Answers may vary. Look at the diagonals as sequences:
(i) 1, 2, 3, 4, 5, 6, 7, 8, 9, 10, ...   arithmetic sequence
(ii) 1, 3, 6, 10, 15, 21, 28, 36, 45, 1st difference = sequence (i)
(iii) 1, 4, 10, 20, 35, 56, 84, 120, ... 1st difference = sequence (ii)
(ii) etc.

Brain Teaser (p. 17)
(a) N, T, E (Rule: <u>O</u>ne, <u>T</u>wo, Three, <u>F</u>our, <u>F</u>ive, <u>S</u>ix, <u>S</u>even, <u>E</u>ight, <u>N</u>ine, <u>T</u>en, <u>E</u>leven) **(b)** Letters composed of only line segments go above the line. Letters with curves go below the line.

Problem Set 1-2
1. (a) 4950 **(b)** n(n+1)/2 **(c)** 251,001
2. If one notices that each number is being added twice and divides the sum 100(101) by 2; then the methods give the same answer: 100(101)/2 = 5050 = 50(101). The advantage of this method is that it works with an even or odd number of terms.
3. The number of squares in an n x n array is $n^2 = 1 + 3 + 5 + ... + 2n-1$
4. 18
5. $1.19
6. (a) 204 squares **(b)** The number of different squares is more than doubled. 8·16 + 7·15 + 6·14 + 5·13 + 4·12 + 3·11 + 2·10 + 9 = 492 squares.
7. Start both the 7-minute and 11-minute timers. When the 7-minute timer stops, put the egg on. When the 11-minute timer stops, restart it. When it stops this time, the egg is done.

8. 12
9. 12
10. 10 boys, 12 dogs
11. $2.45
12. 16 days
13. (a) 42, 55, 68, 81, 94, 107, 120, 133, 146, 159, 172, 185, 198 **(b)** 13
14. (a) 325 cubes **(b) (i)** 10,500 squares **(ii)** $n^2 + 5n$ squares
15. 17 rungs
16. David had 78 marbles, Judy had 42, and Jacobo had 24.
17. Jacobo started with 732 marbles.
18. (a) Weigh 4 against 4, pick the heavier side; weigh 2 against 2, pick the heavier side, and finally, weigh 1 against 1. **(b)** Divide them into groups of 3, 3, and 2 and weigh 3 against 3. If they balance, only one more weighing is necessary. If they do not balance, select any 2 from the heavier side and weigh 1 against 1. Either they balance or they do not.
19. (a) 11 **(b)** 63
20. width = 230 feet, length = 310 feet
21.

17	7	9
3	11	19
13	15	5

22. 1+3+4+5+6+7+8+9+10=53   53/3=17 2/3 which is not a natural number.
23. (a) If both numbers were less than or equal to 9, then their product would be less than or equal to 9·9 = 81 which is not greater than 82. **(b)** Follow the same argument as in (a): 81 is not greater than 81.
24. (a) 260,610 **(b)** 100,701 **(c)** 20,503
25. 170
26. Yes; she can use the 8 1/2-inch side twice to get 17 inches and then use the 11-inch side to get back to 6 inches.
27. $13,500
28. $78, $42, and $24; This is the same problem mathematically as #16.
29. (a) Because each new line can intersect each of the previous lines in at most one point, the number of intersection points is $1 + 2 + 3 + ... + 19 = \left(\dfrac{1+19}{2}\right) \cdot 19 = 190$. **(b)** n lines intersect in at most, $1 + 2 + 3 + ... + n - 1 = (n-1)n/2$ points.
30. 35 moves
31. (a) 21, 24, 27 **(b)** 243, 2, 729
32. 22 + (n-1)10 or 10n+12
33. 21 terms
34. 903

Brain Teaser (p. 36)
Thursday

Problem Set 1-3
1. (a) (i) 541 x 72 **(ii)** divide 12 into 754
(b) (i) 257 x 14 **(ii)** divide 75 into 124
2. (b)
3. $3.99 + 5.87 + 6.47 = $16.33
4. Hint: 259 x 429 = 111,111
5. 17 terms
6. 275,000,000
7. Depends on calculator.
8. Answers may vary.
9. Answers may vary.
10. Answers may vary.

11. $5,256,000 per year
12. Depends upon heart rate.
13. 625
14. 3,628,800
15. (a) If the product were abcd, then a + c = 9 and b + d = 9.
(b) If the product were abcde, then c = 9, a + d = 9 and b + e = 9.
16. The display should be divided by 10.
17. Answers may vary: approximately 26,680,000.
18. 5459 = 53x103. Divide by primes up to 73 which is close to the square root of 5459.
19. Play second and make sure that the sum showing when you hand the calculator to your opponent is a multiple of 3.
20. Play first and press 4. After that, make sure that each time that you hand your opponent the calculator, it displays 4 more than a multiple of 5.
21. Play first and press 3. After that, make sure that each time you hand your opponent the calculator, it displays 3 more than a multiple of 10.
22. Play second. Make sure that the calculator displays a multiple of 3 each time you hand your opponent the calculator.
23. Play second; use a strategy similar to that of problem 22 but use a multiple of 4.
24. Play first and subtract 3; after that, make sure that the calculator displays a multiple of 10 each time you hand your opponent the calculator.
25. (a) $2^6 - 1$ (b) $2^n - 1$
26. (a) 35, 42, 49 (b) 1, 16, 1
27. 20n - 8
28. 21 terms
29. 9 ways

Brain Teaser (p. 42)
Christmas (Notice that there is no L (NOEL) in the display.)

Chapter Test
1. (a) 15, 21, 28 (b) 32, 27, 22 (c) 400, 200, 100
(d) 21, 34, 55 (e) 17, 20, 23 (f) 256, 1024, 4096
(g) 16, 20, 24 (h) 125, 216, 343
2. (a) neither (b) arithmetic (c) geometric (d) neither
(e) arithmetic (f) geometric (g) arithmetic
(h) neither
3. (a) $3n + 2$ (b) n^3 (c) 3^n
4. (a) 5, 8, 11, 14, 17, ... (b) 2, 6, 12, 20, 30, ...
(c) 3, 7, 11, 15, 19, ...
5. (a) 10,100 (b) 10,201
6. (a) 123456, 1234567, 12345678, ...
(b) 1234567890. The last digit of the nth term in the sequence matches the last digit of the number n.
7.

16	3	2	13
5	10	11	8
9	6	7	12
4	15	14	1

8. 89 years
9. The worm will climb out on the 10th day.
10. 26
11. $2.00
12. 21 posts
13. 128 matches
14. $19,305 = 3 \cdot 5 \cdot 9 \cdot 11 \cdot 13$
15. 44,000,000 rotations
16. 20 students

17. 39 boxes
18. 48 triangles
19. (a) $\left(10^{13} - 1\right)\big/9$ (b) $\left(10^{n+1} - 1\right)\big/9$ (c) $\left(10^n - 1\right)\big/9$
20. 9 hours
21. width is 10 feet, length is 24 feet

CHAPTER 2

Brain Teaser (p. 58)
Because the town barber is a male, then he shaves himself. Because he shaves only those who do not shave themselves, he cannot shave himself. Consequently, the barber is not a male, but we know he is. Thus we have a paradox.

Problem Set 2-1
1. Answers vary.
2. (a) {m,a,t,h,e,i,c,s} (b) { x|x is a state in the United States, but neither Alaska nor Hawaii} (c) {January, June, July} (d) { x|x > 20 and x ∈ N } (e) { x|x is a state in the United States} (f) ∅ (g) {Alaska, Hawaii, Washington, California, Oregon}
3. (a) B = {x, y, z, w} (b) 3 ∉ B (c) {1,2} ⊂ {1,2,3,4}
(d) D ⊄ E (e) A ⊄ B (f) 0 ∉ ∅ (g) {0} ≠ ∅
4. Answers vary.
5. (a) Yes (b) No (c) Yes (d) No (e) No
6. 1 ↔ a 1 ↔ b
   2 ↔ b 2 ↔ a
   (1)   (2)
7. (a) 24 (b) 120 (c) n!
8. Answers vary.
9. A, C and D are equal; E and H are equal.
10. $\overline{A}$ is the set of all college students without a straight A average.
11. (a) 7 (b) 1
12. (a) 5 (b) They are equal.
13. Answers vary.
14. (a) ∈ (b) ∉ (c) ∉ (d) ∉ (e) ∉
15. (a) ⊄ (b) ⊄ (c) ⊆ (d) ⊆ (e) ⊆
16. No, because they might not have any members in common, in which case A ⊄ B and B ⊄ A.
17. (a) True (b) False. If A = B, then A ⊆ B but A ⊄ B.
(c) True (d) False. If A ⊂ B, then A ⊆ B but A ≠ B.
18. (a) A = {1, 2}; n(A) = 2. B = { 1, 2, 3, 4}; n(B) = 4. A is a proper subset of B. (b) A = {1, 2, 3}; n(A) = 3. B = {x|x is a natural number less than 101}; n(B) = 100. A is a proper subset of B. (c) A = ∅; n(A) = 0. B = { 1, 2, 3}; n(B) = 3. A is a proper subset of B.
19. Answers vary.
20. (a) 63 (b) $2^n - 1$
21. 35

Problem Set 2-2
1. (a) Yes (b) Yes (c) Yes (d) Yes (e) No (f) Yes
2. (a) True (b) False. If A = {1, 2, 5} and B = {1, 2, 3}, then A - B = {5} ≠ B - A = {3} (c) True (d) False. If A = {1, 2, 3, 4}, B = {1, 6} and U = {x|x is a natural number}, A ∩ B = {x|x is any natural number except 1} whereas $\overline{A} \cap \overline{B}$ = {x|x is any natural number except 1, 2, 3, 4, and 6} (e) True
(f) True (g) True
3. (a) B (b) A

4.

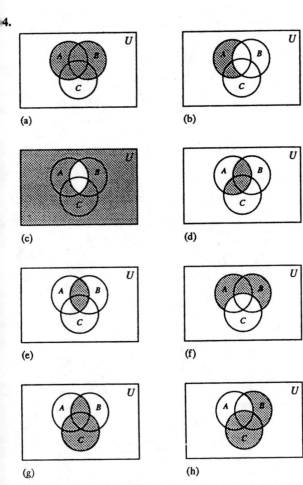

(a) (b)

(c) (d)

(e) (f)

(g) (h)

5. (a) U (b) U (c) S (d) ∅ (e) S (f) U (g) ∅
(h) S (i) $\bar{S}$ (j) S (k) ∅ (l) $\bar{S}$

6. Answers vary.

7. (a) A (b) ∅ (c) ∅ (d) ∅

8. Answers may vary. (a) B∩$\bar{A}$ (b) $\overline{A∪B}$
(c) A∩B∩C (d) A∩B (e) (A∩C)∩$\bar{B}$
(f) $\left((A∪C)∩\bar{B}\right)∪(A∩B∩C)$

9.

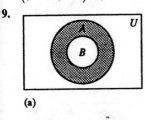

(a) (b)

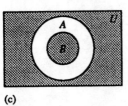

(c) (d)

10. (a) False (b) False (c) False (d) False (e) False

11. (a) (i) 5, (ii) 2 (b) (i) m + n (ii) m if m < n, n if n < m, (n or m if n = m)

12. Answers vary.

13. (a) The set of all natural numbers (b) ∅ (c) E, the set

of all even natural numbers (d) O, the set of all odd natural numbers

14.

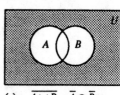

(a) $\overline{A∪B}=\bar{A}∩\bar{B}$ (b) $\overline{A∩B}=\bar{A}∪\bar{B}$

(c) (a) A = {1, 2, 3}; B = {5}; U = {x|x is a natural number};
$\overline{A∪B}=\{4,6,7,8...\}=\{4,5,6,7...\}∩\{1,2,3,4,6...\}=\bar{A}∩\bar{B}$
(b) A = {x|x is a one-eyed jack}, B = {x|x is a face card},
U ={x|x is a playing card in a standard deck}. $\overline{A∩B}$ ={x|x
is any card except a one-eyed jack}, $\bar{A}∪\bar{B}$ ={x|x is any card
except a one-eyed jack}

15. A = B

16. (a) The set of college basketball players/students who are
more than 200 cm tall. (b) The set of all humans who either
aren't college students or aren't more than 200 cm tall. (c) The
set of all college basketball players or college students who are
more than 200 cm tall. (d) The set of all humans who are
neither college basketball players and who are neither students
nor more than 200 cm tall. (e) The set of all college students
more than 200 cm tall who are not basketball players. (f) The
set of all college basketball players who are either not students
or are not more than 200 cm tall.

17. (a) is the set of all eighth grade students at Paxson
School taking band but not choir. (b) is the set of all eighth
grade students at Paxson School taking both band and choir.
(c) is the set of all eighth grade students at Paxson School
taking choir but not band. (d) is the set of all eighth grade
students at Paxson School taking neither band nor choir.

18. 18

19. 4 students

20.

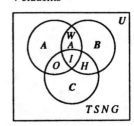

21. (a) 20 (b) 10 (c) 10

22. (a) False. If A = {apples, oranges}, B = {1, 2},
n(A) = n(B) but A ≠ B (b) False. If A = {monkey, telephone},
B = {monkey, telephone}, A ~ B and A∪B is equivalent to B.
(c) False If A = {1, 2, 3, 5}, B = {1, 2, 3, 4, 5}, A - B = ∅ but
A ≠ B. (d) True (e) True; unless A and B are infinite sets; in
that case, n(A) needs to be defined. (f) False. If A = { β,∂ },
B = {π,≠,<,∅}, n(A) < n(B) but A ⊄ B.

23. Cowboys vs. Giants, Steelers vs. Jets, Vikings vs.
Packers, Redskins vs. Bills

24. (a) $\{(x,a),(x,b),(x,c),(y,a),(y,b),(y,c)\}$

(b) $\{(a,x),(a,y),(b,x),(b,y),(c,x),(c,y)\}$ (c) ∅ (d) $\{(0,0)\}$

(e) ∅

(f) $\{(x,a),(x,b),(x,c),(y,a),(y,b),(y,c),(x,0),(y,0)\}$

(g) $\{(x,0),(y,0),(a,0),(b,0),(c,0)\}$

(h) $\{x,y,(a,0),(b,0),(c,0)\}$

25. Answers vary.

26. (a) C = {a}, D = {b, c, d, e}
(b) C = {1, 2}, D = {1, 2, 3}   (c) C = {0, 1}, D = {1,0}
27. (a) 20   (b) mn   (c) (mn)p
28. (a) 0   (b) 0   (c) 0
29. 5
30. Yes
31. 30
32. 60
33. 93
34. Answers vary.
35. Answers vary. The poll is inaccurate because the stats imply a total of 490 students polled, not 500.
36. {a, b, c},{a, b}, {a, c}, {b, c}, {a}, {b}, {c}, ∅
37. Yes
38. {p}, {q}, {r}, {s}, {p, q}, {p, r}, {p, s}, {q, r}, {q, s}, {r, s}, {p, q, r}, {q, r, s}, {p, r, s}, {q, s, p}
39. (a) {Maine, Minnesota, Michigan, Mississippi, Missouri, Maryland, Massachusetts, Montana}   (b) Z = {x|x is a state in the United States that begins with the letter M}

BRAIN TEASER (p. 69)
Gaussfunbel is incorrect.

Problem Set 2-3
1. (a) "is the square root of"; (5, 25) (10, 100)
(b) "is the spouse of"; (Charles, Diana) (Steve, Jane)
(c) "is the lowercase form of"; (q, Q)(p, P)
(d) "at 3 1/3¢ each cost"; (9, candies, 30¢)(12 candies, 40¢)
2. Answers vary.
3. Answers vary. An example is (Garfield, Jon Arbuckle)
4.

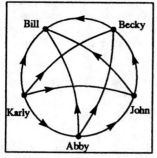

5. (a) Not reflexive, not symmetric, not transitive.
(b) Reflexive, symmetric, transitive. Equivalence relation.
(c) Reflexive, symmetric, transitive. Equivalence relation.
(d) Reflexive, symmetric, transitive. Equivalence relation.
(e) Not reflexive, symmetric, not transitive.
(f) Reflexive, symmetric, not transitive.
(g) Not reflexive, not symmetric, transitive.
6. (a) Reflexive, symmetric, transitive. Equivalence relation.
(b) Not reflexive, not symmetric, transitive.
(c) Not reflexive, symmetric, not transitive.
7. Answers vary.
8. (a) f(x) = 2x   (b) f(x) = x - 2   (c) f(x) = x + 6
(d) $f(x) = x^2 + 1$
9. (a) Not a function, since 1 is paired with a and d.
(b) Not a function, since 2 has no element in the range.
(c) Function   (d) Not a function, since 1 is paired with a, b, and c.
10. f(x) = 4
11. Answers vary.
12. Answers vary.
13. (a) 5   (b) 11   (c) 35   (d) 3a + 5

14. (a) Answers vary

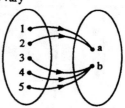

(b) 32
15. (a)

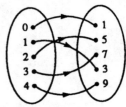

(b) {(0,1),(1,3),(2,5),(3,7),(4,9)}
(c)

x	f(x)
0	1
1	3
2	5
3	7
4	9

(d)

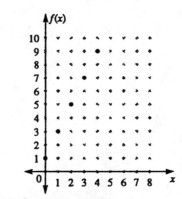

16. (a) ⁻5   (b) 16   (c) 65
17. (a) C(x) = $.29x, where x is the number of ounces.
(b) 57¢
18. (a) 2 chirps/second   (b) 50° F
19. (a) $5.50   (b) f(n) = 2n + $1.50
20. Rule 1; f (x) = x/3, Rule 2; f(x) = x + 2
21. (a) 51   (b) 55   (c) 2
22. (a) 5n - 2   (b) 3^n (c) 2n
23. (a) Yes   (b) No
24.

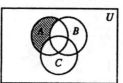

(a) $A - (B \cup C) = (A - B) \cap (A - C)$

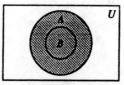

(b) $A \cup B = B$

9. (a) No (b) Yes (c) No (d) Yes
10. Answers vary.
11.

~p	~q	~p∨q
F	F	T
F	T	F
T	F	T
T	T	T

12. (a) Today's not Wednesday or this is not the month of June. (b) Yesterday I didn't eat breakfast or I didn't watch television. (c) It's not true that it's both raining and the month is July.

Brain Teaser (p. 88)
The second native is an Abe and the third native is a Babe. This is true since no matter to which tribe the first native belonged, he would have responded that he was an Abe. The second native reported this truthfully; thus, he is an Abe. The third native lied about the first native's response, then he is a Babe. (Note that the first native could be either an Abe or a Babe.)

Problem Set 2-5
1. (a) $p \rightarrow q$ (b) $\sim p \rightarrow q$ (c) $p \rightarrow \sim q$ (d) $p \rightarrow q$
(e) $\sim q \rightarrow \sim p$ (f) $q \rightarrow p$
2. (a) Converse: If you're good in sports, then you eat Meaties. Inverse: If you don't eat Meaties, then you're not good in sports. Contrapositive: If you're not good in sports, then you don't eat Meaties. (b) Converse: If you don't like mathematics, then you don't like this book. Inverse: If you like this book, then you like mathematics. Contrapositive: If you like mathematics, then you like this book.
(c) Converse: If you have cavities, then you don't use Ultra Brush toothpaste. Inverse: If you use Ultra Brush toothpaste, then you don't have cavities. Contrapositive: If you don't have cavities, then you use Ultra Brush toothpaste. (d) Converse: If your grades are high, then you're good at logic. Inverse: If you're not good at logic, then your grades aren't high. Contrapositive: If your grades aren't high, then you're not good at logic.
3. (a)

p	q	p∨q	p→(p∨q)
T	T	T	T
T	F	T	T
F	T	T	T
F	F	F	T

(b)

p	q	p∧q	(p∧q)→q
T	T	T	T
T	F	F	T
F	T	F	T
F	F	F	T

(c)

p	~p	~(~p)	p→~(~p)
T	F	T	T
F	T	F	T

---

5. Answers vary.
6. (a) $\{x | x = 2n;\ n > 6;\ n \in N\}$ (b) $\{x | x < 14;\ x \in N\}$
7. (a) $\{a,b,c,d\}$ (b) $\{a,d\}$ (c) $\varnothing$ (d) $\varnothing$ (e) $\varnothing$
8. Answers vary. {black, green, orange}; {truth, beauty, goodness}
9. Answers vary. {1, 2, 3, 4}
10. (a) 6 (b) 9
11. $(A \cup B) \cup C = \{h,e,l,p,m\} \cup \{n,o,w\} = \{h,e,l,p,m,n,o,w\} = \{h,e,l,p\} \cup \{m,e,n,o,w\} = A \cup (B \cup C)$

Brain Teaser (p. 83)
The plan fails because we have not accounted for the eleventh man. The first and second men are in room 1, the third through tenth men are in rooms 2 through 9. Where is the eleventh man? He has not been mentioned. If the extra man in room 1 is put in room 10, then the eleventh man still has no room. Confusion results from the fact that by the time that we read that the tenth man has been put into room 9, we think that the extra man in the first room is the eleventh man, when actually he is either the first or the second.

Problem Set 2-4
1. (a) False statement (b) Not a statement (c) False statement (d) Not a statement (e) Not a statement (f) Not a statement (g) True statement (h) Not a statement (i) Not a statement (j) Not a statement
2. (a) There exists x = 3 such that x + 8 = 11. (b) For all natural numbers x, x + 0 = x. (c) There exists a natural number x such that $x^2 = 4$. (d) There is no natural number x such that x + 1 = x + 2.
3. (a) For all natural numbers x, x + 8 = 11. (b) There is no natural number x such that x + 0 = x. (c) For all natural numbers x, $x^2 = 4$. (d) There exists a natural number x such that x + 1 = x + 2.
4. (a) The book does not have 500 pages. (b) Six is not less than eight. (c) $3 \cdot 5 \neq 15$ (d) No one has blond hair. (e) There exists a dog which does not have 4 legs. (f) All cats have nine lives. (g) There exists a square which is not a rectangle. (h) All rectangles are squares. (i) There exists a natural number x such that x + 3 ≠ 3 + x. (j) For all natural numbers x, 3(x + 2) = 12. (k) There exists a counting number not divisible by itself and 1. (l) All natural numbers are divisible by 2. (m) There exists a natural number x such that 5x + 4x ≠ 9x.
5. (a)

~p	~(~p)
F	T
T	F

(b)

~p	p∨(~p)	p∧(~p)
F	T	F
T	T	F

(c) Yes (d) No
6. (a) $q \wedge r$ (b) $r \vee (\sim q)$ (c) $\sim (q \wedge r)$ (d) $\sim q$
7. (a) F (b) T (c) T (d) F (e) F (f) T (g) F (h) F (i) F (j) F
8. (a) F (b) F (c) T (d) T (e) F (f) T (g) F (h) T (i) T (j) T

(d)

p	q	p → q	~(p → q)
T	T	T	F
T	F	F	T
F	T	T	F
F	F	T	F

4. (a) T (b) T (c) F (d) F (e) T (f) F
5. (a) T (b) F (c) T (d) T (e) F (f) T
6. Answers vary.
7. No
8. (a) No (b) Yes (c) No
9. If a number is not a multiple of 4, it is not a multiple of 8.

10. (a)

p	q	r	(p → q)	(p ∧ r)	[(p ∧ r) → q]	(p → q) → [(p ∧ r) → q]
T	T	T	T	T	T	T
T	T	F	T	F	T	T
T	F	T	F	T	F	T
T	F	F	F	F	T	T
F	T	T	T	F	T	T
F	T	F	T	F	T	T
F	F	T	T	F	T	T
F	F	F	T	F	T	T

(b)

p	q	(p → q)	(p → q) ∧ p	[(p → q) ∧ p] → q
T	T	T	T	T
T	F	F	F	T
F	T	T	F	T
F	F	T	F	T

(c)

p	q	~p	~q	p → q	[(p → q) ∧ (~ q)]	[(p → q) ∧ (~ q)] → ~ p
T	T	F	F	T	F	T
T	F	F	T	F	F	T
F	T	T	F	T	F	T
F	F	T	T	T	T	T

(d)

p	q	r	p → q	q → r	(p → q) ∧ (q → r)	p → r	[(p → q) ∧ (q → r)] → (p → r)
T	T	T	T	T	T	T	T
T	T	F	T	F	F	F	T
T	F	T	F	T	F	T	T
T	F	F	F	T	F	F	T
F	T	T	T	T	T	T	T
F	T	F	T	F	F	T	T
F	F	T	T	T	T	T	T
F	F	F	T	T	T	T	T

11. Answers vary.
12. (a) It's false. (b) It's false. (c) Yes, if q is true, then p is false, and p → q can still be true and all conditions are met.
13. Answers vary.
14. (a) Valid (b) Valid (c) Valid (d) Invalid
15. (a) Helen is poor. (b) Some freshmen are intelligent.
(c) If I study for the final, I will look for a teaching job.
(d) There may exist triangles that are not equilateral.
16. (a) If a figure is a square, then it's a rectangle.
(b) If a number is an integer, then it's a rational number.
(c) If a figure has exactly 3 sides, then it may be a triangle.
(d) If it rains, it must be cloudy.

Chapter Test 2

1. {x|x is a letter in the Greek alphabet}

2. {m}, {a}, {t}, {h}, {m, a}, {t, h}, {a, t}, {a, h}, {t, m}, {h, m}, {m, a, t}, {a, t, h}, {t, h, m}, {h, a, m}, {m, a, t, h}, ∅
3. Answers vary.
4. (a) {r, a, v, e} (b) {l, e} (c) {u, n, i, v, r} (d) {r, v}
(e) {u, v, s} (f) {l, a, e} (g) {i, n} (h) {e} (i) 5 (j) 16
5.

(a) A ∩ (B ∪ C)

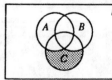

(b) (A ∪ B) ∩ C

6. (a) {(i, s), (i, e), (i, t), (d, s), (d, e), (d, t), (e, s), (e, e), (e, t), (a, s), (a, e), (a, t)} (b) {(s, s), (s, e), (s, t), (e, s), (e, e), (e, t), (t, s), (t, e), (t, t)} (c) 0 (d) 3

7. 7! or 5040

8. **(a)** {t, h, e}
   ↕ ↕ ↕
   {e, n, d}

(b) There are 3! = 6 possible one-to-one correspondences.

9.

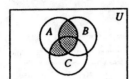 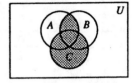

   (a) $A \cap (B \cup C)$ $(A \cap B) \cup C$

10. **(a)** $B \cup (A \cap C)$ **(b)** $\overline{C} \cap B$

11. **(a)** $(A \cap B) \cap C = A \cap (B \cap C)$,

$\{2,3\} \cap \{3,4,5,6,7\} = \{1,2,3\} \cap \{3,4,5\}$, $\{3\} = \{3\}$

(b) $A \cup B = B \cup A$, $\{1,2,3,4,5\} = \{1,2,3,4,5\}$

12. **(a)** False; if, for example, they have no members in common, neither is a subset of the other. **(b)** False; it is not a proper subset of itself. **(c)** False; $\{1, 2, 3\} \sim \{3, 4, 5\}$ but the two sets are not equal. **(d)** False; it's infinite.

(e) False; infinite sets are equivalent to proper subsets of themselves. **(f)** False; B could always be the null set, which is not infinite. **(g)** True **(h)** False, A = {1, 2}; B = {3, 4} provide counterexamples.

13. **(a)** 17 **(b)** 34 **(c)** 0 **(d)** 17

14. 7 students

15. Answers vary.

16. **(a)** 36 students **(b)** 6 **(c)** 5

17. **(a)** Yes **(b)** No **(c)** Yes

18. **(a)** 7 **(b)** 31 **(c)** 37

19. **(a)** Answers vary, but a function assigns exactly one Zipcode to each post office. **(b)** Answers vary.

20. **(a)** range = {3, 4, 5, 6} **(b)** range = {14, 29, 44, 59} **(c)** range = {0, 1, 4, 9, 16} **(d)** range = {5, 9, 15}

21. **(a)** Reflexive, symmetric, transitive **(b)** Transitive **(c)** Symmetric **(d)** None

22. **(a)** Yes **(b)** Yes **(c)** No **(d)** Yes

23. **(a)** No women smoke. **(b)** $3 + 5 \neq 8$ **(c)** Some heavy metal rock is not loud. **(d)** Beethoven did not write only classical music.

24. **(a)**

p	q	~q	p∨~q	$[p \vee (\sim q)] \wedge p$
T	T	F	T	T
T	F	T	T	T
F	T	F	F	F
F	F	T	T	F

(b)

p	q	~q	$p \to (\sim q)$	$[p \to (\sim q)] \vee q$
T	T	F	F	T
T	F	T	T	T
F	T	F	T	T
F	F	T	T	T

(c)

p	q	~q	$p \to (\sim q)$	$(\sim q) \to p$	$[p \to (\sim q)] \wedge [(\sim q) \to p]$
T	T	F	F	T	F
T	F	T	T	T	T
F	T	F	T	T	T
F	F	T	T	F	F

(d)

p	q	~p	~q	~p∨~q	q∧p	$[\sim p \vee \sim q] \to (q \wedge p)$
T	T	F	F	F	T	T
T	F	F	T	T	F	F
F	T	T	F	T	F	F
F	F	T	T	T	F	F

25. **(a)** Equivalent **(b)** Not equivalent

26. Converse: If someone faints, then we'll have a rock concert. Inverse: If we don't have a rock concert, then no one will faint. Contrapositive; If no one faints, then we won't have a rock concert.

27. **(a)** Joe Czernyu loves Mom and apple pie. **(b)** The structure of the Statue of Liberty will eventually rust.

(c) Albertina will pass Math 100.

28. $[(p \to q) \wedge (q \to r) \wedge (r \to s) \wedge (\sim s \to r)] \to \sim p$.

p = You are fair skinned. q = You sunburn. r = You don't go to the dance. s = Your parents want to know why you don't go to the dance. Argument is valid.

29. **(a)** Valid **(b)** Valid **(c)** Valid

CHAPTER 3

Problem Set 3-1

1. (a) $\overline{\text{MCDXXIV}}$ (b) 46,032 (c)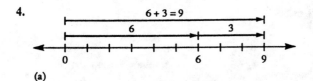(d)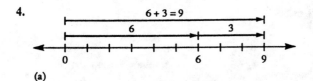 (e)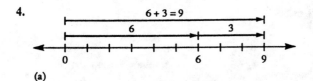
2. (a) MCML; MCMXLVIII (b) $\overline{\text{MII}}$; $\overline{\text{M}}$; (c) M;

CMXCVIII (d) << <▼▼; << < (e) ⨼99⏌; ⨼9;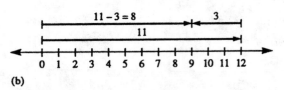

(f) 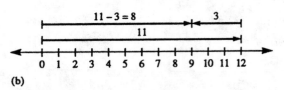 ;

3. 1922
4. (a) Use place value in columns as done in the Hindu-Arabic system. Group the numerals in each column; trade symbols and shift columns if possible. (b) Group all the same symbols for each number; trade if possible to make the sum using as few symbols as possible.

5.

6. (a) CXXI (b) XLII (c) LXXXIX (d) $\overline{\text{V}}$CCLXXXII
7. (a) ∩∩∩∩∩ II (b) 9 III (c) ⟋III (d) ∩∩∩IIIIIIII
8. (a) ▼ <▼▼; ∩∩∩∩∩∩∩II; LXXII; ●●/●●

(b) 602; 999/999 II; DCII; ●/●●

(c) 1223; << << ▼▼▼; MCCXXIII; ●●●/●●●

9. Answers may vary.
10. Answers may vary.
11. Answers may vary.
12. Answers may vary.
13. (a) Hundreds (b) Tens (c) Thousands (d) Hundred thousands
14. (a) 3,004,005 (b) 20,001 (c) 3,560 (d) 9,000,099
15. Answers may vary.
16. (a) 86 (b) 11
17. 811 or 910
18. Answers may vary.
19. 4,782,969
20. Assume an eight-digit display without scientific notation. (a) 98,765,432 (b) 12,345,678 (c) 99,999,999 (d) 11,111,111
21. (a) Answers vary, e.g. subtract 2020 (b) Answers vary, e.g., subtract 50

Brain Teaser (p. 111)

One box contains 2 nickels, one box contains 2 dimes, and one box contains a nickel and a dime. You would reach in the box labeled 15¢. If a nickel is drawn, the correct label for this box is 10¢. The 20¢ label would then be shifted to the box which was labeled 10¢ and then the 15¢ label would be placed on the remaining box. If a dime were drawn from the box labeled 15¢, then the 20¢ label would be placed on this box. Then the 10¢ label would be shifted to the box which was labeled 20¢ and the 15¢ label would be placed on the remaining box.

Problem Set 3-2

1. (a) k = 2 (b) k = 3
2. No. If k = 0, we would have k = 0 + k, implying k > k.
3. For example, let A = {1, 2}, B = {2, 3}, then

A ∪ B = {1,2,3}. Thus n(A) = 2, n(B) = 2, n(A ∪ B) = 3 , but

n(A) + n(B) = 2 + 2 = 4 ≠ n(A ∪ B).

4.

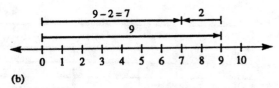

(a)

(b)

5. (a) 5 (b) 2 (c) 0,1, 2 (d) 3, 4, 5, 6, . . .
6. (a) 3 (b) 13 (c) a (d) 0 (e) 3, 4, 5, 6, 7, 8, 9
(f) 10, 11, 12, . . .
7. (a) Yes (b) Yes (c) Yes (d) No, $3+5 \notin V$ (e) Yes
8. (a) x = 119 + 213 (b) 213 = x + 119 (c) 213 = 119 + x
9. (a) Commutative Property for Addition (b) Associative Property for Addition (c) Commutative Property for Addition
10. (a) 3820, 3802, 8023 (b) 2830, 3280, 3208, 3028, 3802, 3082
11. (a) 33, 38, 43 (b) 56, 49, 42
12.

$$\overbrace{\text{X X X X X X X X X X}}^{9}$$

X X | X X X X X X X X (↑↓ ↑↓) 7 left

0 0

(a)

9 − 2 = 7 | 2
9

0 1 2 3 4 5 6 7 8 9 10

(b)

13. Answers may vary; for example, let A = {a, b},
B = {a, b, c, d}. Then 4 − 2 = n(B − A) = n({c, d}) = 2
14. (a) For example, 5 - 3 ≠ 3 - 5 (b) (7 - 5) - 1 ≠ 7 - (5 - 1)
(c) 4 - 0 ≠ 0 - 4 and 0 - 4 ≠ 4
15. (a) 9 (b) 8 (c) 3 (d) 6 or 8 (e) 5 (f) 4 or 8 (g) 9
16. (a) 1 (b) No, because C = 1 (c) 8 or 9 (d) 2
17. 0
18.

8	1	6
3	5	7
4	9	2

(a)

17	10	15
12	14	16
13	18	11

(b)

19.

8	3
4	12

20.

1	5	9
6	7	2
8	3	4

21.

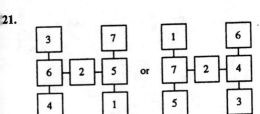

22.

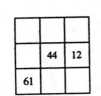

23.

(a) Answers may vary

(b) Yes, for example,

1	2
3	5
4	6

,

1	3
2	5
4	6

, or

1	4
2	5
3	6

24. 28
25. 5 months
26. 45 points
27. 400
28. Answers may vary.
29. Answers may vary.
30. Answers may vary.
31. Answers may vary.
32. (a) 70 (b) 9000 (c) 1100 (d) 560 (e) 3470
33. Depends on the calculator.
34. Depends on the calculator.
35. 26
36. (a) CMLIX (b) XXXVIII
37. There are fewer symbols to remember and place value is used.
38. $5 \cdot 10^3 + 2 \cdot 10^2 + 8 \cdot 10^1 + 6 \cdot 1$

Brain Teaser (p. 122)

Answers may vary, for example,

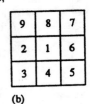

1	2	3
8	9	4
7	6	5

9	8	7
2	1	6
3	4	5

(a)   (b)

Problem Set 3-3

1.

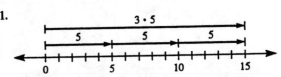

2. $35.00
3. (a) Yes (b) Yes (c) Yes (d) Yes (e) Yes
(f) No, $2 \cdot 2 = 4$, which does not belong to the set.
4. (a) No, $2 + 3 = 5$ (b) Yes (c) Not closed for either,
$2 + 4 = 6$ and $2 \cdot 3 = 6$.
5. This is false, consider the set $A = \{1\}$.
6. $8 \cdot 3 = (6 + 2) \cdot 3 = 6 \cdot 3 + 2 \cdot 3 = 18 + 6 = 24$

7. (a) Commutative Property for Multiplication
(b) Associative Property for Multiplication (c) Commutative Property of Addition (d) Zero Multiplication Property
(e) Identity Property of Multiplication (f) Commutative Property of Multiplication (g) Distributive Property of Multiplication over Addition (h) Distributive Property of Multiplication over Addition
8. (a) 5 (b) 4 (c) Any whole number
9. (a) ac + ad + bc + bd (b) 3x + 3y + 15
(c) $\square \cdot \triangle + \square \cdot \bigcirc$ (d) $x^2 + xy + xz + yx + y^2 + yz$,
or $x^2 + 2xy + xz + y^2 + yz$
10. (a) 11 (b) 16 (c) 16 (d) 13
11. (a) $(4+3) \times 2 = 14$ (b) $(9+3)+1=4$
(c) $(5+4+9)+3=6$ (d) $3+6-2+1=7$ or $(3+6-2)+1=7$
12. $a(b+c+d) = a[(b+c)+d] = a(b+c) + ad = ab + ac + ad$
13. Only (a)
14. $(m+n)(x+y) = (m+n)x + (m+n)y = (mx+nx)+(my+ny) = mx + (nx+my) + ny = mx + (my+nx) + ny = mx + my + nx + ny$
15. (a) 6 (b) 0 (c) 4
16.

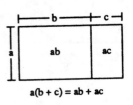

$a(b+c) = ab + ac$

(a)

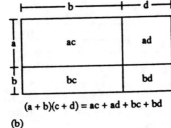

$(a+b)(c+d) = ac + ad + bc + bd$

(b)

17. (a) $40 = 8 \cdot 5$ (b) $326 = 2 \cdot x$ (c) $48 = x \cdot 16$
(d) $x = 5 \cdot 17$
18. The number is always equal to the original number. It works all the time.
19. (a) $(5 \times 2) + 6 = 16$ (b) $(5+3) \times 5 = 40$
(c) $(15+3) - 4 = 1$ (d) $(6+3) + (5-3) = 4$
20. (a) $2+1 \neq 1+2$ (b) $(8+4)+2 \neq 8+(4+2)$
(c) $8 + (2+2) \neq (8+2) + (8+2)$ (d) $3 + 4 \notin W$
21. $32
22. 2; 3 left
23. 9 minutes
24. (a)

$\square$	$\triangle$
0	34
1	26
2	18
3	10
4	2

(b) $\triangle = 66$

25. 1 and 36, 2 and 18, 3 and 12, 4 and 9, 6 and 6
26. 12
27. 30
28. 12
29. Answers may vary
30. Answers may vary
31. (a) Yes (b) Yes (c) Yes, a (d) Yes

32. (a) 3 (b) 2 (c) 2 (d) 6 (e) 4

33. The answers depend upon the keys available on your calculator.

(a)

$$3 = 1 + 9 - 7 \qquad 12 = 19 - 7$$
$$4 = 1^7 + \sqrt{9} \qquad 13 = 91 + 7$$
$$5 = 7 - \sqrt{9} + 1 \qquad 14 = 7(\sqrt{9} - 1)$$
$$6 = 7 - 1^9 \qquad 15 = 7 + 9 - 1$$
$$7 = 7 \cdot 1^9 \qquad 16 = (7 + 9) \cdot 1$$
$$8 = 7 + 1^9 \qquad 17 = 7 + 9 + 1$$
$$9 = 1^7 \cdot 9 \qquad 18 = \sqrt{9}(7 - 1)$$
$$10 = 1^7 + 9 \qquad 19 = ?$$
$$11 = 7 + 1 + \sqrt{9} \qquad 20 = 7\sqrt{9} - 1$$

(b) For example, $4 \cdot 4 - (4 + 4) - (4 + 4) - (4 + 4)$. (c) For example, $22 + 2$. (d) For example, $111 - 11$.

34. (i) ⋂⋂⋂⋂⋂⋂ | | | | | (ii) LXXV (iii) ▼ <▼▼▼▼▼▼▼

35. $3 \cdot 10^4 + 5 \cdot 10^3 + 2 \cdot 10^2 + 0 \cdot 10^1 + 6$

36. For example, $\{0, 1\}$

37. No. For example, $5 - 2 \neq 2 - 5$.

38.

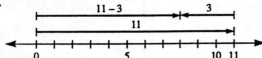

Brain Teaser (p. 133)

Rosalie made $20 on the transaction. The best way for students to understand this problem is to use play money and act the problem out.

Problem Set 3-4

1. (a) $^13^27^18\ 9$
$$\cancel{9}\ \cancel{12}\ \cancel{9}\ \cancel{6}$$
$$+\ 6^38^14^83^25$$
$$\overline{1\ 9\ 9\ 2\ 8}$$

(b) $^15^22\ 4$
$$3\ 2\ \cancel{8}$$
$$\cancel{8}\ \cancel{6}\ 7^2$$
$$+\ 1^43^2\cancel{5}_4$$
$$\overline{1\ 5\ 5\ 4}$$

2. The "scratch marks" represent the normal "carries."

3. The columns separate place value and show that $7 + 8 = 15$ and $20 + 60 = 80$. Finally, $15 + 80 = 95$

4. (a)   981
$$+\ 421$$
$$1402$$
$$6369$$

(b)   2025
$$1196$$
$$+3148$$

(c)   1,069
$$2,094$$
$$9,546$$
$$9,003$$
$$+\ 7,064$$
$$\overline{28,776}$$

(d)   291
$$451$$
$$+\ 584$$
$$1326$$

5. (a) 87693   (b) 8135   (c) 383   (d) 13296
$$\underline{-46414} \qquad \underline{-4682} \qquad \underline{-\dot{1}59} \qquad \underline{-8309}$$
$$41279 \qquad\ \ 3453 \qquad\ \ 224 \qquad\ \ 4987$$

6. (a) One possibility: 863   (b) One possibility: 368
$$\underline{+752} \qquad\qquad\qquad\qquad\qquad \underline{+257}$$
$$1615 \qquad\qquad\qquad\qquad\qquad\ \ 625$$

7. Only if positive numbers are used:

(a)   876   (b)   623
$$\underline{-235} \qquad\qquad\quad \underline{-587}$$
$$641 \qquad\qquad\qquad\ 36$$

8. 15,782

9. (a) 34, 39, 44 (b) 82, 79, 76

10. 30¢

11. No, not all at dinner. He can have either the steak or the salad.

12. Molly, 55 lbs; Karly, 50 lbs; Samantha, 65 lbs.

13. $124

14.   3428
$$\underline{+5631}$$
$$9059$$

15. (a) (i) No, not clustered (ii) Yes, clustered around 500
(b) Answers vary

16. Too high

17. (a) About 121 weeks (b) About 3 years (c) Answers vary (d) Answers vary

18.

Hawks	15	32	40	33	120
Warriors	20	25	47	39	131

19. Answer may vary

20. Answer may vary

21. Answer may vary

22. (i) 1,236 (ii) 1,032

23. Answer may vary

24. Answer may vary

25. Answer may vary

26. Answers may vary, for example,   000
$$770$$
$$000$$
$$330$$
$$\underline{+011}$$
$$1111$$

27. $8 + 8 + 8 + 88 + 888$

28.

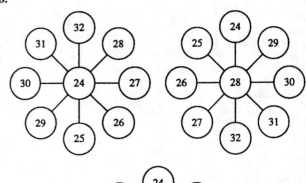

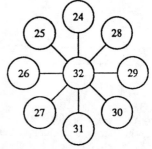

(b) 3

9. It is doubling the second number in the operation

10. (a) 34; 34; 34   (b) 34   (c) 34   (d) Yes
(e) Yes

31. $5280 = 5 \cdot 10^3 + 2 \cdot 10^2 + 8 \cdot 10 + 0 \cdot 1$

32.   For example, $2 + (3 + 4) = (2 + 3) + 4$
$$2 + 7 = 5 + 4$$
$$9 = 9$$

33.

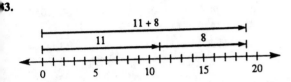

34.   1,000,410

35.   (a) $a \cdot (x + 1)$ (b) $(3 + a) \cdot (x + y)$

36.   15

Brain Teaser (p. 145)
The license plate number is 10968.

Laboratory Activity (p. 147)

1.

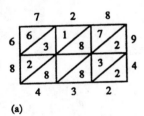

(a)

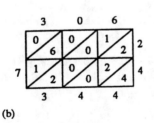

(b)

Problem Set 3-5

1.

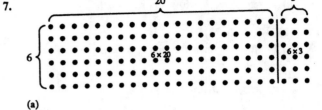

(a)   (b)

2.   Diagonals separate place value as placement does in the traditional algorithm.

3.   (a)   426   (b)   327
          × 783   × 941
          1278   327
          3408   1308
          2982   2943
         333558   307707

4.   Answers may vary.

5.   (a) 5^{19} (b) 6^{15} (c) 10^{313} (d) 10^{12}

6.   (a) 2^{100} (b) 2^{102}

7.

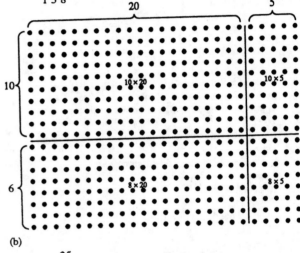

(a)

          23
        × 6
          18   (6×3)
         120   (6×20)
         138

(b)

          25
        × 18
          40   (8×5)
         160   (8×20)
          50   (10×5)
         200   (10×20)
         450

8.   (a) $293 \cdot 476 = 139,468$ (b) Placement still indicates place value.   (c)   363
                                                             × 84
                                                            2904
                                                            1452
                                                           30492

9.   →17 × 63   63
          8   126   + 1008
          2   504   1071
       → 1   1008

10.   (a) 21   (b) 355   (c) 304   (d) 164

11.   (a) 22   (b) 190   (c) 7   (d) 39

12.   (a) $15 \cdot (10 + 2) = 150 + 30 = 180$
(b) $14 \cdot (100 + 2) = 1400 + 28 = 1428$
(c) $30 \cdot 99 = 30(100 - 1) = 3000 - 30 = 2970$

13.

a	b	a·b	a+b
67	56	3752	123
32	78	2496	110
15	18	270	33

14.   (a) 1332   (b) Jane, 330 more calories   (c) Maurice, 96 more calories

15.   No, only 2352 calories

16. $60

17. (a) 77 remainder 7   (b) 8 remainder 10
(c) 10 remainder 91

18. (a) $3\overline{)876}$ (b) $8\overline{)367}$

19. (a) Monthly payments are more expensive.   (b) $3,700

20. 65,536 bits

21. 3

22. 8 cars (remember the match)

23.

2	11
4	15
0	7
6	19
12	31

24. (f) Yes, suppose the 3 numbers are a, b, and c. The 6 different numbers are

ab
ac
bc
bd
cb
+cd . The sum is 2(a + b + c) 10 + 2(a + b + c) = (a + b + c)·22. Now if we divide by (a + b + c), we always obtain 22.

25. (a) Answers vary   (b) If ab·cd=ba·dc then ac = bd

26. 1022

27. The result is always 4.

28. 3 hrs

29. Her estimate is high, discussions vary.

30. Answers vary.

31. 10 seconds

32. 21 weeks

33. 58 buses needed, not all full

34. 11 km/L

35. Answers vary

36. (a) (i) $70 (ii) $10   (b) On the 12th trip

37. (a) (i) 27·198 = 5346 (ii) 48·159 = 7632
(iii) 39·186 = 7254   (b) (i) 1963·4 = 7852
(ii) 483·12 = 5796 (iii) 297·18 = 5346   (c) 1

38. (a)   763   (b)   678
        × 8   × 3
       6104   2034

39. (a)   762   (b)   378
        × 83   × 26
      63,246   9,828

40. 7,500,000 cows

41. (a)   37   (b)   93   (c) $9\overline{)123}$
        × 43   × 36   - 9
        111   558   33
       1480   2790   - 27
       1591   3348   6

42. (a) 1; 121; 12,321; 1,234,321; your calculator may not produce the pattern after this term, but it continues through 111,111,111·111,111,111.   (b) 9801, 998001, 99980001, 9999800001, 999998000001

43. $60; $3600; $86,400; $604,800; $2,592,000 (30 days); $31,536,000 (365 days); $630,720,000 or $631,152,000 (with leap years)

44. 19

45. 999999ⵔⵔⵔⵔⵔⵔⵔⵔⵔⵔ||||

46. 300,260

47. For example, 3 + 0 = 3 = 0 + 3.

48. (a) x·(a + b + 2)   (b) (3 + x)(a + b)

49. 6979 miles.

50. 724

Brain Teaser (p. 158)
(a)   570,140   (b)   38   39
        ×   6   38   or   39
       3,420,840   +38   +39
                                   114   117

Problem Set 3-6

1. (a) $(1, 10, 11, 100, 101, 110, 111, 1000, 1001, 1010, 1011, 1100, 1101, 1110, 1111)_{two}$ (b) $(1, 2, 10, 11, 12, 20, 21, 22, 100, 101, 102, 110, 111, 112, 120)_{three}$ (c) $(1, 2, 3, 10, 11, 12, 13, 20, 21, 22, 23, 30, 31, 32, 33)_{four}$
(d) $(1, 2, 3, 4, 5, 6, 7, 10, 11, 12, 13, 14, 15, 16, 17)_{eight}$

2. 20

3. $2032_{four} = \left(2 \cdot 10^3 + 0 \cdot 10^2 + 3 \cdot 10 + 2\right)_{four}$

4. (a) 111_{two} (b) 555_{six} (c) 999_{ten} (d) EEE_{twelve}

5. (a) ETE_{twelve}; $EE1_{twelve}$ (b) 11111_{two}; 100001_{two}
(c) 554_{six}; 1000_{six} (d) 66_{seven}; 101_{seven} (e) 444_{five}; 1001_{five}
(f) 101_{two}; 111_{two}

6. (a) There is no numeral 4 in base four.   (b) There are no numerals 6 or 7 in base 5.   (c) There is no numeral T in base three.

7. (a) 3212_{five} (b) 1177_{twelve} (c) 12110_{four}
(d) 100101_{two} (e) $1E3T4_{twelve}$

8. 100010_{two}

9. (a) 117   (b) 45   (c) 1331   (d) 1451   (e) 157   (f) 181

10. 72¢; 242_{five}

11. 1 prize of $625, 2 prizes of $125, and 1 of $25.

12. 3 quarters, 4 nickels, and 2 pennies.

13. (a) 8 weeks, 2 days   (b) 4 years; 6 months
(c) 1 day, 5 hours   (d) 5 feet, 8 inches

14. $E66_{twelve}$; 1662

15. (a) 6   (b) 1   (c) nine

16. 1 hour 34 minutes 15 seconds

17. 4; 1, 2, 4, 8; 1, 2, 4, 8, 16

18. (a) 9, (4 quarters 3 nickels 2 pennies)   (b) 73 pennies

19. (a) 121_{five} (b) 20_{five} (c) 1010_{five} (d) 14_{five}
(e) 1001_{two} (f) 1010_{two}

20.

+	0	1	2	3	4	5	6	7
0	0	1	2	3	4	5	6	7
1	1	2	3	4	5	6	7	10
2	2	3	4	5	6	7	10	11
3	3	4	5	6	7	10	11	12
4	4	5	6	7	10	11	12	13
5	5	6	7	10	11	12	13	14
6	6	7	10	11	12	13	14	15
7	7	10	11	12	13	14	15	16

Base eight

•	0	1	2	3	4	5	6	7
0	0	0	0	0	0	0	0	0
1	0	1	2	3	4	5	6	7
2	0	2	4	6	10	12	14	16
3	0	3	6	11	14	17	22	25
4	0	4	10	14	20	24	30	34
5	0	5	12	17	24	31	36	43
6	0	6	11	22	30	36	44	52
7	0	7	16	25	34	43	52	61

Base eight

1. (a) 9 hours 33 minutes 25 seconds (b) 1 hour 39 minutes 40 seconds
2. (a) 2 quarts, 1 pint, 0 cups, or 1 half-gallon, 0 quarts, 1 pint, 0 cups (b) 1 pint, 0 cups (c) 2 quarts, 1 pint, 1 cup
3. $2\frac{1}{2}$ so buy 3 gallons
24.

$3_3 1_1 2$

$1\ 3_0$

$2\ 2$

$4_3 3_0$

$2_0 3$

$1\ 2_0$

$\overline{3\ 1\ 0}_{\text{five}}$

25. (a) 3 gross 10 dozen 9 ones (b) 6 gross 3 dozen 4 ones
26. (a) 22 students on Tuesday; (b) 1 gal., 1 half-gallon, 1 qt., 1 pint, and 1 cup
27. (a) 70 (b) 87
28. There is no numeral 5 in base five; $2_{\text{five}} + 3_{\text{five}} = 10_{\text{five}}$.
29. (a) 230_{five} (b) 20010_{three}

$-\ 22_{\text{five}}$ $-\ 2022_{\text{three}}$

$\overline{203_{\text{five}}}$ $\overline{10211_{\text{three}}}$

30. (a) 233_{five} (b) 4_{five} R 1_{five} (c) 2144_{five}
(d) 31_{five} (e) 67_{eight} (f) 15_{eight} R 3_{eight}
(g) 110_{two} (h) 1101110_{two}
31. (a) Nine (b) Four (c) Six (d) Any base greater than or equal to 2.
32. 30221_{five}
33. a=5, b=7
34. Answers may vary.

Laboratory Activity (p. 166)

1. (a) A computer
2. When a person tells his or her age by listing cards, the person is giving the base two representation for his or her age. The number can then be determined by adding the numbers in the upper left-hand corners of the named cards.

Chapter Test

1. (a) 400,044 (b) 117 (c) 1704 (d) 11 (e) 1448
2. (a) CMXCIX (b) ⌒⌒⌒⌒⌒⌒⌒⌒|||||
(c) $\overset{\bullet}{\underset{\bullet\bullet\bullet}{}}$ (d) 2341_{five} (e) 1000_{twelve} (f) 11011_{two}
(g) 1241_{nine} (h) 1011_{two}
3. (a) 3^{17} (b) 2^{21} (c) 3^5 (d) 2^{82}
4. (a) Distributive Property for Multiplication over Addition
(b) Commutative Property of Addition
(c) Identity Property for Multiplication
(d) Distributive Property for Multiplication over Addition
(e) Commutative Property for Multiplication
(f) Associative Property of Multiplication
5. (a) 3 < 13, because 3 + 10 = 13 (b) 12 > 9, because 12 = 9 + 3
6. $1000 \cdot 483 = 10^3 \left(4 \cdot 10^2 + 8 \cdot 10 + 3 \right)$

$= 4 \cdot 10^5 + 8 \cdot 10^4 + 3 \cdot 10^3$

$= 4 \cdot 10^5 + 8 \cdot 10^4 + 3 \cdot 10^3 + 0 \cdot 10^2 + 0 \cdot 10^1 + 0 \cdot 1$

$= 483,000$

7. (a) 1119 (b) $173E_{\text{twelve}}$.
8. (a) 60,074 (b) 14150_{eight}
9. (a) 5 remainder 243 (b) 91 remainder 10
(c) 120_{five} remainder 2_{five} (d) 11_{two} remainder 10_{two}
10. (a) $5 \cdot 912 + 243 = 4803$ (b) $91 \cdot 11 + 10 = 1011$
(c) $23_{\text{five}} \cdot 120_{\text{five}} + 2_{\text{five}} = 3312_{\text{five}}$
(d) $11_{\text{two}} \cdot 11_{\text{two}} + 10_{\text{two}} = 1011_{\text{two}}$
11. (a) tens (b) thousands (c) hundreds
12. (a) 10, 11, 12, 13, 14, 15 (b) 10
(c) All whole numbers (d) 0, 1, 2, ..., 26
13. (a)
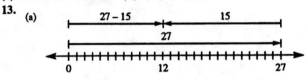

(b)
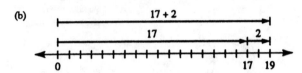

14. (a) 15a (b) $5x^2$ (c) xa + xb + xy (d) (x + 5)(3 + y)
15. (a) 1 (b) 6 (c) 9
16. $395
17. $4380
18. 2600
19. $3842
20. Several answers are possible. For example,

$\begin{array}{r} 296 \\ +\ 541 \\ \hline 837 \end{array}$ $\begin{array}{r} 569 \\ +\ 214 \\ \hline 783 \end{array}$

21. 69 miles
22. 40 cans
23. 12 outfits
24.

+	5	7	9
8	13	15	17
11	16	18	20
21	26	28	30

25. 26
26. $2.16
27. $6000
28. There are 36 bikes and 18 trikes
29. $214
30. $400

CHAPTER 4

Problem Set 4-1

1. (a) ⁻2 (b) 5 (c) ⁻m (d) 0 (e) m
(f) ⁻a + ⁻b or ⁻(a + b)
2. (a) 2 (b) m (c) 0
3. (a) 5 (b) 10 (c) ⁻5 (d) ⁻5

4.

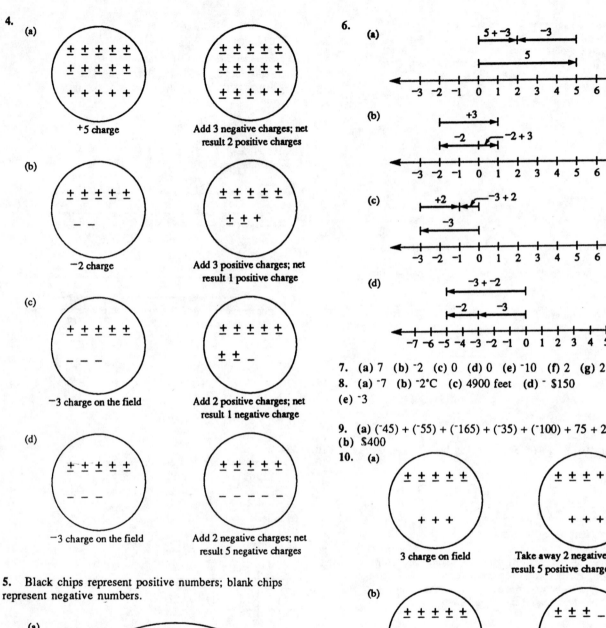

(a)

+5 charge

Add 3 negative charges; net
result 2 positive charges

(b)

−2 charge

Add 3 positive charges; net
result 1 positive charge

(c)

−3 charge on the field

Add 2 positive charges; net
result 1 negative charge

(d)

−3 charge on the field

Add 2 negative charges; net
result 5 negative charges

5. Black chips represent positive numbers; blank chips
represent negative numbers.

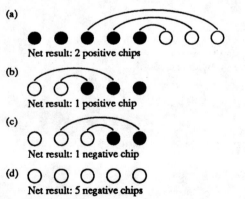

(a)

Net result: 2 positive chips

(b)

Net result: 1 positive chip

(c)

Net result: 1 negative chip

(d) Net result: 5 negative chips

6.

(a)

(b)

(c)

(d)

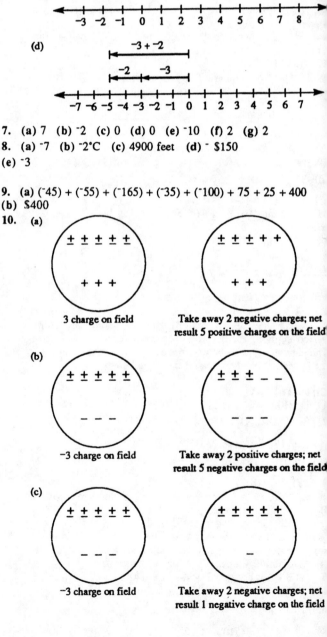

7. (a) 7   (b) −2   (c) 0   (d) 0   (e) −10   (f) 2   (g) 2

8. (a) −7   (b) −2°C   (c) 4900 feet   (d) − $150
(e) −3

9. (a) (−45) + (−55) + (−165) + (−35) + (−100) + 75 + 25 + 400
(b) $400

10. (a)

3 charge on field

Take away 2 negative charges; net
result 5 positive charges on the field

(b)

−3 charge on field

Take away 2 positive charges; net
result 5 negative charges on the field

(c)

−3 charge on field

Take away 2 negative charges; net
result 1 negative charge on the field

11. (a)

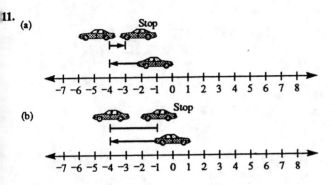

(b)

12. (a) ⁻4 - 2 = ⁻6; ⁻4 -1 = ⁻ 5; ⁻4 - 0 = ⁻4; ⁻4 - ⁻1 = ⁻3
(b) 3 - 1 = 2; 2 - 1 = 1; 1- 1 = 0; 0 - 1 = ⁻1; ⁻1 - 1 = ⁻2; ⁻2 - 1 = ⁻3
13. (a) ⁻1   (b) 1   (c) 3
14. (a) ⁻9   (b) ⁻10   (c) 13   (d) ⁻4
15. (a) ⁻9   (b) 3   (c) 1   (d) ⁻19   (e) ⁻13   (f) ⁻6
16. (a) (i) 55 - 60   (ii)   55 + (⁻60)   (iii) ⁻5
(b) (i) 200 - 220   (ii) 200+ (⁻220)   (iii) ⁻20
17. (a) 1 + 4x   (b) 2x + y   (c) x - 2
18. (a) All negative integers   (b) All positive integers
(c) All positive integers less than ⁻1   (d) 2 or ⁻2   (e) There are none.   (f) All integers except 0   (g) There are none.
19. 783 BC
20. (a) I   (b) W   (c) I - {0}   (d) ∅   (e) ∅   (f) I
(g) {0}   (h) W   (i) I
21.

2	⁻13	8
5	⁻1	⁻7
⁻10	11	⁻4

other answers are possible

22.

	3	5	
7	1	8	2
	4	6	

other answers are possible

23. 33 points
24. (a) 59   (b) ⁻269°C   (c) 192° F   (d) 56 or 80
25. 2
26. ⁻4 pounds
27. (a) 10W-40 or 10W-30   (b) 5W-30   (c) 10W-40 or 10W-30   (d) none   (e) 10W-30 or 10W-40
28. (a) 0   (b) ⁻101   (c) 1   (d) ⁻4
29. (a) 9   (b) 2   (c) 0 or 2   (d) The set of all integers greater than or equal to 0
30. (a) All nonnegative integers
(b) (i) 5   (ii) 5   (iii) 0   (iv) ⁻7
31. (a) 89   (b) 19   (c) 19   (d) y - x - 1 or y - (x+ 1)
32. Greatest possible value: a - (b - c) - d, or 8. Least possible value: a - b - (c- d), or ⁻6
33. (a) ⁻3; ..., ⁻12, ⁻15, ...   (b) ⁻4; ..., ⁻9, ⁻13, ...
(c) ⁻y; ..., x - 2y, x- 3y ...   (d) 2x; ..., 1 + 3x, 1 + 5x, ...
34. (a) 0   (b) 3775   (c) 2538
35. (a) ⁻14   (b) ⁻24   (c) 2   (d) 5
36. (a) ⁻18   (b) ⁻106   (c) ⁻6   (d) 22   (e) ⁻11   (f) 2
(g) ⁻18   (h) 23
37. (a) ⁻101   (b) 516   (c) 10,894   (d) 5,995
38. b - a = b + (⁻a) = ⁻a + b = ⁻a - (⁻b) = ⁻(a - b)
39. (a) (a + b) + (⁻a + ⁻b) = a + b + ⁻a + ⁻b = a + ⁻a + b + ⁻b
= (a + ⁻a) + (b + ⁻b) = 0 + 0 = 0

(b) From part (a), ⁻a + ⁻b is a solution of the equation (a + b) + x = 0. Because ⁻(a + b) is the unique solution of this equation, we must have ⁻a + ⁻b = ⁻(a + b).
40. Find the difference of the absolute values of the integers. The sum has the same sign as the integer with the larger absolute value.
41. (a) True   (b) True   (c) True   (d) True
(e) False; let x= ⁻1   (f) True

Brain Teaser (p. 187)
123 - 45 - 67 + 89 = 100

Brain Teaser (p. 195)
Answers may vary. $1 = 4^4/4^4$; $2 = (4 \cdot 4)/4 + 4$;
$3 = 4 - (4/4)^4$; $[(4-4)/4] + 4$; $5 = 4 + 4^{(4-4)}$;
$6 = 4 + [(4+4)/4]$; $7 = (44/4) - 4$; $8 = 4 \cdot 4/4 + 4$;
$9 = 4 + 4 + 4/4$; $10 = (44 - 4)/4$

Problem Set 4-2
1. $3(^-1) = {}^-1 + {}^-1 + {}^-1 = {}^-3$; $2(^-1) = {}^-1 + {}^-1 = {}^-2$; $1(^-1) = {}^-1$;
$0(^-1) = 0$; $(^-1)(^-1) = 1$, by continuing the pattern.
2.

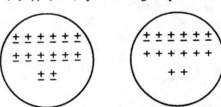

0 charge   Take away four groups of two negative charges; net result is eight positive charges.

3.
If you are now at 0 moving west at 4 km/h, you will be at 8 km west of 0 two hours from now.

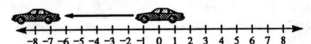

4. (a) ⁻20·4   (b) +20·4   (c) ⁻20n   (d) 20n
5. (a) 12   (b) ⁻15   (c) ⁻15   (d) 0   (e) 30   (f) ⁻30   (g) 0
(h) 16
6. (a) 5   (b) ⁻13   (c) ⁻ 11   (d) 0   (e) Impossible; division by 0 is not defined.   (f) Impossible; division by 0 is not defined.
7. (a) ⁻10   (b) ⁻40   (c) a; if a/b is defined   (d) ⁻10
(e) a; If b ≠ 0   (f) ⁻32   (g) ⁻5   (h) 0   (i) Impossible
(j) ⁻4   (k) Impossible   (l) 13   (m) ⁻1   (n) ⁻2
8. (a) 32°C - 30·(3°C)   (b) 0°C + 25·(4 °C)
(c) ⁻20°C + 30·(4°C)   (d) 25 °C - 20·(3°C)
(e) 0°C + m·(d°C)   (f) 20°C - m·(d°C)
9. (a) 4(⁻11) = ⁻44   (b) ⁻66 divided by 11 = ⁻6; He lost 6 yards.
10. 14(⁻12,000), i.e., a loss of 168,000 acres.
11. (a) ⁻1(⁻5 + ⁻2) = ⁻1(⁻7) = 7; (⁻1)(⁻5) + (⁻1)(⁻2) = 5 + 2 = 7
(b) ⁻3(⁻3 + 2) = ⁻3(⁻1) = 3; (⁻3)(⁻3) + (⁻3)(2) = 9 + ⁻6 = 3
(c) ⁻5(2 + ⁻6) = ⁻5(⁻4) = 20; (⁻5)(2) + (⁻5)(⁻6) = ⁻10 + 30 = 20
12. (a) ⁻8   (b) 16   (c) ⁻1000   (d) 81   (e) 1   (f) ⁻1
(g) 1   (h) ⁻1
13. (a) 12   (b) 0   (c) ⁻5   (d) 19   (e) 9   (f) ⁻9   (g) ⁻13
(h) ⁻8   (i) ⁻32   (j) ⁻16

14. (b), (c), (g), (h) are always positive (a), (f) are always negative

15. (b) = (c); (d) = (e); (9) = (h)

16. (a) Commutative Property of Multiplication (b) Closure Property of Addition (c) Associative Property of Multiplication (d) Distributive Property of Multiplication over Addition

17. (a) Distributive Property of Multiplication over Addition (b) Subtraction as the Inverse of Addition (c) Commutative Property of Multiplication (d) Commutative Property of Addition (e) Addition as the inverse of subtraction

18. (a) xy (b) 2xy (c) 0 (d) $^-$x (e) x + 2y (f) b (g) x (h) y

19. (a) $^-$2 (b) 2 (c) 0 (d) $^-$6 (e) $^-$36 (f) 6 (g) All integers except 0 (h) All integers except 0 (I) No solution is possible with integers. (J) 3 or $^-$3 (k) No solution is possible with integers. (l) All integers except 0 (m) All integers except 0 (n) All integers (o) All integers

20. (a) $^-$2x + 2 (b) $^-$2x + 2y (c) $x^2 - xy$ (d) $^-x^2 + xy$ (e) $^-$2x - 2y + 2z (f) $^-x^2 + xy + 3x$ (g) $^-25 - 10x - x^2$ (h) $x^2 - y^2 - 1 - 2y$ (I) $^-x^4 + 3x^2 - 2$

21. (a) $(50 + 2)(50 - 2) = 50^2 - 2^2 = 2500 - 4 = 2496$ (b) 25 - 10,000 = $^-$9975 (c) $x^2 - y^2$ (d) $4 - 9x^2$ (e) $x^2 - 1$ (f) $(213 + 13)(213 - 13) = 226 \times 200 = 45,200$

22. No; it is not of the form (a - b)(a + b)

23. (a) 8x (b) (a + 2)x (c) x(y + 1) (d) (a - 2)x (e) x(x + y) (f) 6x (g) x(3y + 2 - z) (h) x(3x + y - 1) (I) a(b(c + 1) - 1) (J) (a + b)c (k) (4 + a)(4 - a) (l) (x + 3y)(x - 3y) (m) (2x + 5y)(2x - 5y) (n) (x + y)(x - y) + x + y = (x + y)(x - y + 1)

24. (a) $(a - b)^2 = a^2 + 2ab + b^2$ (b) (i) $98^2 = (100 - 2)^2 = 100^2 - 2(200) + 2^2 = 10,000 - 400 + 4 = 9604$ (ii) $99^2 = (100 - 1)^2 = 100^2 - 2(100) + 1^2 = 10,000 - 200 + 1 = 9801$ (iii) $997^2 = (100 - 3)^2 = 1000^2 - 2(3000) + 3^2 = 1,000,000 - 6000 + 9 = 994,009$

25.
$$a^2 + 2a\left(^-b\right) + \left(^-b\right)^2$$
$$= a^2 + \left(^-2ab\right) + \left(^-b\right)^2 \quad \text{since } 2a(^-b) = ^-2ab$$
$$= a^2 - 2ab + \left(^-b\right)^2$$
$$= a^2 - 2ab + b^2 \quad \text{since } \left(^-b\right)^2 = b^2$$

26. (a) False (b) True (c) True (d) True

27. (a) The sums are 9 times the middle number. (b) Let a be the middle number. Then we have the following 9 numbers:

a - 8	a - 7	a - 6
a - 1	a	a + 1
a + 6	a + 7	a + 8

The sum of these numbers is 9a which is 9 times the middle number.

28. (a) 8, 11, d = 3, nth term is 3n - 13 (b) $^-$8, $^-$11, d = $^-$3, nth term is $^-$3n + 13 (c) $^-$128, $^-$256, r = 2, nth term $^-(2)^n$

(d) $^-$128, 256, r = $^-$2, nth term is $\left(^-2\right)^n$

(e) $2^7, ^-2^8$, r = $^-$2, nth term is $2 \cdot \left(^-2\right)^{n-1}$ or $^-\left(^-2\right)^n$

(f) $^-8 \cdot 2^4, 9 \cdot 2^8$

29. (a) 13,850 (b) $^-$13,850

30. (a) $^-$9, $^-$6, $^-$1, 6, 15 (b) $^-$2, $^-$7, $^-$12, $^-$17, $^-$22 (c) $^-$3, 3, $^-$9, 15, $^-$33, (d) 0, 8, 0, 32, 0, (e) $^-$1, 4, $^-$9, 16, $^-$25, (f) 2, $^-$8, 24, $^-$64, 160, (g) 9, 8, 7, 6, 5, (h) 0, 8, 0, 32, 0,

31. 7, 2

32. (a) $(^-a)b + ab = (^-a + a)b = 0b = 0$, so $(^-a)b = ^-(ab)$ (b) $(^-a)(^-b) + ^-(ab) = (^-a)(^-b) + (^-a)b = (^-a)(^-b + b) = (^-a)0 = 0$, so $(^-a)(^-b) = ^-(^-(ab)) = ab$

33. $(^-1)a + a = (^-1)a + (1)a = (^-1 + 1)a = 0a = 0$, so $(^-1)a = ^-a$
Now:
$$(^-a)b = [(^-1)a]b$$
$$= ^-1(ab) \quad \text{by the Associative Property of Multiplication}$$
$$= ^-(ab) \quad \text{by first part}$$

34. $^-(a + b) = (^-1)(a + b) \quad$ by first part of problem 33.
$$= (^-1)a + (^-1)b \quad \text{by Distributive Property}$$
$$= ^-a + ^-b \quad \text{by first part of problem 33.}$$

35. (a) $^-$81 (b) 184 (c) $^-$2 (d) 2

36. (a) $^-$3 (b) 1 (c) 13 (d) 3 (e) $^-$3 (f) - 13

37.

38. (a) 5 (b) $^-$7 (c) 0

39. (a) 14 (b) 21 (c) $^-$4 (d) 22

Brain Teaser (p. 197)
0 because (x - x) = 0

Brain Teaser (p. 212)
The part of the explanation that is incorrect is the division by (e - a - d) which is equal to 0. Division by 0 is impossible.

Problem Set 4-3

1. (a) $^-$20, $^-$13, $^-$5, $^-$3, 0, 4 (b) $^-$6, $^-$5, 0, 5, 6 (c) $^-$100, $^-$20, $^-$15, $^-$13, 0 (d) $^-$3, $^-$2, 5, 13

2. (a) $^-$5 + 2 = $^-$3 (b) $^-$6 + 6 = 0 (c) $^-$10 + 2 = $^-$8 (d) $^-$5 + 9 = 4

3. (a) $^-$18 (b) x > $^-$18 and x is an integer (c) 18 (d) x < 18 and x is an integer (e) $^-$18 (f) x < $^-$18 and x is an integer (g) $^-$7 (h) x < $^-$7 and x is an integer (I) $^-$2 (J) x ≥ $^-$2 and x is an integer (k) $^-$1 (l) x < $^-$1 and x is an integer (m) $^-$2 (n) x < $^-$3 and x is an integer

4. (a) True (b) False except when x = 3 (c) True (d) True (e) True (f) False

5. (a) {1, $^-$2, 0} (b) {9} (c) {$^-$6, $^-$7} (d) {$^-$3, $^-$2, $^-$1, 0, 1, 2, 3}

6. (a) $^-$3 (b) 0 (c) 1 (d) 0

7. (a) n - 6 or 6 - n (b) n + 14 (c) 4n - 7 (d) 8 + 3n (e) n + 10 (f) 4n (g) 13 - n (h) n - 4

8. (a) 60t (b) 4g + 30 (c) $20 + $25x (d) 175d cents (e) 3x + 3 (f) 3x + 6 (g) 3m (h) $m^3 - m$ (I) $q \cdot 2^n$ (J) 40°F - (3 °F)·t (k) $2(s + 5000)

9. North America: 8,055,800 square miles
Asia: 17,093,600 square miles
South America: 6,869,800 square miles
Europe: 3,672,800 square miles

10. Tom is older than 11.

12. Rick has $100 and David has $300.

13. Let a, b, c be on the same line and x be the distance from B to A. Point A is twice as far from point C as point B is from point A can be translated as "point A is 2x from point C and point B is x from point A." From this information, we can infer that the distance from B to C is also x. The distance from B to C is 5 inches. Hence, the distance from A to C is 10 inches. An alternate answer is 3 1/3 inches.

14. Factory A produces 2800 cars per day Factory B produces 1400 cars per day Factory C produces 3100 cars per day

15. 40 pounds of the $0.60/lb tea, 60 pounds of the $0.45/lb tea

16. 524 student tickets

17. 78, 79, 80

18. 78, 80, 82

19. 14 + 7

20. Eldest, $30,000; middle, $24,000; youngest, $10,000

21. 10, 12, 14

22. 200 student tickets, 800 adult tickets

23. 720 km from Albuquerque

24. The second troop should start counter clockwise around the lake and they will meet the first troop in 2 hours. If they went clockwise, it would take them 3 hours to catch up.

25. 48 miles

26. (a) $-4 < x < 4$ (b) $-3 < y < 3$ (c) $0 \le |x + y| \le 6$ and $0 \le |x - y| \le 6$

27. (a) Yes. $(x-y)^2 \ge 0$ is always true; this implies $x^2 - 2xy + y^2 \ge 0$ which implies $x^2 + y^2 \ge 2xy$

(b) $x^2 + y^2 = 2xy$ if and only if $x = y$

28. Proof: $0 < a < b$ implies that $0 < a$ and $0 < b$. Now $a < b$ and $0 < a$ imply $a^2 < ab$. Also $a < b$ and $0 < b$ imply $ab < b^2$. Hence $a^2 < b^2$.

29. No; $-5 < 2$, but $(-5)^2 > 2^2$.

30. Proof: $a < b$ implies $-a > -b$. Hence $c + -a > c + -b$, or $c - a > c - b$.

31. (a) $-3, -2, -1, 0, 1$ (b) $-2, -3, -4, ...$

32. (a) 7 (b) -5 (c) -3 (d) -10

33. (a) -10 (b) 4 (c) -4 (d) 10 (e) -21 (f) 21
(g) -4 (h) -3 (i) 3 (j) -4 (k) 7 (l) -21 (m) 21
(n) 56 (o) 15 (p) -1

34.

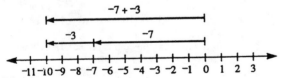

Brain Teaser (p. 214)
42,857

Chapter 4 Test

1. (a) -3 (b) a (c) 0 (d) $-x - y$ (e) $x - y$ (f) 32
(g) 32

2. (a) -7 (b) 8 (c) 8 (d) 0 (e) 8 (f) 15

3. (a) 3 (b) -5 (c) Any integer except 0 (d) No integer will work (e) -41 (f) Any integer

4. $2(-3) = -3 + -3 = -6$; $1(-3) = -3$; $0(-3) = 0$; if the pattern continued then: $-1(-3) = 3$; $-2(-3) = 6$

5. (a) $10 - 5 = 5$ (b) $1 - (-2) = 3$

6. (a) $(x - y)(x + y) = (x - y)x + (x - y)y$
$$= x^2 - yx + xy - y^2$$
$$= x^2 - xy + xy - y^2$$
$$= x^2 - y^2$$

(b) $4 - x^2$

7. (a) $-x$ (b) $y - x$ (c) $3x - 1$ (d) $2x^2$ (e) 0
(f) $-9 - 6x - x^2$

8. (a) $-2x$ (b) $x(x + 1)$ (c) $(x - 6)(x + 6)$
(d) $(9y^3 + 4x^2)(9y^3 - 4x^2)$ (e) $5(1 + x)$ (f) $(x - y)x$

9. (a) -2 (b) 5 or -5 (c) 1, 2, 3, 4, ... (d) $-3, -4, -5, -6, ...$

10. (a) False (b) False (c) False (d) True (e) False

11. (a) $2/1 \ne 1/2$ (b) $3 - (4 - 5) \ne (3 - 4) - 5$ (c) $1/2$ is not an integer (d) $8/(4 - 2) \ne 8/4 - 8/2$

12.

(a)
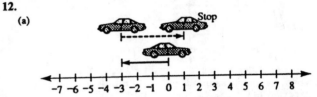

(b)
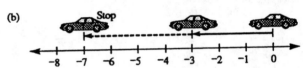

(c) If you are at 0, moving west at 3 km/hr, you were 12 km east of 0 four hours ago.

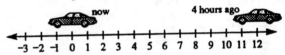

13. $-7°C$

14. 115 2-kg packages, 35 1-kg packages

15. 7 nickels, 17 dimes

16. 1790 freshmen, 2020 sophomores, 895 juniors, 1010 seniors

17. 42 gallons

18. 4000 pounds of Spanish peanuts, 4000 pounds of cashews, 2000 pounds of pecans

CHAPTER 5

Problem Set 5-1

1. (a) True (b) True (c) True (d) True (e) True
(f) False

2. (a) Answers will vary. $7|35$ (b) $d|213$ (c) $d|a$
(d) $7|245$ (e) $d|213$ (f) $d|a$

3. Yes.

4. No.

5. (a) True by Theorem 5-1 (b) True by Theorem 5-2(b)
(c) None (d) True by Theorem 5-2(b) (e) True by Theorem 5-1

6. (a) No; $17|34,000$ and $17 \nmid 15$ imply $17 \nmid (34,000 + 15)$

(b) Yes; $17|34,000$ and $17|51$ imply $17|(34,000 + 51)$

(c) No; $19|19,000$ and $19 \nmid 31$ imply $19 \nmid (19,000 + 31)$

(d) No; $31 \nmid 19,000$ and $31|31$ imply $31 \nmid (19,000 + 31)$

(e) No.; $2^{14}|2^{64}$ and $2^{14} \nmid 1$ imply $2^{14} \nmid \left(2^{64}+1\right)$

(f) No; Each of 2, 3, 5, 7, 13, and 17 divide $2 \cdot 3 \cdot 5 \cdot 7 \cdot 13 \cdot 17$, but since $2 \nmid 1, 3 \nmid 1, 5 \nmid 1, 7 \nmid 1, 13 \nmid 1, 17 \nmid 1$, then none of 2, 3, 5, 7, 13, or 17 divides $2 \cdot 3 \cdot 5 \cdot 7 \cdot 13 \cdot 17 + 1$.

7. **(a)** 1, 2, 4, 5, 8, 11

(b) 2 ways;

Touchdown	Extra pt.	Field Goal
4	4	4
1	1	11

(c) Impossible if one scores an extra point with every touchdown. If not, then 5.

8. **(a)** (i) 1 (ii) 2 (iii) 3 (iv) 7 (v) 3 (vi) 6 (vii) 6 (viii) 0

(b) The remainder is a.   **(c)** The remainder is the sum of the digits.

9.

(a)	4	4	4
(b)	8	8	8
(c)	3	12	3
(d)	8	26	8
(e)	2	20	2

(f) The remainder when n is divided by 9 is equal to the remainder when the sum of the digits of n is divided by nine.

10. **(a)** 12,343 + 4546 + 56 = 16,945

     4 + 1 + 2 =   7

(b) 987 + 456 + 8765 = 10,208

     6 + 6 + 8   = 20 has a remainder of 2 when divided by 9 as does 1 + 0 + 2 + 0 + 8 = 11.

(c) 10,034 + 3004 + 400 + 20 = 13,458

     8 + 7 + 4 + 2 = 21 has a remainder 3 when divided by 9 as does 1 + 3 + 4 + 5 + 8.

(d) Answers vary.   **(e)** 1003 - 46 = 957

     4 - 1 = 3 has remainder 3 when divided by 9 as does 9 + 5 + 7 = 21   **(f)** $345 \cdot 56 = 19{,}320$. 345 has remainder 3 when divided by 9; 56 has remainder 2 when divided by 9; $3 \cdot 2 = 6$ as does $345 \cdot 56 = 19{,}320$ when divided by 9.   **(g)** Answers vary.

11. **(a)** False; 2|4, but $2 \nmid 1$ and $2 \nmid 3$ **(b)** False (same example as in 11 (a))   **(c)** True   **(d)** False; 12|72 but $12 \nmid 8$ and $12 \nmid 9$ **(e)** True   **(f)** True   **(g)** True   **(h)** False; If a = 5 and b = ‾5, then a|b and b|a, but a ≠ b.   **(i)** True   **(j)** False; $2 \nmid 3$ and $2 \nmid 9$ but 2|(3 + 9)   **(k)** False; $50|10^2$, but $50 \nmid 10$ **(l)** False; $50 \nmid 10$, but 50|100   **(m)** True

12. **(a)** True   **(b)** False   **(c)** False   **(d)** True   **(e)** True   **(f)** False   **(g)** true

13. **(a)** Always   **(b)** Sometimes   **(c)** Never   **(d)** Always   **(e)** Always   **(f)** Sometimes   **(g)** Always

14. **(a)** A number is divisible by 16 if and only if the last four digits form a number divisible by 16.   **(b)** A number is divisible by 25 if and only if the number formed by the last two digits is divisible by 25.

15. Yes, $651 for each of those installments.

16. Each candy bar costs $.19.

17. 85,041

18. **(a)** 2, 3, 4, 6, 11.   **(b)** 2, 3, 6, 9.   **(c)** 2, 3, 5, 6, 10.   **(d)** 2, 3, 4, 6.   **(e)** 3, 5   **(f)** 2,4   **(g)** 7,11   **(h)** None   **(i)** 2, 4, 5, 10.

19. **(a)** No. If $5 \nmid d$ for any integer d, then there is no integer m such that 5m=d. If we assume 10|d, this means there exists n such that 10n = d or 5(2n) = d. This contradicts the original assumption that d is not divisible by 5.   **(b)** Yes. All odd multiples of 5 are not divisible by 10 but are divisible by 5.

20. **(a)** 7   **(b)** 7   **(c)** 6

21. Answers vary.

22. Prove the following theorem. For any integers a, b, and c, with a ≠ 0 and b ≠ 0, if a|b and b|c, then a|c.

If a|b, there exists an integer m such that ma=b.
If b|c, there exists an integer n such that nb= c.
Using substitution, n(ma) = c.
Using the associative property of multiplication,
   (nm)a = c. Because m and n are integers, mn is an integer and a|c.

23. **(a)** Yes   **(b)** No   **(c)** Yes   **(d)** Yes

24. **(a)** (i) Yes; (ii) Yes; (iii) Yes; (iv) Yes   **(b)** By definition, a four-digit palindrome is of the form abba for any integers a and b. (a might equal b.)
The divisibility test for 11 states that an integer is divisible by 11 if and only if the sum of the digits in the places that are even powers of 10 minus the sum of the digits in the places that are odd powers of 10 is divisible by 11.
For abba, then, (a + b) - (b + a) = 0 is divisible by 11. Therefore, the four-digit palindrome abba is always divisible by 11.
(c) Answers vary.   **(d)** Answers vary.

25. **(a)** The result is always 9.   **(b)** The result is always 18.
(c) Let the number be $a \cdot 10 + b$. The number with the digits reversed is $b \cdot 10 + a$.
Now, $a \cdot 10 + b - (b \cdot 10 + a) = a \cdot 10 + b - b \cdot 10 - a$
$= a \cdot 10 - a + b - b \cdot 10$
$= 9a - 9b$
$= 9(a - b)$
Thus, the difference is a multiple of 9.
(d) The result is a multiple of 9.

26. No. Both 6 and 15 are multiples of 3, but 286 is not.

27. Answers vary.

28. **(a)** Consider any sequence a, a + 1, a + 2. According to the division algorithm, there exists a unique quotient and remainder for a, a + 1, and a + 2 when we divide by three. Since there are only 3 possible remainders when dividing by 3, namely 1, 2, and 0, when we divide by 3, we get a quotient g with a remainder of 1, 2, or 0. If the quotient is g and r = 1, then a + 1 divided by 3 has a quotient of g and r = 2. Also, a + 2 divided by 3 yields a quotient of g with r = 0. In fact, the remainders for the sequence a, a + 1, a + 2 when dividing by three will follow the sequence 0, 1, 2, 0, 1, 2, 0, 1, 2 . . . with 0 a member of any sequential triple.
(b) Among any n consecutive integers, there is always one that is divisible by n.

29. Suppose that d|a, $d \nmid b$, and d|(a+b).
d|a implies that there exists an integer c such that cd = a. d|(a + b) implies that there exists an integer e such that ed = a + b
Using substitution: ed = cd + b
     ed - cd = b
     (e - c)d = b which implies d|b. This contradicts the assumption that $d \nmid b$.
     Therefore $d \nmid (a + b)$.

30. Let $n = a \cdot 10^4 + b \cdot 10^3 + c \cdot 10^2 + d \cdot 10 + e$

$a 10^4 = a \cdot (10{,}000) = a \cdot (9999 + 1) = a \cdot 9999 + a$

$b \cdot 10^3 = b \cdot (1000) = b \cdot (999 + 1) = b \cdot 999 + b$

$c \cdot 10^2 = c \cdot (100) = c \cdot (99 + 1) = c \cdot 99 + c$

$d \cdot 10 = d \cdot (10) = d \cdot (9 + 1) = d \cdot 9 + d$

Thus, $n = (a \cdot 9999 + b \cdot 999 + c \cdot 99 + d \cdot 9) + (a + b + c + d + e)$
Because 9|9, 9|99, 9|999, 9|9999, it follows that
$9 | [(a \cdot 9999 + b \cdot 999 + c \cdot 99 + d \cdot 9) + (a + b + c + d + e)]$; that is, 9|n. If, on the other hand, $9 \nmid (a + b + c + d + e)$ it follows, that $9 \nmid n$.

31. 243. Yes. For n of the form, n = abcabc.
Therefore,

$$n = (a \cdot 10^5) + (b \cdot 10^4) + (c \cdot 10^3) + (a \cdot 10^2) + (b \cdot 10^1) + c$$
$$= a(10^5 + 10^2) + b(10^4 + 10^1) + c(10^3 + 1)$$
$$= a(100,000 + 100) + b(10,000 + 10) + c(1001)$$
$$= a(1001 \cdot 100) + b(1001 \cdot 10) + c(1001)$$
$$= (1001)[(a \cdot 100) + b(10) + c(1)]$$
$$= (7 \cdot 11 \cdot 13)[(a \cdot 100) + b(10) + c(1)]$$

Therefore, 7|n, 11|n, and 13|n.

32. $(3 \times \$20) + (11 \times \$50)$, or
$(8 \times \$20) + (9 \times \$50)$, or
$(13 \times \$20) + (7 \times \$50)$, or
$(18 \times \$20) + (5 \times \$50)$, or
$(23 \times \$20) + (3 \times \$50)$, or
$(28 \times \$20) + (1 \times \$50)$

The answer is not unique.

Brain Teaser (p. 231)
The number is 381-65-4729

Problem Set 5-2

1.

(a)   504

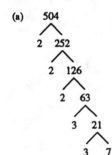

$504 = 2^3 \cdot 3^2 \cdot 7$

(b)   2475

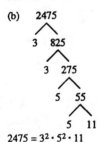

$2475 = 3^2 \cdot 5^2 \cdot 11$

(c)   11250

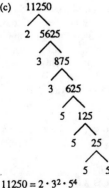

$11250 = 2 \cdot 3^2 \cdot 5^4$

2. **(a)** 149 is prime. **(b)** 923 is not prime. **(c)** 433 is prime. **(d)** 101 is prime. **(e)** 463 is prime. **(f)** 897 is not prime.

3. 73

4. Answers vary.

5. 101, 103, 107, 109, 113, 127, 131, 137, 139, 149, 151, 157, 163, 167, 173, 179, 181, 191, 193, 197, 199

6. 90

7. **(a)** 1×48, 2×24, 3×16, 4×12 **(b)** Only one, 1×47.

8. Yes; 177 flotillas of 1 ship each, 1 flotilla of 177 ships; 59 flotillas of 3 ships each; 3 flotillas of 59 ships.

9. **(a)** 3, 5, 15, 29, people **(b)** 145 committees of 3; 87 committees of 5; 29 committees of 15; 15 committees of 29.

10. **(a)** 1, 2, 3, 4, 6, 9, 12,18 or 36 **(b)** 1, 2, 4, 7, 14 or 28 **(c)** 1 or 17 **(d)** 1, 2, 3, 4, 6, 8, 9, 12, 16, 18, 24, 36, 48, 72, or 144

11. Answers vary.

12. **(a)** $2^7 \cdot 41$ **(b)** 16 divisors **(c)** No

13. **(a)** Answers may vary. For example,
$82^2 - 82 + 41 = 6683 = 41(163)$. **(b)** Let $n = 41a$ where $a \in N$.
Then $n^2 - n + 41 = (41a)^2 - 41a + 41 = 41(41a^2 - a + 1)$

14. 27,720

15. Answers vary.

16. 3, 5; 5, 7; 11, 13; 17, 19; 29,31; 41,43; 59, 61; 71, 73; 101, 103; 107, 109; 137, 139; 149, 151; 179, 181; 191, 193; 197, 199

17. **(a)** The Fundamental Theorem of Arithmetic says that n can be written as a product of primes in one and only one way. Since 2|n and 3|n and 2 and 3 are both prime, they must be included in the unique factorization.

That is, $2 \cdot 3 \cdot p_1 \cdot p_2 \cdot \ldots \cdot p_m = n$

Therefore, $(2 \cdot 3)(p_1 \cdot p_2 \cdot \ldots \cdot p_m) = n$

Thus, 6|n.

(b) Yes. If a|n, there exists an integer c such that ca = n. If b|n, there exists an integer d such that db = n.

Therefore, $(ca)(db) = n^2$

$(cd)(ab) = n^2$

Hence, $ab | n^2$

18. Answers vary.

19. Every number would have its "usual" factorization $1(p_1 \cdot p_2 \cdot p_3 \cdot \ldots \cdot p_n)$, along with infinitely many such other factorizations because $1^n = 1$; n may, be any natural number.

20. 1, 2, 3, 6, 7, 14, 21

21. No, because 5^2 has no factors of either 2 or 3.

22. **(a)** 4, 6, 8, 0 **(b)** 1 and 9 **(c)** 23, 29, 31, 37, 53, 59, 71, 73, 79 **(d)** Answers vary. For example, 233

23. **(a)** 49, 121, 169 Squares of prime numbers (column 2) **(b)** 81, 625, 2401 Squares of squares of prime numbers (squares of column 3) **(c)** 38, 39, 46
Products of 2 primes or cubes of primes.

24. Answers vary.

25. $97^2 = 9409$

26. None of the primes 2, 3, 5. . ., p divides N because if any one of the primes divided N, then it must also divide 1 which is impossible.

27. Answers vary.

28. Answers vary.

29. There are infinitely many composites of the form 1, 11, 111, 1111, 11111, 111111. . . since every 3rd member of this sequence will be divisible by 3.

30. $3n + 1$, where $n \in \{1,2,3,...\}$

When n is odd, $3n + 1$ is even. Thus, $3n + 1$ is divisible by 2, and is not prime. Since there are infinitely many even integers, there are infinitely many composites in the sequence, $3n + 1$ when n is odd.

31. Composites are obtained when n = 16 or 17.

32. (a) False (b) True (c) True (d) True

33. (a) 2, 3, 6 (b) 2, 3, 5, 6, 9 10

34. If 12|n, there exists an integer a such that $12a = n$.

$$(3 \cdot 4)a = n$$
$$3(4a) = n$$

Thus, 3|n.

35. Yes, among 8 people. Each would get $422.

Problem Set 5-3

1. (a) $D_{18} = \{1,2,3,6,9,18\}$

$D_{10} = \{1,2,5,10\}$

GCD(18, 10) = 2

$M_{18} = \{18,36,54,72,90...\}$

$M_{10} = \{10,20,30,40,50,60,70,80,90,...\}$

LCM(18,10) = 90

(b) $D_{24} = \{1,2,3,4,6,8,12,24\}$

$D_{36} = \{1,2,3,4,6,9,12,18,36\}$

GCD(24,36) = 12

$M_{24} = \{24,48,72,96,120,144,168...\}$

$M_{36} = \{36,72,108,144,180...\}$

LCM(24,36) = 72

(c) $D_8 = \{1,2,4,8\}$

$D_{24} = \{1,2,3,4,6,8,12,24\}$

$D_{52} = \{1,2,4,13,26,52\}$

GCD(8,24,52) = 4

$M_8 = \{8,16,24,32,40,48,56,64,72,80,88,96...\}$

$M_{24} = \{24,48,72,96,120,144,168,192,216,240,$
$\qquad 264,288,312...\}$

$M_{52} = \{52,104,156,208,160,312...\}$

LCM(8,24,52) = 312

2. (a) $132 = 2^2 \cdot 3 \cdot 11$

$504 = 2^3 \cdot 3^2 \cdot 7$

$GCD(132,504) = 2^2 \cdot 3 = 12$

$LCM(132,504) = 2^3 \cdot 3^2 \cdot 7 \cdot 11 = 1690$

(b) $65 = 5 \cdot 13$

$1690 = 2 \cdot 5 \cdot 13^2$

$GCD(65,1690) = 5 \cdot 13 = 65$

$LCM(65,1690) = 2 \cdot 5 \cdot 13^2 = 1690$

(c) $96 = 2^5 \cdot 3$

$900 = 2^2 \cdot 3^2 \cdot 5^2$

$630 = 2 \cdot 3^2 \cdot 5 \cdot 7$

$GCD(96,900,630) = 2 \cdot 3 = 6$

$LCM(96,900,630) = 2^5 \cdot 3^2 \cdot 5^2 \cdot 7 = 50,400$

(d) $108 = 2^2 \cdot 3^3$

$360 = 2^3 \cdot 3^2 \cdot 5$

$GCD(108,360) = 2^2 \cdot 3^2 = 36$

$LCM(108,360) = 2^3 \cdot 3^3 \cdot 5 = 1080$

(e) $63 = 3^3 \cdot 7$

$147 = 3 \cdot 7^2$

$GCD(63,147) = 3 \cdot 7 = 21$

$LCM(63,147) = 3^2 \cdot 7^2 = 441$

(f) $625 = 5^4$

$750 = 2 \cdot 3 \cdot 5^3$

$1000 = 2^3 \cdot 5^3$

$GCD(625,750) = 5^3 = 125$

$LCM(625,750) = 2^3 \cdot 3 \cdot 5^4 = 15,000$

3. (a) GCD(2924, 220) = GCD(220, 64) = GCD(64, 28) = GCD(28, 8) = GCD(8, 4) = GCD(4, 0) = 4 (b) GCD(14,595, 10,856) = GCD(10,856, 3739) = GCD(3739, 3378) = GCD(3378, 361) = GCD(361, 129) = GCD(129, 103) = GCD(103, 26) = GCD(26, 25) = GCD(25, 1) = 1 (c) GCD(123,152, 122,368) = GCD(122,368, 784) = GCD(784, 64) = GCD(64, 16) = GCD(16, 0) = 16

4. (a) 72 (b) 1440 (c) 630

5. (a) 220·2924/4 or 160,820 (b) 14,595·10,856/1 or 158,443,320 (c) 123,152·122,368/16 or 941,866,496

6. GCD(6, 10) = 2, LCM(6, 10) = 30

7. (a) LCM(15, 40, 60)= 120 minutes = 2 hours
So the clocks alarm again together at 8:00 A.M. (b) No

8. 5

9. (a) $60 (b) $12 each (c) 30

10. 24

11. 24 nights

12. 15 cookies

13. After 7 1/2 hours, or 2:30 A.M.

14. 36 minutes

15. (a) ab (b) GCD(1, a) = a; LCM(a, a) = a

(c) $GCD(a^2,a) = a$; $LCM(a^2,a) = a^2$ (d) GCD(a,b) = a;

$LCM(a,b) = b$ (e) GCD(a,b) = 1; LCM(a,b) = ab (f) a|b

(g) b|a

16. Answers vary.

17. GCD(120, 75) = 15; GCD(15, 105) = 15; GCD(120, 75, 105) = 15

18. Answers vary.

19. (a) $4 = 2^2$. Since 97,219,988,751 is odd, it has no prime factors of two. Consequently, 1 is their only common divisor and they are relatively prime. (b) 11 only has prime factor 11. 181,345,913 is not divisible by 11; therefore 1 is the only common divisor and they're relatively prime. (c) 33 has prime factors 3 and 11. 181,345,913 is divisible by neither 3 nor 11. Therefore, they're relatively prime.

20. {1, 2, 3, 4, 6, 7, 8, 9, 11, 12, 13, 14, 16, 17, 18, 19, 21, 22, 23, 24}

21. (a) 28 (b) Proper Divisors of 220 = {1, 2, 4, 5, 10, 11, 20, 22, 44, 55, 110}. 1 + 2 + 4 + 5 + 10 + 11 + 20 + 22 + 44 + 55 + 110 = 284. Proper Divisors of 284 = {1, 2, 4, 71, 142}. 1 + 2 + 4+ 71 + 142 = 220
Therefore, 220 and 284 are amicable.

22. Yes. If d|GCD(a,b), then since GCD(a,b)|a and GCD(a,b)|b, then d|a and d|b.

23. x = 15,625; y = 64

24. (a) 83,151; 83,451; 83,751 (b) 86,691 (c) 10,396

25. $17 \cdot 183 = 3111$; thus 3111 is not prime.
26. Answers may vary. $30{,}030 = 2 \cdot 3 \cdot 5 \cdot 7 \cdot 11 \cdot 13$
27. 27,720
28. 43
29. 70
30. (a) 67 (b) 41 (c) 93,87,51 (d) 91

Brain Teaser (p. 254)
If n is the width of the rectangle and m is the length of the rectangle, then the number of squares the diagonal crosses is (n+m)-GCD(n,m) or (n+m)-1.

Problem Set 5-4
1. (a) 3 (b) 2 (c) 6 (d) 8 (e) 3 (f) 4 (g) Does not exist (h) 10
2. (a) 2 (b) 1 (c) 2 (d) 4 (e) 2 (f) 1 (g) 2 (h) 4

3. (a)

$\oplus$	1	2	3	4	5	6	7
1	2	3	4	5	6	7	1
2	3	4	5	6	7	1	2
3	4	5	6	7	1	2	3
4	5	6	7	1	2	3	4
5	6	7	1	2	3	4	5
6	7	1	2	3	4	5	6
7	1	2	3	4	5	6	7

(b) $6 = 6 \ominus 5$; $4 = 2 \ominus 5$ (c) Every subtraction problem can be written as an addition problem, which can always be performed.

4. (a)

$\otimes$	1	2	3	4	5	6	7
1	1	2	3	4	5	6	7
2	2	4	6	1	3	5	7
3	3	6	2	5	1	4	7
4	4	1	5	2	6	3	7
5	5	3	1	6	4	2	7
6	6	5	4	3	2	1	7
7	7	7	7	7	7	7	7

(b) $3 \oplus 5 = 2$; $4 \oplus 6 = 3$ (c) Yes. Division by numbers different than 7 is possible since each row and column in the table contains every element 1 through 6.

5. (a)

$\otimes$	1	2	3
1	1	2	3
2	2	1	3
3	3	3	3

$\otimes$	1	2	3	4
1	1	2	3	4
2	2	4	2	4
3	3	2	1	4
4	4	4	4	4

$\otimes$	1	2	3	4	5	6
1	1	2	3	4	5	6
2	2	4	6	2	4	6
3	3	6	3	6	3	6
4	4	2	6	4	2	6
5	5	4	3	2	1	6
6	6	6	6	6	6	6

$\otimes$	1	2	3	4	5	6	7	8	9	10	11
1	1	2	3	4	5	6	7	8	9	10	11
2	2	4	6	8	10	1	3	5	7	9	11
3	3	6	9	1	4	7	10	2	5	8	11
4	4	8	1	5	9	2	6	10	3	7	11
5	5	10	4	9	3	8	2	7	1	6	11
6	6	1	7	2	8	3	9	4	10	5	11
7	7	3	10	6	2	9	5	1	8	4	11
8	8	5	2	10	7	4	1	9	6	3	11
9	9	7	5	3	1	10	8	6	4	2	11
10	10	9	8	7	6	5	4	3	2	1	11
11	11	11	11	11	11	11	11	11	11	11	11

(b) Answers vary. (c) The rows and columns in each contain all the elements except for the identity.
6. (a) 10 (b) 9 (c) 7 (d) 7 (e) 1 (f) 6
7. (a) 2, 9, 16, 30 (b) 3, 10, 17, 24, 31 (c) $366 \equiv 2(\bmod 7)$; Wednesday
8. (a) 4 (b) 0 (c) 0 (d) 7
9. (a) $8|(81 - 1)$ (b) $10|(81 - 1)$ (c) $13|(1000 - (^-1))$
(d) $10^1 \equiv 1(\bmod 9)$ implies $10^{84} \equiv 1^{84}(\bmod 9)$
(e) $10^2 = 1(\bmod 11)$ implies $\left(10^2\right)^{50} \equiv 1^{50}(\bmod 11)$
(f) $100|(937-37)$
10. (a) $a \equiv 0(\bmod m)$ if and only if $m|a$. By definition, $a \equiv b(\bmod m)$ if and only if $a - b$ is a multiple of m; where m is a positive integer greater than 1. Suppose $a \equiv 0(\bmod m)$. $(a - 0) = nm$ where n is a positive integer. Therefore, $a = nm$ so that $m|a$. Suppose $m|a$. $mn = a$ where n is an integer $mn = a - 0$ which implies $a \equiv 0(\bmod m)$.
11. (a) $24 \equiv 0(\bmod m)$ (b) $^-90 \equiv 0(\bmod m)$ (c) $0 \equiv 0(\bmod m)$
12. (a) $x = 2k$, k is an integer $x\{.., ^-4, ^-2, 0, 2, 4, ..\}$ (b) $x - 1 = 2k$ implies $x = 2k + 1$ where k is an integer. $x\{... ^-3, ^-1, 1, 3, 5, ...\}$ (c) $x - 3 = 5k$ implies $x = 3 + 5k$ where k is an integer. $x \in \{.., ^-7, ^-2, 3, 8, 13, ...\}$
13. (a) 1 (b) 5 (c) 10 (d) 1
14. Answers vary.
15. (a) $^-1$ (b) 12
16. $N = a_{k-1} \cdot 10^k + a_{k-1} \cdot 10^{k-1} + ... + a^2 \cdot 10^2 + a_1 \cdot 10^1 + a_0$
$4|N$ if and only if $4|(a_1 \cdot 10 + a_0)$.

Proof. $100 \equiv 0(\bmod 4)$. Hence,

$$N = 100\left(a_k \cdot 10^{k-2} + a_{k-1} \cdot 10^{k-3} + ... + a_2\right)$$

$+a_1 \cdot 10 + a_0 \equiv a_1 \cdot 10 + a_0(\bmod 4)$

Consequently, $4|n$ if and only if $4|(a_1 \cdot 10 + a_0)$
17. For example, $2 \cdot 11 \equiv 1 \cdot 11(\bmod 11)$ but $2 \equiv 1(\bmod 11)$ is false.

Brain Teaser (p. 259)
There are no primes in this list.

Chapter 5 Test
1. (a) False (b) False (c) True (d) False; 12, for example (e) False; 9, for example
2. (a) False; $7|7$ and $7 \nmid 3 \cdot 7$ yet $7|3 \cdot 7$ (b) False; $3 \nmid (3 + 4)$ but 313 and $3 \nmid 4$ (c) True (d) True (e) True (f) False; $4 \nmid 2$ and $4 \nmid 22$ but $4|44$
3. (a) Divisible by 2, 3, 4, 5., 6, 7, 8, 9, 11. (b) Divisible by 3, 11.
4. If 10,007 is prime, $17 \nmid 10{,}007$ We know $17|17$, so $17 \nmid (10{,}007 + 17)$ by Theorem 5-2 (b).
5. (a) 8724; 8654; 8784 (b) 41,856; 44,856; 47,856 (c) 87,174; 87,464; 87,754
6. (a) Composite (b) Prime
7. Answers vary.
8. (a) 4 (b) 73
9. (a) $2^4 \cdot 5^3 \cdot 7^4 \cdot 13 \cdot 17$ (b) 77, 562
10. Answers vary.
11. 1, 2, 3, 4, 6, 8, 9, 12, 16, 18, 24, 36, 48, 72, 144
12. (a) $2^2 \cdot 43$ (b) $2^5 \cdot 3^2$ (c) $2^2 \cdot 5 \cdot 13$ (d) $3 \cdot 37$
13. 15 minutes

14. $.31
15.   9:30 A M.
16.   One month of 365 days; five months of 73 days; 365 months of 1 day; 73 months of 5 days
17.   3
18.   Answers vary.
19. $n = a \cdot 10^2 + b \cdot 10 + c$
$n = a(99+1) + b(9+1) + c$
$n = 99a + 9b + c$
Since $9 | 99a$ and $9 | 9b$, $9 | [99a + 9b + (a+b+c)]$ if and only if $9 | (a+b+c)$
20.   (a) 1   (b) 4   (c) 3
21.   Friday
22.   mod 360. It would cover all the area encircling the lighthouse.

CHAPTER 6

Problem Set 6-1
1.   (a) The solution to $8x = 7$ is 7/8. (b) Jane ate seven eighths of Jill's candy. (c) The ratio of boys to girls is seven to eight.
2.   (a) 1/6   (b) 1/4   (c) 2/6   (d) 7/12   (e) 5/16   (f) 2/16
3.   (a) 2/3   (b) 4/6   (c) 6/9   (d) 8/12. The diagram illustrates the Fundamental Law of Fractions
4.

(a)

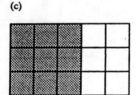

(b)

● ● ● ○ ○

(c)

(d)

● ● ● ○ ○
● ● ● ○ ○

(e)

(f)

5.   (a) 9/24 or 3/8   (b) 12/24 or 1/2   (c) 4/24 or 1/6   (d) 8/24 or 1/3
6.   (a) 4/18, 6/27, 8/36   (b) ⁻4/10, 2/⁻5, ⁻10/25   (c) 0/1, 0/2, 0/4   (d) 2a/4, 3a/6, 4a/8
7.   (a) 52/31   (b) 3/5   (c) ⁻5/7   (d) 0/1   (e) 144/169   (f) Reduced
8.   Impossible to determine. Because 20/25 = 24/30 = 4/5, so the same fraction of students passed in each

class, but the actual scores in one class could have been higher than in the other.
9.   (a) undefined   (b) undefined   (c) 0   (d) cannot be simplified   (e) cannot be simplified   (f) 2/3   (g) 5/3
10.   (a) 1   (b) 2x/9y   (c) a/1   (d) $(a^3 + 1)/a^3 b$ (e) 1/(3 + b)   (f) a/(3a + b)
11.   (a) equal   (b) equal   (c) equal   (d) not equal
12.   (a) not equal   (b) not equal   (c) equal   (d) not equal
13.   Yes, 1/32 in.
14.

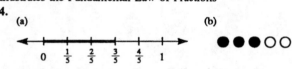

15.   36/48
16.   A, 12 minutes
17.

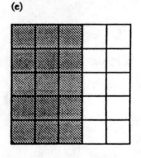

18.   (a) $2\frac{7}{8}$ (b) $2\frac{3}{8}$ (c) $1\frac{3}{8}$-   (d) $\frac{7}{8}$
19.   It is less than either factor
20.   0 has no reciprocal because 1/0 is undefined
21.   No, depends on the context of problem.
22.   12/21, 24/42, 48/84
23.   (a) 32/3   (b) ⁻36   (c) x is any rational number except 0
24.   (a) $a = b, c \neq 0$ (b) $b = c \neq 0$ or $a = 0$, but $b \neq 0$ and $c \neq 0$.
25.   (a) T   (b) T   (c) F   (d) F   (e) T
26.   (a) not equal   (b) not equal   (c) equal

Problem Set 6-2
1.

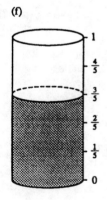

2.   (a) $\frac{-11}{16}$ (b) $\frac{-4}{12}$, or $\frac{-1}{3}$ (e) $\frac{19}{18}$ (d) $\frac{-5}{42}$
3.   (a) $\frac{-31}{20}$ (b) $\frac{58}{35}$ (c) $\frac{-19}{40}$ (d) $\frac{5y-3x}{xy}$
4.   (a) $\frac{-6y+6x-1}{4xy}$ (b) $\frac{-9y+5x+42y^2}{6x^2y^2}$
5.   (a) $18\frac{2}{3}$ (b) $2\frac{4}{5}$ (c) $-2\frac{93}{100}$ (d) $-5\frac{7}{8}$
6.   (a) $\frac{27}{4}$ (b) $\frac{15}{2}$ (c) $\frac{-29}{8}$ (d) $\frac{-14}{3}$
7.   (a) $\frac{71}{24}$ (b) $\frac{-23}{3}$ (c) $\frac{43}{2^4 \cdot 3^4}$ (d) $\frac{472}{45}$
8. $\frac{2}{6} + \frac{5}{8}$
9.   (a) 1/3, high   (b) 1/6, low   (c) 3/4, low   (d) 1/2, low
10.   (a) Beavers   (b) Ducks   (c) Bears   (d) Tigers   (e) Lions   (f) Wildcats, Badgers

11. (a) 1/2, high (b) 0, low (c) 3/4, high (d) 1, high
(e) 1, low (f) 0, high (g) 3/4, low (h) 1/2, low
12. (a) 2 (b) 3/4 (c) 0 (d) 0
13. (a) 10 (b) 0 (c) 13 (d) 151
14. (a) No (b) No
15. (a) 1/4 (b) $5\frac{1}{8}$ (c) 0 (d) 10
16. (a) A (b) H (c) T (d) H
17. (a) $\dfrac{dc+a}{bc}$ (b) $\dfrac{a^2+2ab-b^2}{a^2-b^2}$ (c) $\dfrac{a-ab-b^2}{a^2-b^2}$
18. (a) $\dfrac{3+3}{3}\neq\dfrac{3}{3}+3$ (b) $\dfrac{4}{2+2}\neq\dfrac{4}{2}+\dfrac{4}{2}$ (c) $\dfrac{ab+c}{a}\neq\dfrac{ab+c}{\not a}$
(d) $\dfrac{a\cdot a-b\cdot b}{a-b}\neq\dfrac{\not a\cdot a-\not b\cdot b}{\not a-\not b}$ (e) $\dfrac{a+c}{b+c}\neq\dfrac{a+\not c}{b+\not c}$
19. $\dfrac{1}{4}$
20. (a) $\dfrac{1}{30}$ (b) $\dfrac{2}{10}$ or $\dfrac{1}{10}$ (c) $\dfrac{1}{60}$ (d) No, the total number
of dollars might have been greater, so the fraction of the total dollars might still be greater.

21.

$\dfrac{5}{3}$	$\dfrac{1}{12}$	1
$\dfrac{1}{4}$	$\dfrac{11}{12}$	$\dfrac{19}{12}$
$\dfrac{5}{6}$	$\dfrac{7}{4}$	$\dfrac{1}{6}$

22. $6\dfrac{7}{12}$ yards
23. Answers vary
24. Answers vary
25. $1\dfrac{3}{4}$ cups
26. Answers vary
27. $2\dfrac{5}{6}$ yards
28. $22\dfrac{1}{8}$ inches
29. (a) Team 4, $76\dfrac{11}{16}$ pounds (b) $3\dfrac{11}{16}$ pounds
30. Answers vary
31. (a) $\dfrac{1}{2}+\dfrac{3}{4}\in Q$ (b) $\dfrac{1}{2}+\dfrac{3}{4}=\dfrac{3}{4}+\dfrac{1}{2}$
(c) $\left(\dfrac{1}{2}+\dfrac{1}{3}\right)+\dfrac{1}{4}=\dfrac{1}{2}+\left(\dfrac{1}{3}+\dfrac{1}{4}\right)$
32. (a) Yes. If a, b, c, and d are integers, then
$\dfrac{a}{b}-\dfrac{c}{d}=\dfrac{ad-bc}{bd}$ is a rational number.
(b) No. For example, $\dfrac{1}{2}-\dfrac{1}{4}\neq\dfrac{1}{4}-\dfrac{1}{2}$
(c) No. For example, $\dfrac{1}{2}-\left(\dfrac{1}{4}-\dfrac{1}{8}\right)\neq\left(\dfrac{1}{2}-\dfrac{1}{4}\right)-\dfrac{1}{8}$.
(d) No. If there is an identity for subtraction it must be 0, since only for 0 does $\dfrac{a}{b}-0=\dfrac{a}{b}$. However, in general $0-\dfrac{a}{b}\neq\dfrac{a}{b}-0$, and hence there is no identity. (e) No. Since there is no identity, an inverse cannot be defined.

33. (a) $\dfrac{6}{4},\dfrac{7}{4},2$; arithmetic, $\dfrac{1}{2}-\dfrac{1}{4}=\dfrac{3}{4}-\dfrac{1}{2}=1-\dfrac{3}{4}=\dfrac{5}{4}-1$
(b) $\dfrac{6}{7},\dfrac{7}{8},\dfrac{8}{9}$; not arithmetic; $\dfrac{2}{3}-\dfrac{1}{2}\neq\dfrac{3}{4}-\dfrac{2}{3}$
(c) $\dfrac{17}{3},\dfrac{20}{3},\dfrac{23}{3}$; arithmetic; $\dfrac{5}{3}-\dfrac{2}{3}=\dfrac{8}{3}-\dfrac{5}{3}=\dfrac{11}{3}-\dfrac{8}{3}=\dfrac{14}{3}-\dfrac{11}{3}$
(d) $\dfrac{^-5}{4},\dfrac{^-7}{4},\dfrac{^-9}{4}$; arithmetic;
$\dfrac{3}{4}-\dfrac{5}{4}=\dfrac{1}{4}-\dfrac{3}{4}=\dfrac{^-1}{4}-\dfrac{1}{4}=\dfrac{^-3}{4}-\left(\dfrac{^-1}{4}\right)$
34. (a) $\dfrac{1}{4}n$ (b) $\dfrac{n}{n+1}$ (c) $\dfrac{3n-1}{3}$ (d) $\dfrac{^-2n+7}{4}$
35. $1,\dfrac{7}{6},\dfrac{8}{6},\dfrac{9}{6},\dfrac{10}{6},\dfrac{11}{6},2$
36. (a) (i) $\dfrac{3}{4}$ (ii) $\dfrac{25}{12}$ (iii) 0 (b) (i) $\dfrac{1}{4}$ (ii) $\dfrac{^-7}{4}$ (iii) $\dfrac{^-1}{4}$
37. (a) $f(0)=^-2$ (b) $f(^-2)=0$ (c) $f(^-5)=\dfrac{1}{2}$
(d) $f(5)=\dfrac{7}{4}$
38. (b) $\dfrac{1}{n}=\dfrac{1}{n+1}+\dfrac{1}{n(n+1)}$
(c) $\dfrac{1}{n+1}+\dfrac{1}{n(n+1)}=\dfrac{n}{n(n+1)}+\dfrac{1}{n(n+1)}=\dfrac{n+1}{n(n+1)}=\dfrac{1}{n}$
39. (a) $\dfrac{2}{3}$ (b) $\dfrac{13}{17}$ (c) $\dfrac{25}{49}$ (d) $\dfrac{a}{1}$, or a (e) Reduced
40. (a) equal (b) Not equal (c) equal (d) Not equal

Brain Teaser (p. 288)
Let x = number of students, $\dfrac{1}{2}x+\dfrac{1}{7}x+20=x$
$$20=\dfrac{5}{14}x$$
$$56=x$$

Brain Teaser (p. 298)
Observe that after crossing each bridge, the prince was left with half the bags he had previously minus one additional bag of gold. To determine the number he had prior to crossing the bridge, we can use the inverse operations; that is, add 1 and multiply by 2. The prince had one bag left after crossing the fourth bridge. He must have had two before he gave the guard the extra bag. Finally he must have had four bags before he gave the guard at the fourth bridge any bags. The entire procedure is summarized in the following table.

Bridge	Bags After Crossing	Bags Before Guard Given Extra	Bags Prior to Crossing
Fourth	1	2	4
Third	4	5	10
Second	10	11	22
First	22	23	46

Problem Set 6-3
1. (a) $\dfrac{1}{4}\cdot\dfrac{1}{3}=\dfrac{1}{12}$ (b) $\dfrac{2}{4}\cdot\dfrac{3}{5}=\dfrac{6}{20}$

2.

(a)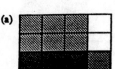

(b)

(c)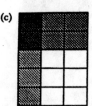

3. B

4. (a) $\dfrac{1}{5}$ (b) $\dfrac{b}{a}$ (c) $\dfrac{za}{x^2y}$ (d) $\dfrac{35}{4}$ (e) $\dfrac{44}{3}$ (f) $\dfrac{^-25}{4}$

5. (a) $10\dfrac{1}{2}$ (b) $8\dfrac{1}{3}$ (c) $24{,}871\dfrac{1}{20}$

6. (a) $^-3$ (b) $\dfrac{3}{10}$ (c) $\dfrac{y}{x}$ (d) $\dfrac{^-1}{7}$

7. Yes, $1\dfrac{3}{8}$ ft.

8. (a) $\dfrac{11}{5}$ (b) $\dfrac{77}{12}$ (c) $\dfrac{22}{3}$ (d) $\dfrac{5}{2}$ (e) 5 (f) $^-42$

(g) 2 (h) $\dfrac{z}{y}$ (i) z (j) $\dfrac{5}{x}$ (k) $\dfrac{xy}{z}$

9. (a) 20 (b) 16 (c) 2 (d) 1

10. (a) 18 (b) 25 (c) 7 (d) 6

11. (a) Less than 1 (b) Less than 1 (c) Greater than 2
(d) Less than 4 (e) Greater than 4

12. C

13. (a) 26 (b) 29 (c) 92 (d) 18 (e) 6 (f) 7 (g) 9
(h) $2\dfrac{1}{4}$

14. It is less than 1

15. (a) $\dfrac{21}{8}$ (b) $\dfrac{3}{35}$ (c) $^-28$ (d) $\dfrac{^-56}{5}$ (e) $\dfrac{1}{5}$ (f) $\dfrac{15}{32}$

(g) $\dfrac{^-45}{28}$ (h) $\dfrac{^-7}{15}$

16. Answers may vary.

17. 400

18. $\dfrac{1}{6}$

19. (a) 39 uniforms (b) $\dfrac{1}{4}$ yards left

20. Never less than n

21. (a) $2+1 \neq 1+2$ (b) $(1+2)+3 \neq 1+(2+3)$ (c) There is
no rational number a such that $2+a=a+2=2$ (d) Because
there is no identity, there can be no inverse.

22. $\dfrac{29}{36}$

23. 9600

24. $240

25. (a) $121,000 (b) $90,000 (c) $300,000

26. 1/4

27. 246

28. $225

29. (a) Peter, 30 min.; Paul, 25 min.; Mary, 20 min.
(b) Peter, 10; Paul, 12; Mary, 15

30. 8

31. (a) $89\dfrac{6}{10}$°F (b) $^-40$°C

32. $2253\dfrac{1}{8}$

33. 32 marbles

34. Answers vary

35. $\left(\dfrac{1}{4}\cdot 12\right)\cdot 15 = 3\cdot 15 = 45$

36. 7 ounces

37. (i) $\dfrac{1}{32}, \dfrac{1}{64}$; geometric ratio $=\dfrac{1}{2}$ (ii) $\dfrac{^-1}{32}, \dfrac{1}{64}$;

geometric ratio $=\dfrac{^-1}{2}$ (iii) $\dfrac{81}{256}, \dfrac{243}{1024}$; geometric ratio $=\dfrac{3}{4}$

(iv) $\dfrac{5}{3^5}, \dfrac{6}{3^6}$; not geometric, $\dfrac{2}{3^2}+\dfrac{1}{3} \neq \dfrac{3}{3^3}+\dfrac{2}{3^2}$

38. (a) $n(n+1)+\left(\dfrac{1}{2}\right)^2$ (b) $\left(n+\dfrac{1}{2}\right)^2 = n^2+2n\cdot\dfrac{1}{2}+\left(\dfrac{1}{2}\right)^2$

$= n^2+n+\left(\dfrac{1}{2}\right)^2 = n(n+1)+\left(\dfrac{1}{2}\right)^2$

39. (a) (i) $\dfrac{^-4}{5}$ (ii) $\dfrac{^-26}{17}$ (iii) $\dfrac{^-14}{33}$ (b) (i) $\dfrac{^-4}{3}$ (ii) $\dfrac{^-30}{7}$

(iii) $\dfrac{^-3}{10}$ (c) $\dfrac{5}{4}$

40. (a) First 3, second 4, third 5. Guess 6. The guess is
correct since

$\left(1+\dfrac{1}{1}\right)\left(1+\dfrac{1}{2}\right)\left(1+\dfrac{1}{3}\right)\left(1+\dfrac{1}{4}\right)\left(1+\dfrac{1}{5}\right) = 5\left(1+\dfrac{1}{5}\right) = 6$ (b) 102
(c) n+2

41. $c = 0$ or $a = b$, where $b \neq 0$

42. (a) $2S = 2\left(\dfrac{1}{2}+\dfrac{1}{2^2}+\ldots+\dfrac{1}{2^{64}}\right) = 1+\dfrac{1}{2}+\dfrac{1}{2^2}+\ldots+\dfrac{1}{2^{63}}$

(b) Note that $2S = 1+S-\dfrac{1}{2^{64}}$. Hence, $2S-S = 1+S-\dfrac{1}{2^{64}}-S$

$= 1-\dfrac{1}{2^{64}}$ (c) $1-\dfrac{1}{2^n}$

43. (a) $1\dfrac{49}{99}$ (b) $25\cdot\left(2\dfrac{49}{99}\right) = 62\dfrac{37}{99}$

44. (a) $\dfrac{25}{16}$ (b) $\dfrac{25}{18}$ (c) $\dfrac{5}{216}$ (d) $\dfrac{259}{30}$ (e) $\dfrac{37}{24}$

(f) $\dfrac{^-39}{4}$

45. 120 students

Brain Teaser (p. 302)
No. The legacy is impossible because the fractions of cats to be
shared do not add up to the whole units of cats.
$\dfrac{1}{2}x+\dfrac{1}{3}x+\dfrac{1}{9}x = \dfrac{17}{18}x$, but the sum should be 1x, or $\dfrac{18}{18}x$.

Brain Teaser (p. 310)
Both cyclists covered the same distance, so it follows that the
one who rode longer is the slower one. If we denote David's
riding time in hours (or any other unit of time) by d and Sara's
riding time, also in hours, by s, it would be sufficient to
determine if $d < s$. Because David rode three times as long as
Sara rested, we can deduce that Sara rested one third as long as
David rode, that is, $\dfrac{d}{3}$ hours. Similarly, because Sara rode four

times as long as David rested, we can deduce that David rested one fourth as long as Sara rode, that is, $\frac{s}{4}$. Using the expressions $\frac{d}{3}$ and $\frac{s}{4}$, we can write expressions for the total time of the trip, as shown in the following table.

	Riding Time	Resting Time	Total Time of Trip
David	d	$\frac{s}{4}$	$d+\frac{s}{4}$
Sara	s	$\frac{d}{3}$	$s+\frac{d}{3}$

Both cyclists started and returned at the same time, so their total trip times are the same. As shown in the table, David's total trip time is $d+\frac{s}{4}$ and Sara's total trip time is $s+\frac{d}{3}$. Consequently, we have the following equation and solution in terms of s.

$$d+\frac{s}{4}=s+\frac{d}{3}$$

$$d-\frac{d}{3}=s-\frac{s}{4}$$

$$\frac{2}{3}d=\frac{3}{4}s$$

$$d=\frac{3}{2}\cdot\frac{3}{4}s$$

$$d=\frac{9}{8}s$$

Because $\frac{9}{8}>1$, it follows that $\frac{9}{8}s>s$, or that $d>s$. Thus, it took David longer to travel the same distance that Sara traveled, so Sara rode faster than David.

Problem Set 6-4

1. (a) > (b) > (c) < (d) < (e) = (f) =

2.
-2 1/4 -1 3/8 -1/2   1 1/8   2 5/8
```
←|——|—●|●—|——|——|—●|——|—●—|→
 -3   -2   -1    0    1    2    3
```

3. (a) $\frac{11}{13},\frac{11}{16},\frac{11}{22}$ (b) $3,\frac{33}{16},\frac{23}{12}$ (c) $\frac{-1}{5},\frac{-19}{36},\frac{-17}{30}$

4. (a) $x\le\frac{27}{16}$ (b) $x<\frac{17}{5}$ (c) $x\ge\frac{115}{3}$ (d) $x\ge\frac{141}{22}$

5. (a) No. Multiplication by bd, which is negative, reverses the order. (b) Yes, Multiplication by bd, which is positive, retains same order.

6. (a) $399\frac{80}{81}$ (b) $180\frac{89}{90}$ (c) $3\frac{699}{820}$

7. (a) over 7 (b) under 13 (c) under 1 (d) over 6 (e) over 6

8. Bren's class

9. (a) about 180 (b) about 729 (c) about 468 (d) about 6 (e) about 3

10. Every 3 pounds of bird seed yields about 4 packages. Thus, there are about 28 packages.

11. (a) A proper fraction is greater than its square.

(b) Let $\frac{a}{b}$ be a positive proper fraction, that is $0<\frac{a}{b}<1$.

Therefore, $\frac{a}{b}>0$, $\frac{a}{b}<1$ implies $\frac{a}{b}\cdot\frac{a}{b}<1\cdot\frac{a}{b}$ or $\left(\frac{a}{b}\right)^2<\frac{a}{b}$.

(c) If a fraction is greater than 1, it is less than its square.

(d) Let $\frac{a}{b}$ be a fraction greater than 1. Then $\frac{a}{b}\cdot\frac{a}{b}>1\cdot\frac{a}{b}$ or $\left(\frac{a}{b}\right)^2>\frac{a}{b}$.

12. $\frac{a}{b}<1$ and $\frac{c}{d}>0$ imply $\frac{a}{b}\cdot\frac{c}{d}<1\cdot\frac{c}{d}$ or $\frac{a}{b}\cdot\frac{c}{d}<\frac{c}{d}$.

13. $xy>y$ because $x>1$ and $y>0$ implies $x\cdot y>1\cdot y$ or $xy>y$.

14. We need to show that $\frac{n}{n+1}<\frac{n+1}{n+2}$. This inequality is equivalent to $n^2+2n<n^2+2n+1$, or $0<1$.

15. Answers vary.

16. (a) There is no whole number between two consecutive whole numbers — for example, between 0 and 1. (b) Same as (a).

17. Answers may vary. The following are possible answers.

(a) $\frac{10}{21},\frac{11}{21}$ (b) $\frac{-22}{27},\frac{-23}{27}$ (c) $\frac{997}{1200},\frac{998}{1200}$

(d) $0,\frac{1}{2}$

18. (a) 33 (b) 133 (c) $x<\frac{4}{7}$, so $x=0$

(d) no such x exists

19. Answers vary

20. (a) 1 (b) 1 (c) No, let x equal the top circled number, then the sum of the circled numbers is x + (x + 12)+ (x + 19)+ (x + 31) = 4x + 62. The sum of the four interior numbers is (x + 10)+ (x + 11)+ (x + 20)+ (x + 21) = 4x + 62. Here the ratio is always 1.

21. (a) They are equal $\frac{1}{3}$

(b) $\frac{1+3+5+7+...+201}{203+-205+207+...+403}=\frac{1}{3}$ (c) The nth term is

$\frac{1+3+5+...+(2n+1)}{(2n+3)+(2n+5)+...+(4n+3)}=\frac{n(n+1)}{3n(n+1)}=\frac{1}{3}$

22. $0<\frac{a}{b}<\frac{c}{d}$ so that $0<\frac{1}{2}\cdot\frac{a}{b}<\frac{1}{2}\cdot\frac{c}{d}$. Also,

$0<\frac{a}{b}=\frac{1}{2}\cdot\frac{a}{b}+\frac{1}{2}\cdot\frac{a}{b}<\frac{1}{2}\cdot\frac{a}{b}+\frac{1}{2}\cdot\frac{c}{d}=\frac{1}{2}\left(\frac{a}{b}+\frac{c}{d}\right)$. Similarly,

$\frac{1}{2}\left(\frac{a}{b}+\frac{c}{d}\right)<\frac{c}{d}$, and therefore $0<\frac{a}{b}<\frac{1}{2}\left(\frac{a}{b}+\frac{c}{d}\right)<\frac{c}{d}$

23. We are considering $\frac{a}{b}$ and $\frac{a+x}{b+x}$ when $a<b$. $\frac{a}{b}<\frac{a+x}{b+x}$ because $ab+ax<ab+bx$.

24. (a) $\frac{29}{8}$ (b) $\frac{87}{68}$ (c) $\frac{25}{144}$ (d) 1 (Provided that $|x|\ne|y|$)

25. $6\frac{7}{18}$ hours

26. (a) $\frac{-4}{3}$ (b) $\frac{-11}{8}$ (c) $\frac{24}{17}$ (d) $^-3$

27. $26\frac{1}{4}$ hours

28. (a) 3 and 4 (b) (4 and 5) or (3 and 6) depending on estimates used.

Problem Set 6-5

1. (a) 3:2 (b) 2:3
2. (a) 5:21 (b) Answers vary

3. (a) 30 (b) $^-3\frac{1}{3}$ (c) $23\frac{1}{3}$ (d) $10\frac{1}{2}$

4. 36 pounds

5. 2469

6. \$1.19

7. 270 miles

8. 64

9. 72 minutes for 30 inches

10. (a) 42, 56 (b) 24, 32

11. 500 ft. by 900 ft.

12. \$14,909.09, \$29,818.18, \$37,272.73

13. \$77 and \$99

14. 135

15. (a) $\frac{5}{7}$ (b) 6 ft.

16. 120 ft.

17. 8 days

18. (a) 27 (b) 20

19. Approximately 34 cm

20. 312 pounds

21. (a) $\frac{40}{700}$ or $\frac{4}{70}$ or $\frac{2}{35}$ (b) 525 cm

(c) probably not, $\frac{2}{5} \neq \frac{3}{5}$

22. $9\frac{9}{14}$ days

23. No, the ratio of the prices is proportional to the ratio of the areas.

24. (a) 2:5. Because the ratio is 2:3, there are 2x boys and 3x girls, hence the ratio of boys to all the students is $2x/(2x+3x) = 2/5$ (b) m:(m + n)

25. $1\frac{1}{3}$ days

26. $13\frac{1}{3}$ hours

27. $\frac{a}{b} = \frac{c}{d}$ implies $ad = bc$, which is equivalent to $d = \frac{bc}{a}$; then, $\frac{d}{c} = \frac{b}{a}$.

28. We need to prove that if $0 < \frac{a}{b} < 1$ and $0 < \frac{c}{d} < 1$ then

$\frac{a}{b} \cdot \frac{c}{d} < \frac{a}{b}$ and $\frac{a}{b} \cdot \frac{c}{d} < \frac{c}{d}$. We prove this as follows: $\frac{c}{d} < 1$ and

$\frac{a}{b} > 0$ implies $\frac{c}{d} \cdot \frac{a}{b} < 1 \cdot \frac{a}{b}$ or $\frac{a}{b} \cdot \frac{c}{d} < \frac{a}{b}$. Similarly, $\frac{a}{b} < 1$ and

$\frac{c}{d} > 0$ implies $\frac{a}{b} \cdot \frac{c}{d} < 1 \cdot \frac{c}{d}$ or $\frac{a}{b} \cdot \frac{c}{d} < \frac{c}{d}$.

29. (a) $\frac{1}{2}$ (b) Let $\frac{a}{b} = \frac{c}{d} = \frac{e}{f} = r$.

Then $a = br$
$c = dr$
$e = fr$

So, $a + c + e = br + dr + fr$
$a + c + e = r(b + d + f)$
$\frac{a+c+e}{b+d+f} = r$

30. (a) $\frac{a}{b} = \frac{c}{d}$ implies $\frac{a}{b} + 1 = \frac{c}{d} + 1$, which implies

$\frac{a+b}{b} = \frac{c+d}{d}$. (b) By inverting (Problem 27), $\frac{b}{a} = \frac{d}{c}$ and by

part (a), $\frac{b+a}{a} = \frac{d+c}{c}$. Then inverting again gives

$\frac{a}{a+b} = \frac{c}{d+c}$. (c) $\frac{a}{b} = \frac{c}{d}$ implies $\frac{a}{b} - 1 = \frac{c}{d} - 1$, which implies

$\frac{a-b}{b} = \frac{c-d}{d}$. From part (a) and this last result we have

$\frac{a+b}{b} + \frac{a-b}{b} = \frac{c+d}{d} + \frac{c-d}{d}$ which implies $\frac{a+b}{a-b} = \frac{c+d}{c-d}$.

31. $\frac{37}{125}$ of a mile

32. (a) $\frac{^-3}{5}, \frac{^-2}{5}, 0, \frac{1}{5}, \frac{2}{5}$ (b) $\frac{13}{24}, \frac{7}{12}, \frac{13}{18}$

33. (a) $x \geq \frac{3}{2}$ (b) $x > 3$ (c) $x > \frac{^-7}{15}$ (d) $x \leq \frac{^-56}{5}$

34. Answers vary. Examples are: (a) $\frac{11}{30}, \frac{12}{30}, \frac{13}{30}$

(b) $\frac{^-1}{12}, \frac{^-1}{9}, \frac{^-5}{36}$

Brain Teaser (p. 318)

Let d be the distance between the houses and v the speed. Then

$\frac{2d + \frac{3}{8}}{v} = \frac{d + \frac{5}{12}}{v}$. Hence $2d + \frac{3}{8} = d + \frac{5}{12}$, $d = \frac{5}{12} - \frac{3}{8} = \frac{1}{24}$ mi.

Problem Set 6-6

1. (a) $\frac{1}{3^{13}}$ (b) 3^{13} (c) 5^{11} (d) 5^{19} (e) $\frac{1}{\left(^-5\right)^2}$ or $\frac{1}{5^2}$

(f) a^5 (g) a^2 (h) $\frac{1}{a}$

2. (a) $\left(\frac{1}{2}\right)^{10}$ (b) $\left(\frac{1}{2}\right)^3$ (c) $\left(\frac{2}{3}\right)^9$ (d) 1 (e) $\left(\frac{5}{3}\right)^3$

(f) $\left(\frac{5}{6}\right)^{21}$

3. (a) False $2^3 \cdot 2^4 \neq (2 \cdot 2)^{3+4}$ (b) False $2^3 \cdot 2^2 \neq (2 \cdot 2)^{3 \cdot 4}$

(c) False $2^3 \cdot 2^3 \neq (2 \cdot 2)^{23}$ (d) False $a^0 = 1$ if $a \neq 0$

(e) False $(2+3)^2 \neq 2^2 + 3^2$ (f) False $(2+3)^{-2} \neq \frac{1}{2^2} + \frac{1}{3^2}$

(g) False $a^{mn} = \left(a^m\right)^n \neq a^m \cdot a^n$ (h) True $\left(\frac{a}{b}\right)^{-1} = \frac{1}{\left(\frac{a}{b}\right)} = \frac{b}{a}$

4. (a) 5 (b) 6 or $^-6$ (c) $^-2$ (d) $^-4$ (e) 0 (f) 15

5. (a) $2 \cdot 10^{11}$ (b) $2 \cdot 10^5$

6. (a) $x \leq 4$ (b) $x \leq 1$ (c) $x \geq 2$ (d) $x > 0$

7. (a) $\frac{1-x^2}{x}$ (b) $\frac{x^2 y^2 - 1}{y^2}$ (c) $6x^2 + 4x$ (d) $\frac{1+y^6}{y^3}$

(e) $(3a-b)^2$ (f) $b/(b+a)$

8. (a) $\left(\frac{1}{2}\right)^3$ (b) $\left(\frac{3}{4}\right)^8$ (c) $\left(\frac{4}{3}\right)^{10}$ (d) $\left(\frac{4}{5}\right)^{10}$ (e) $\left(\frac{4}{3}\right)^{10}$

(f) $\left(\frac{3}{4}\right)^{100}$

9. (a) 10^{10} (b) $10^{10} \cdot (6/5)^2$

10. (a) 3/2, 3/4, 3/8, 3/16, 3/32   (b) Each of the four ratios is $\frac{1}{2}$ (c) 3/1024

11. (a) 3/4   (b) 24   (c) 3/128   (d) n=$^-$7

12. (a) 3^{400} (b) $4^{300} = \left(4^3\right)^{100} = 64^{100}, 3^{400} = \left(3^4\right)^{100} = 81^{100}$ and $81^{100} > 64^{100}$.   (c) You get an error in the display.

13. (a) 32^{50} because $32^{50} = \left(2^5\right)^{50} = 2^{250}$ and $4^{100} = 2^{200}$

(b) $\left(^-3\right)^{-75}$

14. No, it must end in 1, 3, 9, or 7
15. 125
16. 216
17. 27

18. (a) $\frac{2}{7}$ (b) $\frac{40}{3}$ (c) $\frac{1}{3^4}$ (d) $\frac{1}{100}$ (e) $\frac{9}{4}$ (f) $\frac{49}{100}$

(g) $\frac{9}{16}$ (h) $\frac{x}{x+y}$

19. (a) $\frac{^-4}{3}$ (b) $\frac{^-9}{10}$ (c) $\frac{60}{13}$ (d) $\frac{^-9}{4}$ (e) 9 or $^-$9 (f) $\frac{4}{5}$

20. $1\frac{1}{5}$ days

21. It will become greater because $\frac{3x}{8x} < \frac{3x+2}{8x+2}$.

22. $\frac{^-6}{7}, \frac{^-3}{4}, \frac{^-2}{3}, \frac{^-1}{2}, 0, \frac{7}{9}, \frac{4}{5}, \frac{6}{7}, \frac{9}{7}$

Chapter Test

1.

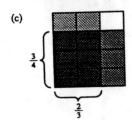

2. $\frac{10}{12}, \frac{15}{18}, \frac{20}{24}$

3. (a) $\frac{6}{7}$ (b) $\frac{ax}{b}$ (c) $\frac{0}{1}$ (d) $\frac{5}{9}$ (e) $\frac{b}{1}$ (f) $\frac{2}{27}$

4. (a) =   (b) >   (c) >   (d) <

5. (a) $\frac{11}{10}$ (b) $\frac{13}{175}$ (c) $\frac{10}{13}$ (d) $\frac{25}{24}$ (e) $\frac{50}{9}$ (f) $\frac{^-26}{27}$

6. (a) $^-3, \frac{1}{3}$ (b) $^-3\frac{1}{7}, \frac{7}{22}$ (c) $\frac{^-5}{6}, \frac{6}{5}$ (d) $\frac{3}{4}, \frac{^-4}{3}$

7. $^-2\frac{1}{3}, ^-1\frac{7}{8}, 0, (71/140)^{300}, 69/140, 1/2, 71/140, (74/73)^{300}$

8. (a) 6 (b) $\frac{5}{4}$ (c) $\frac{^-1}{4}$

9. (a) $x \le \frac{42}{25}$ (b) $x \le \frac{3}{2}$ (c) $x = \frac{8}{9}$ (d) $x = \frac{3}{2}$

10. $\frac{a}{b} + \frac{c}{d} = x$ if and only if $\frac{a}{b} = \frac{c}{d} \cdot x$. $x = \frac{d}{c} \cdot \frac{a}{b}$ is the

solution of the equation because $\frac{c}{d} \cdot \left(\frac{d}{c} \cdot \frac{a}{b}\right) = \frac{a}{b}$.

11. 9

12. (a) $\frac{1}{2^{11}}$ (b) $\frac{1}{5^{20}}$ (c) $\left(\frac{3}{2}\right)^{28}$, or $\frac{3^{28}}{2^{28}}$ (d) 3^{18}

13. 17 pieces, $\frac{11}{6}$ yards left.

14. (a) 15   (b) 15   (c) 4
15. 76/100, 78/100 but answers may vary.
16. $70
17. 6:1
18. ⬚5⬚ ⬚0⬚ ⬚4⬚ ⬚7⬚ ⬚9⬚ ⬚2⬚ ⬚x⬚ ⬚2⬚ ⬚3⬚ ⬚$\frac{1}{x}$⬚ ⬚=⬚
19. $333\frac{1}{3}$ calories
20. 16 minutes
21. 60 credits

CHAPTER 7

Problem Set 7-1

1. (a) $0 \cdot 10^0 + 0 \cdot 10^{-1} + 2 \cdot 10^{-2} + 3 \cdot 10^{-3}$

(b) $2 \cdot 10^2 + 0 \cdot 10 + 6 \cdot 10^0 + 0 \cdot 10^{-1} + 6 \cdot 10^{-2}$

(c) $3 \cdot 10^2 + 1 \cdot 10 + 2 \cdot 10^0 + 0 \cdot 10^{-1} + 1 \cdot 10^{-2} + 0 \cdot 10^{-3} + 3 \cdot 10^{-4}$

(d) $0 \cdot 10^0 + 0 \cdot 10^{-1} + 0 \cdot 10^{-2} + 0 \cdot 10^{-3} + 1 \cdot 10^{-4} + 3 \cdot 10^{-5} + 2 \cdot 10^{-6}$

2. (a) 4356.78   (b) 4000.608   (c) 40,000.03
(d) 0.2004007

3. (a) 536.0076   (b) 3.008   (c) 0.000436
(d) 5,000,000.2

4. (a) 436/1000 = 109/1250   (b) 2516/100 = 629/250
(c) $^-$316,027/1000   (d) 281 ,902/10,000 = 140,951/5000
(e) $^-$43/10   (f) $^-$6201/100

5 (a), (b), (c), (d), (e), (f). and (h) can be represented by terminating decimals.

6. (a) 0.8   (b) 3.05   (c) 0.5   (d) 0.03125   (e) 0.01152
(f) 0.2128   (h) 0.08

7. (a) 39.202   (b) 168.003   (c) $^-$390.6313   (d) 1.49093
(e) $^-$10.4   (f) 4.681

8. (a) 17.702   (b) 8.538   (c) 0.0272   (d) 68
9. $231.24
10. Lining up the decimal points acts as using place value.
11. (a) 463,000,000   (b) 4,000,000   (c) 4,630,000,000
(d) 46,300,000,000   (e) 463,000   (f) 4.63   (g) 0.000463
(h) 0.000004   (i) 0.00463   (j) 0.00000000463   (k) 46,300
(1) 400   (m) 463,000   (n) 0.463
12. (a), (c), and (f)
13. (a) 0.0770   (b) 406
14. Answers may vary
15. 62.298 Ib

16.

8.2	1.9	6.4
3.7	5.5	7.3
4.6	9.1	2.8

17. $8.00
18. (a) It costs $3.21 to heat her house for one day.
(b) The light bulb would have to stay on 358.9 hours.
19. (a) 6390.955 cubic cm   (b) 183.07123 cubic in
20. 21.324 miles/hr

21. Approximately $2098 profit
22. **(a)** $235 cash = 366.60 Swiss francs. $235 traveler's checks = 373.65 Swiss francs   **(b)** Exchange at least $472.76 cash or $463.84 in traveler's checks
(c) $440.00 in travelers checks
23. **(a)** 5.4, 6.3, 7.2, 8.1, 9.0,9.9,10.8, ...   **(b)** 1.3, 1.5, 1.7, 1.9, 2.1, 2.3, ...   **(c)** 0.0625, 0.03125, 0.015625, 0.0078125, ...   **(d)** 6.7, 8.0, 9.3, 10.6, 11.9, 13.2, 14.5, 15.8, 17.1, ...
24. The person might divide the entry by 1000.
25. Do a division problem. Depending upon the type of calculator and how many places in the display, the division may have to be done in parts. It would take 59,424.92 hours.
26. **(a)** 91,000,000.1106   **(b)** ⁻90,753,086.5318
(c) 154 ,815,802 .09496   **(d)** 1 02,880,657,928.6
27. **(a)** System A   **(b)** System B   **(c)** 25 checks
28. No, the bank is over $7.74.
29. Second option; it is $4,368,709.12 more profitable.
30. The number of digits in the terminating decimal is the greater of m or n.

Brain Teaser (p. 340)
One possibility is 77/0.77=100.

Problem Set 7-2
1. **(a)** $0.\overline{4}$ **(b)** $0.\overline{285714}$ **(c)** $0.\overline{27}$ **(d)** $0.0\overline{6}$ **(e)** $0.02\overline{6}$
(f) $0.\overline{01}$ **(g)** $0.8\overline{3}$ **(h)** $0.0\overline{75923}$
2. **(a)** **(i)** $0.\overline{142857}$ **(ii)** $0.\overline{285714}$ **(iii)** $0.\overline{428571}$
(iv) $0.\overline{571428}$ **(v)** $0.\overline{714285}$ **(vi)** $0.\overline{857142}$ **(b)** 6
(c) The answers all contain the same digits, 1, 2, 4, 5, 7, and 8. The digits in each answer repeat in the same sequence; that is, in each case a 1 is always followed by a 4, which is always followed by a 2, which is always followed by an 8, and so on. In each of the answers in (i)-(vi), the starting digit is different, but the sequence of numbers is the same.
3. **(a)** The sum is always 999.   **(b)** Yes   **(c)** It appears that the sum will be a power of 10 less 1.   **(d)** No
4. **(a)** $0.\overline{075923}$ **(b)** $0.\overline{047619}$ **(c)** $0.\overline{1578947368421052632}$
5. **(a)** 221/90   **(b)** 243/99 = 27/11   **(c)** 243/99 = 27/11
(d) 243/990 = 27/110   **(e)** 243/9900 = 27/1100
(f) ⁻2430/99 = ⁻270/11   **(g)** 4/9   **(h)** 6/9 = 2/3   **(i)** 5/9
(j) 34/99
(k) ⁻232/99   **(l)** ⁻2/99
6. **(a)** $3.2\overline{3}$, $3.\overline{23}$, 3.23, $3.\overline{22}$, 3.20
(b) ⁻1.45, ⁻1.454, ⁻$1.45\overline{4}$, ⁻$1.\overline{454}$, ⁻$1.4\overline{54}$
7. Answers may vary: **(a)** 3.25   **(b)** 462.245   **(c)** 0.01515
(d) $462.24\overline{34}$
8. **(a)** 3.25   **(b)** 462.245   **(c)** 462.243   **(d)** .009
9. **(a)** 49,736.5281   **(b)** 41,235.6789
10. **(a)** 200   **(b)** 200   **(c)** 204   **(d)** 203.7   **(e)** 203.65
11. 19 miles per gallon
12. **(a)** Okay, it only totals $2.57   **(b)** Short; answers may vary.
13. $37
14. Estimates may vary. Exact answers are as follows:
(a) 122.06   **(b)** 57.31   **(c)** 25.40   **(d)** 136.15
15. **(a)** 3.325×10^3 **(b)** 4.632×10 **(c)** 1.3×10^{-3}
(d) 9.30146×10^5
16. **(a)** 0.0000000032   **(b)** 3,200,000,000   **(c)** 0.42
(d) 620,000
17. **(a)** 1.27×10^7 **(b)** 5.797×10^6 **(c)** 5×10^7
18. **(a)** 0.0000044   **(b)** 19,900   **(c)** 3,000,000,000
19. **(a)** 4.8×10^{28} **(b)** 4×10^7 **(c)** 2×10^2

20. 1000^5 or 10^{15}
21. 2.35×10^{13}
22. Because 1/99 = 0.0101010101 ..., then 51/99 =51(1/99) = 51(0.0101010101 ...) =0.5151515151 ... However, x/99 behaves differently if x > 99.
23. **(a)** $1.\overline{6}$, 2, $2.\overline{3}$, $2.\overline{6}$, 3, $3.\overline{3}$, $3.\overline{6}$, 4 ...
(b) $6/7 = 0.\overline{857142}$, 7/8 = 0.875, $8/9 = 0.\overline{8}$, $9/10 = 0.9,...$
24. **(a)** $0.\overline{446355}$; 6   **(b)** $1.3\overline{5775}$; yes; 4
25. **(a)** 21.6 pounds   **(b)** 48 pounds
26. $22,761.95
27. A fraction in simplest form, a/b, can be written as a terminating decimal if and only if the prime factorization of the denominator contains no primes other than 2 or 5.
28. **(a)** 1672/100 = 418/25   **(b)** 3/1000   **(c)** ⁻507/100
(d) 123/1000

Problem Set 7-3
1. **(a)** 789 %   **(b)** 3.2 %   **(c)** 19,310 %   **(d)** 20 %
(e) $83.\overline{3}$ % or 83 1/3 %   **(f)** 15 %   **(g)** 12.5 %   **(h)** 37.5 %
(i) 62.5 %   **(j)** $16.\overline{6}$ % or 16 2/3 %   **(k)** 80 %   **(l)** 2.5 %
2. **(a)** 0.16   **(b)** 0.045   **(c)** 0.002   **(d)** $0.00\overline{285714}$
(e) $0.13\overline{6}$ **(f)** 1.25   **(g)** $0.00\overline{3}$ **(h)** 0.0025
3. **(a)** 4   **(b)** 2   **(c)** 25   **(d)** 200   **(e)** 12.5
4. Depends on calculator.
5. **(a)** 2.04   **(b)** 50 %   **(c)** 60   **(d)** 3.43   **(e)** 300%   **(f)** 40
6. 63 boxes
7. $13,960
8. $14,500
9. $437.50
10. **(a)** Bill sold 221   **(b)** Joe sold 90%   **(c)** Ron started with 265
11. 20%
12. 15%
13. 18.4%
14. $\frac{26}{29} \cdot 100\%$ or approximately 89.7%
15. 100%
16. $22.40
17. $5.10
18. 50 cups
19. $336
20. 35%
21. $3200
22. 1200
23. $16.\overline{6}\% = 16\ 2/3\%$
24. $10.37/hr
25. $82,644.63
26. 11.1%
27. $440
28. $33.\overline{3}\%$
29. $187.50
30. Approximately $9207.58
31. **(a)** $3.30   **(b)** $24.00   **(c)** $1.90   **(d)** $24.50
32. **(a)** 4%   **(b)** 32%   **(c)** 64%
33. **(a)** Approximately 4.94%, 34.57%, 60.49%
(b) Approximately 6.25%, 37.50%, 56.25%
(c) Approximately 8.16%, 40.82%, 51.02%
(d) Approximately 2.78%, 27.78%, 69.44%
34. **(a)** False; the price after 2 years is 99% of the original price.   **(b)** False; the price decreased by 1%.
35. **(a)** Answers may vary.   **(b)** **(i)** 0.366 seconds between beats **(ii)** 0.0061 minutes between beats

36. (a) 25% (b) 20% (c) 20% (d) 20%
37. Apprentice makes $700. Journeyman makes $1400. Master makes $2100
38. (a) 4% (b) (i) 44 (ii) 88%
39. $30.43
40. (a) 90% (b) 6.$\overline{6}$% or 6 2/3% (c) 48%
(d) Approximately 60.42%
(e) Children's Cvcs + Corrections + Other
      or
   Mental Health + Adult & Family Svcs + Senior Svcs
(f) Yes
41. (a) $1322.50
(b) Filing separately: $1416.77
       Filing jointly: $1416.77
It doesn't make a difference whether they file separately or jointly.
42. 97 days
43. 3321/100
44. 0.$\overline{2}$
45. 2795/90 = 559/18
46. (a) 3.25×10^6 (b) 1.2×10^{-4}
47. (a) 32.0 (b) 30

Problem Set 7-4

1.	Int. Rate per Per.	# of Periods	Amt. of Int. Pd.
(a)	3%	4	$125.51
(b)	2%	12	$268.24
(c)	10/12% or 0.8$\overline{3}$%	60	$645.31
(d)	12/365%	1460	$615.95

2. $5,460.00
3. $24.45
4. 3.5%
5. Invest $32,040.82
6. $64,800
7. $4,416.35
8. $23,720.58
9. $81,628.83
10. $1944
11. The Pay More Bank offers a better rate.
12. (iii) 13.2%
13. Approximately $2.53
14. Approximately $23,673.64
15. Approximately $3592.89
16. $10,935
17. Approximately 12.79%
18. (a) Decrease (b) 2.97%
19. Approximately $7.026762 \cdot 10^8$
20. Approximately 7.3 years

Problem Set 7-5

1. Answers may vary. One answer is 0.232233222333 ...
2. 0.77, 0.$\overline{7}$, 0.78, 0.787787778 ..., 0.$\overline{78}$, 0.788,
0.7$\overline{8}$ = 0.7$\overline{88}$
3. 0.9, 0.9, 0.$\overline{98}$, 0.9$\overline{88}$, 0.9, 0.$\overline{898}$
4. (a), (d), (e), and (f) represent irrational numbers
5. (a) 15 (b) 15.8 (c) 13 (d) 22.6 (e) Impossible
(f) 25
6. (a) 4.12 (b) 2.65 (c) 4.58 (d) 0.11 (e) 4.51
(f) 1.2
7. (a) False, $\sqrt{2} + 0$ (b) False, $^{-}\sqrt{2} + \sqrt{2}$
(c) False, $\sqrt{2} \cdot \sqrt{2}$ (d) False, $\sqrt{2} - \sqrt{2}$

8. False: $\sqrt{64 + 36} \neq \sqrt{64} + \sqrt{36}$
9. Answers may vary. For example, $\sqrt{2}$, $\sqrt{3}$, and $\sqrt{5}$
10. Answers may vary. For example, assume the following pattern continues 0.54544544454444 ...
11. No; 22/7 is a rational number that can be represented by the repeating decimal 3.$\overline{142857}$.
12. No; $\sqrt{13}$ is an irrational number, so when it is expressed as a decimal, it is nonterminating and nonrepeating.
13. (a) R (b) ∅ (c) 0 (d) ∅ (e) R (f) R
14.

(a) $x \leq \frac{8}{3}$

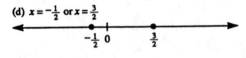

(b) $x \geq \frac{\sqrt{3} - 4}{10}$

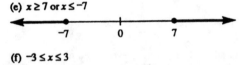

(c) $x \leq \frac{-3\sqrt{3}}{17}$

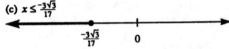

(d) $x = -\frac{1}{2}$ or $x = \frac{3}{2}$

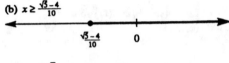

(e) $x \geq 7$ or $x \leq ^{-}7$

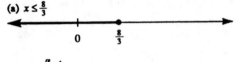

(f) $^{-}3 \leq x \leq 3$

15. (a) N, I, Q, R (b) Q, R (c) R, S (d) N, I, Q, R
(e) ∅ (f) Q, R
16. (a) 64 (b) none (c) $^{-}$64 (d) none
(e) All real numbers greater than 0 (f) none
17. 6.4 feet
18. (a) 8.98 seconds (b) 20.07 seconds
19. 13/99
20. Suppose $\sqrt{3}$ is rational. $\sqrt{3} = a/b$ where a and b are integers and $b \neq 0$. Therefore, $3 = a^2/b^2$, or $3b^2 = a^2$. a^2 has an even number of 3's in its prime factorization but $3b^2$ has an odd number of 3's in its prime factorization and this is impossible. Thus, $\sqrt{3}$ is irrational.
21. Suppose $\sqrt{p}$ is rational, where p is a prime. Then $\sqrt{p}$ = a/b where a and b are integers and $b \neq 0$. Thus, $p = a^2/b^2$ or $pb^2 = a^2$. Since b^2 has an even number of p's in its prime factorization, pb^2 has an odd number of p's in its prime factorization. Also a^2 can have only an even number of p's in its prime factorization and this is impossible. Thus, $\sqrt{p}$ is irrational.
22. (a) m is a perfect square. (b) Use the result of Problem 21.
23. (a) $0.5 + 1/0.5 = 0.5 + 2 = 2.5 \geq 2$ (b) Suppose x + 1/x < 2. Since $x > 0$, $x^2 + 1 < 2x$ so that $x^2 - 2x + 1 < 0$, or $(x - 1)^2 < 2$, which is false. Therefore, $x + 1/x \geq 2$.

24. (a) $4.\overline{9}$ (b) $5.0\overline{9}$ (c) $0.4\overline{9}$
25. 3/12,500
26. 4.09, $4.09\overline{1}$, 4.099, $4.0\overline{9}$
27. 8/33
28. (a) 208,000 (b) 0.00038
29. $20,274
30. 60%

Problem Set 7-6

1. (a) $6\sqrt{5}$ (b) 23 (c) $11\sqrt{3}$ (d) $6\sqrt{7}$ (e) 13/14
(f) 1/2
2. (a) ⁻3 (b) $2\sqrt[5]{3}$ (c) 2 (d) $5\sqrt[3]{2}$ (e) ⁻3 (f) $2\sqrt{2}$
3. (a) $2\sqrt{3}+3\sqrt{2}+6\sqrt{5}$ (b) $2\sqrt[3]{5}$ (c) $30+12\sqrt{6}$
(d) $\sqrt{2}/2$ or $\sqrt{1/2}$ or (e) $17\sqrt{2}$ (f) $\sqrt{6}$
4. (a) 4 (b) 9 (c) 32 (d) 9 (e) 1/256 (f) 9 (9) 1/4
(h) 1/9 (i) 4 (j) 32 (k) 10 (l) 8 (m) 16 (n) 1/4 (o) 4
5. No
6. (a) Sometimes (if a ≥ 0) (b) Sometimes (if x ≤ 0)
(c) Always (d) Sometimes (if a + b ≥ 0) (e) Sometimes
(if a ≥ 0)
7. 22 terms in the sequence
8. (a) 2^{10} (b) 2^{11} (c) 2^{12}
9. $(4/25)^{-1/4}$, $(4/25)^{-1/3} = (25/4)^{1/3}$
10. (a) $\sqrt{3}$ (b) $\sqrt[3]{3}$ (c) $\sqrt{12}+\sqrt{14}$
11. $\sqrt[8]{2^7}$
12. (a) 4 (b) 3/2 (c) ⁻4/7 (d) 5/6
13. $\sqrt[3]{1/16}$
14. (a) n is odd (b) When m is even, then n can be any
number except 0. When m is odd, then n must also be odd.
15. (a) Rational (b) Rational (c) Irrational (d) Rational

Chapter Test

1. (a) ⁻0.693 (b) 31.564 (c) 0.2284 (d) 0.032
(e) ⁻0 097 (f) $1.6 \cdot 10^{-7} = 0.00000016$
2. (a) $3 \cdot 10 + 2 \cdot 10^0 + 0 \cdot 10^{-1} + 1 \cdot 10^{-2} + 2 \cdot 10^{-3}$
(b) $0 \cdot 10^0 + 0 \cdot 10^{-1} + 0 \cdot 10^{-2} + 1 \cdot 10^{-3} + 0 \cdot 10^{-4} + 3 \cdot 10^{-5}$
3. A fraction in simplest form, a/b, can be written as a
terminating decimal if and only if the prime factorization
of the denominator contains no primes other than 2 or 5.
4. 8
5. (a) $0.\overline{571428}$ (b) 0.125 (c) $0.\overline{6}$ (d) 0.625
6. (a) 7/25 (b) 1/3 (c) 94/45
7. (a) 307.63 (b) 307.6 (c) 308 (d) 300
8. (a) $x \leq 3.\overline{3}$ (b) 0 (c) 20,000 (d) 20% (e) 34
(f) $0.\overline{6}$
9. (a) 25% (b) 192 (c) $56.\overline{6}$ (d) 20%
10. (a) 12.5% (b) 7.5% (c) 627% (d) 1.23%
(e) 150%
11. (a) 0.60 (b) $0.00\overline{6}$ (c) 1
12. (a) No; $^{-}\sqrt{2}+\sqrt{2}$ is not an irrational number.
(b) No; see part (a). (c) No; $\sqrt{2} \cdot \sqrt{2}$ is not an irrational
number. (d) No; $\sqrt{2}/\sqrt{2}$ is not an irrational number.
13. 4.7958
14. (a) $4.26 \cdot 10^5$ (b) $2.37 \cdot 10^{-6}$ (c) $3.2 \cdot 10$
(d) $3.25 \cdot 10^{-1}$
15. (a) 3 (b) 3 (c) 2 (d) 3

16. (a) Irrational (b) Irrational (c) Rational
(d) Irrational
17. $9280
18. $3.\overline{3}$%
19. 88.6%
20. $5750
21. It makes no difference.
22. $80
23. $15,000
24. $15,110.69
25. (a) $11\sqrt{2}$ (b) $12\sqrt{2}$ (c) $6\sqrt{2}$ (d) $3\sqrt[3]{6}$
26. (a) $1/2^{11}$ (b) $1/5 1/5^{20}$ (c) $(3/2)^{28}$ (d) 3^{18}

CHAPTER 8

Problem Set 8-1

1. (a) {Bush, Reagan, Carter, Ford, Nixon, Johnson,
Kennedy, Eisenhower, Truman, F. Roosevelt} (b) Answers
vary. (c) Answers vary.
2. (a) {0, 1, 2, 3, 4, 5, 6, 7, 8, 9} (b) {0, 1, 2, 3, 4}
(c) {1, 3, 5, 7, 9} (d) {0, 1, 3, 4, 5, 6, 7, 8, 9}
(e) (b) 5/10, or 1/2 (c) 5/10, or 1/2 (d) 9/10
3. (a) 3/8 (b) 2/8, or 1/4 (c) 4/8, or 1/2 (d) 2/8, or 1/4
(e) 0 (f) 3/8 (g) 1/8
4. (a) 26/52, or 1/2 (b) 12/52, or 3/13 (c) 28/52, or 7/13
(d) 4/52, 1/13 (e) 48/52, or 12/13 (f) 22/52, or 11/26
(g) 3/52 (h) 30/52, or 12/26
5. (a) 4/12, or 1/3 (b) 8/12 or 2/3 (c) 0 (d) 6/12 or 1/2
6. (a) 5/26 (b) 21/26
7. 0.8
8. (a) 1/6 (b) 3/6, or 1/2
9. (a) 8/36, or 2/9 (b) 4/36, or 1/9 (c) 24/36, or 2/3
(d) 6 and 8 both have 5/36 probability. (e) 0 (f) 1
(g) 10 times
10. Answers vary.
11. (a) 18/38, or 9/19 (b) 2/38, or 1/19 (c) 26/38, or
13/19 (d) 20/38, or 10/19
12. 10 times
13. (a) No (b) Yes (c) Yes (d) Yes (e) No (f) Yes
(g) No (h) No
14. 45/150, or 3/10
15. (a) 2/4 or 1/2 (b) 3/4 (c) 3/4
16. 0.7
17. Answers vary.
18. (a) 45/80, or 9/16 (b) 10/80, or 1/8 (c) 60/80, or 3/4
(d) 30/80, or 3/8

Brain Teaser (p. 395)

You should choose your die second, because then you can base
your choice on the die that was picked first. The best second
choices are given below, along with the probability of the
second choice winning.

1st Person's Choice	2nd Person's Choice	Probability 2nd Choice Winning
A	D	$\frac{2}{3}$
B	A	$\frac{2}{3}$
C	B	$\frac{2}{3}$
D	C	$\frac{2}{3}$

The table on page 202 can be verified by constructing a sample space for the various first and second choices. For more information, see R. Billstein, "A Fun Way to Introduce Probability," The Arithmetic Teacher 24 (January 1971): 39–42.

Problem Set 8-2

1. (a)

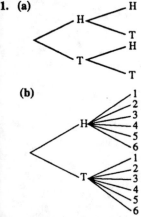

(b)

2. (a) {(1, 1), (1, 2), (1, 3), (2, 1), (2, 1), (2, 3)}
(b) {(2, 2)}   **(c)** {(1, 2), (2, 1), (2, 2), (2,3)}
(d) {(1, 2),(2, 1),(2, 3)}
3. (a) 1/216   **(b)** 1/120
4. (a) 1/24   **(b)** 1/64   **(c)** 1/84   **(d)** 7/36
5. Answers vary.
6. (a) Box 1, with probability 1/3 (Box 2 has probability 1/5   **(b)** Either, with. probability 4/27
7. (a) 64/75   **(b)** 11/75
8. Answers vary.
9. (a) 1/5   **(b)** 4/5   **(c)** 11/15   **(d)** 8/15
10. 5/16
11. 1/16
12. (a) 1/4   **(b)** 5/8   **(c)** 1/8
13. Answers vary.
14. (a) 1/320   **(b)** 63/4000   **(c)** 0   **(d)** 171/320
15. 1/32
16. 1
17. (a) 16/81   **(b)** 8/27
18. 1/256
19. 1/34,650
20. (a) 1/25   **(b)** 8/25   **(c)** 16/25
21. (a) 100 square units
(b)   P(Region A) = 4/100, or 1/25
         P(Region B) = 12/100, or 3/25
         P(Region C) = 20/100, or 1/5
         P(Region D) = 28/100, or 7/25
         P(Region E) = 36/100, or 9/25
(c) 1/625   **(d)** 36/100, or 9/25
22. 0.7
23. 1/12
24. 271/1000
25. 2/5
26. 3 Reds, one Black
27. Answers vary.
28. Answers vary.
29. 25/30, or 5/6
30. 2/28, or 1/14
31. Answers vary.
32. 0.0005
33. 69/3000, or 23/1000
34. (a) Spinner A   **(b)** Choose C, with a winning probability of 35/99

35. The probabilities of Abe's winning the game are summarized below:

		Abe's Choice			
		HH	HT	TH	TT
Your	HH	--	0.50	0.75	0.50
Choice	HT	0.50	--	0.50	0.25
	TH	0.25	0.50	--	0.50
	TT	0.50	0.75	0.50	--

Of the 12 possible games, only 8 result in choices with equally likely probabilities.
36. She should serve the first one hard; It does not matter with the next one.
37. (a) v   **(b)** iii   **(c)** ii   **(d)** i   **(e)** iv
38. (a) 1/30   **(b)** 0   **(c)** 19/30

Brain Teaser (p. 408)

The probability that at least two people share the same birthday is one minus the probability that no two people share the same birthday. We calculate the latter probability first. Let's pick a first person. Since there are 364 birthdays that a second person can have which are different from the first person's birthday the probability that the second person's birthday differs from the first is $\frac{364}{365}$. In order for the third person to have a birthday different from the first and the second person, he or she must be born on one of the 363 days which are different from the first two person's birthdays. Thus the probability that the third person's birthday differs from the first and second is $\frac{363}{365}$. Hence the probability that the first three people have different birthdays is $\frac{364}{365} \cdot \frac{363}{365}$. Continuing in this way we find the probability that all n people have different birthdays is $\frac{364}{365} \cdot \frac{363}{365} \cdot \frac{362}{365} \cdot \ldots \cdot \frac{365-(n-1)}{365}$. To find the value of n for which the above product is less than $\frac{1}{2}$, we can use a calculator and try various values of n. For n = 23 the above product is slightly less than $\frac{1}{2}$. Hence if there are 23 people in the room, the probability that no two people share the same birthday is slightly less than $\frac{1}{2}$; therefore the complementary probability that at least 2 people share the same birthday is slightly greater than $\frac{1}{2}$.

Problem Set 8-3

1. Answers vary.
2. Answers vary.
3. (a) Answers vary.**(b)** Answers vary.   **(c)** 0.0000001
4. (a) Let 1, 2, 3, 4, 5 and 6 represent the numbers of the die and ignore the numbers 0, 7, 8, 9.   **(b)** Number the persons 01, 02, 03, ...,18, 19, 20. Go to the random digit table and mark off groups of two. The three persons chosen are the first three whose numbers appear.   **(c)** Represent Red by the numbers 0,1,2,3, 4; Green by the number 5, 6, 7; Yellow by the number 8 and White by the number 9.
5. 1200 fish
6. 3/10
7. Pick a starting spot in the table and count the number of digits it takes before all the numbers 1 through 9 are obtained. Repeat this experiment many times and find the average number of coupons.

8. Answers vary.
9. Answers vary
10. 13 cards
11. (a) 7 (b) Answers vary
12. Answers may vary, e.g., use a random digit table. Let the digits 1-8 represent a win and the digits 0 and 9 represent losses. Mark off blocks of 3. If only the digits 1-8 appear then this represents 3 wins in a row.
13. Answers may vary, e.g., mark off blocks of 2 digits and let the digits 00, 01, 02, ..., 13, 14 represent contracting the disease and 15 to 99 represent no disease. Mark off blocks of 6 digits to represent the 3 children. If at least one of the numbers is in the range 00 to 14, then this represents a child in the 3-child family having strep.
14. Let the 10 ducks be represented by the digits 0, 1, 2, 3, ..., 8, 9. Then pick a starting point in the table and mark off 10 digits to simulate which ducks the hunters shoot at. Count how many of the digits 0 through 9 are not in the 10 digits and this represents the ducks that escaped. Do this experiment many times and take the average to determine an answer. See how close your simulation comes to 3.49 ducks.
15. (a) 1/4 (b) 1/52 (c) 48/52 or 12/13 (d) 3/4
(e) 1/2 (f) 1/52 (g) 16/52 or 4/13 (h) 1
16. (a) 15/19 (b) 56/361 (c) 28/171

Problem Set 8-4
1. (a) 12 to 40, or 3 to 10 (b) 40 to 12, or 10 to 3
2. 30 to 6, or 5 to 1
3. 15 to 1
4. (a) 1/2 (b) $(1/2)^{10}$ or 1/1024 (c) 1023 to 1
5. 5/8
6. 7 to 1
7. 4 to 6 or 2 to 3
8. 20 to 18, or 10 to 9
9. Answers vary.
10. $3.50
11. $3.00
12. 3 hours
13. 1000/1001
14. Approximately 8 cents
15. $10,000
16. (a) Since Al's probability of winning at this point was 3/4 and Betsy's was 1/4, Al should get $75 and Betsy $25.
(b) 3 to 1 (c) Al gets about $89.00; Betsy gets about $11.00.
(d) 57 to 7
17. Yes.
18. No.
19. 1/1,000,000,001
20. Answers vary.
21. 1/27
22. (a) {1, 2, 3, 4} (b) {Red, Blue} (c) {(1, Red, (1, Blue), (2, Red), (2, Blue), (3, Red), (3, Blue), (4, Red), (4, Blue)}
(d) {(Blue, 1), (Blue, 2), (Blue, 3), (Blue, 4), (Blue 5), (Blue, 6), (Red, 1), (Red, 2), (Red, 3), (Red, 4), (Red, 5), (Red, 6)}
(e) {(1, 1), (1, 2), (1, 3), (1, 4), (2, 1), (2, 2), (2, 3), (2, 4), (3, 1), (3, 2), (3, 3), (3, 4), (4, 1), (4, 2), (4, 3), (4, 4)}
(f) {(Red, Red), (Red, Blue), (Blue, Red), (Blue, Blue)}
23. The blue section must have 300°; the red has 60°.
24. 25/676

Problem Set 8-5
1. Answers vary.
2. (a) (i) 12 (ii) 4,989,600 (b) 13,860
3. (a) 1,000,000 (b) Montana, Wyoming, Alaska,

Delaware, North Dakota, South Dakota, Vermont
(c) Answers vary.
4. 224
5. 32
6. 10,000
7. 1352 with 3 letter call letters; 35,152 with 4 letter call letters.
8. 180
9. (a) True (b) False (c) False (d) False (e) True
(f) True (g) True
10. 8! = 40,320
11. 15
12. (a) 12 (b) 210 (c) 3360 (d) 34,650 (e) 3780
13. (a) 24,360 (b) 4060
14. 792
15. 362,880
16. 1/120
17. 45
18. 1000
19. 1260
20. (a) 6 (b) 36
21. 8 people
22. (a) 1/13 (b) 8/65
23. (a) 10 (b) 1 (c) 1 (d) 3
24. Approximately 0.228
25. 3840

Brain Teaser (p. 423)
(a) The probability of a successful flight with 2 engines is 0.9999
(b) The probability of a successful flight with 4 engines is 0.99999603.

Chapter 8 Test
1. (a) {Monday, Tuesday, Wednesday, Thursday, Friday, Saturday, Sunday} (b) {Tuesday, Thursday} (c) 2/7
2. There's at least one other colored bean, besides red and blue; there are 800 blue ones; there are 125 red ones.
3. (a) Approximately 0.501 (b) Approximately 0.499
(c) 34,226,731 to 34,108,157
4. (a) 5/12 (b) 9/12, or 3/4 (c) 5/12 (d) 9/12, or 3/4
(e) 0 (f) 1
5. (a) 13/52, or 1/4 (b) 1/52 (c) 22/52, or 11/26
(d) 48/52 or 12/13
6. (a) 64/729 (b) 24/504 or 1/21
7. 6/25
8. 14/80, or 7/40
9. 7/45
10. 4 to 48, or 1 to 12
11. 3 to 3, or 1 to 1
12. 3/8
13. $.30
14. 33 1/3¢, or 34¢
15. 900
16. 120
17. 5040
18. 2/20, or 1/10
19. (a) 5·4·3, or 60 (b) 3/60, or 1/20 (c) 1/60
20. 15/36
21. 2/5
22. 0.027
23. 63/80
24. Answers vary.
25. (a) 1/8 (b) 1/4 (c) 1/16
26. 8/20, or 2/5

CHAPTER 9

Problem Set 9-1

1.

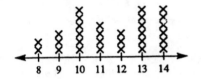

Glasses of Lemonade Sold

Friday	
Thursday	
Wednesday	
Tuesday	
Monday	

represents 10 glasses

2. (a) 225 million (b) 375 million (c) 550 million

3.

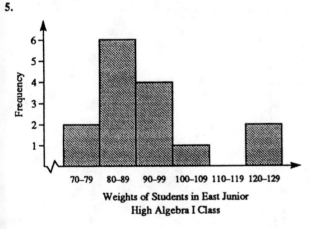

8   9   10   11   12   13   14

4. (a) 72, 74,81, 81, 82, 85, 87, 88, 92, 94, 97, 98, 103, 123, 125 (b) 72 Ibs. (c) 125 lbs.

5.

Frequency

70–79   80–89   90–99   100–109   110–119   120–129

Weights of Students in East Junior
High Algebra I Class

6. Answers may vary.

7. (a) November, 30 cm (b) 50 cm

8. (a)

Ages of HXM Employees

6	332	
5	8224	
4	8561511	
3	474224	3	4 represents
2	1433361730136539	34 years old
1	898	

(b) There are more employees in their 40's. (c) 20 (d) 17.5%

9. (a) Approximately 3800 km (b) Approximately 1900 km

10.

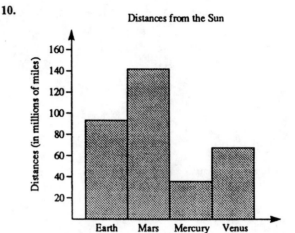

Distances from the Sun

Distances (in millions of miles)

Earth   Mars   Mercury   Venus

11.

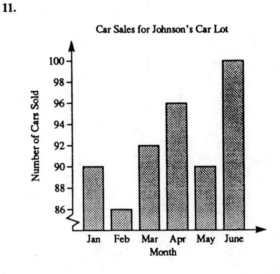

Car Sales for Johnson's Car Lot

Number of Cars Sold

Jan   Feb   Mar   Apr   May   June
Month

12.

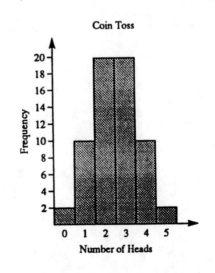

Coin Toss

Frequency

0   1   2   3   4   5
Number of Heads

13. (a)

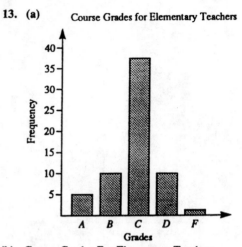

Course Grades for Elementary Teachers

(b) Course Grades For Elementary Teachers

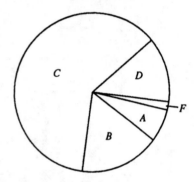

14. (a) Fall Textbook Costs

```
1 | 6
2 | 3  3
3 | 0  3  5  7  7  9  9
4 | 0  1  2  2  5  8  9
5 | 0  0  1  3  8
6 | 0  2  2      2 | 3 represents $23
```

(b)

Fall Textbook Costs

Classes	Tally	Frequency
$15–19	I	1
$20–24	II	2
$25–29		0
$30–34	II	2
$35–39	HHT	5
$40–44	IIII	4
$45–49	III	3
$50–54	IIII	4
$55–59	I	1
$60–64	III	3
		25

(c) (d) Frequency polygon and histogram on same graph.

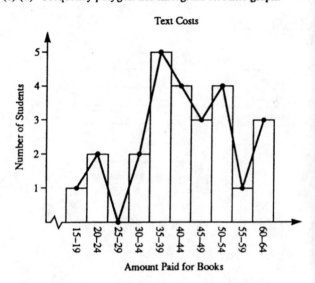

15. The line graph is more helpful since we can approximate the point midway between 8:00 and 12:00 noon and then draw a vertical line upward until it hits the line graph. An approximation for the 10:00 temperature can then be obtained from the vertical axis.

16. (a) A line graph is more appropriate since we have continuous data changing over time.

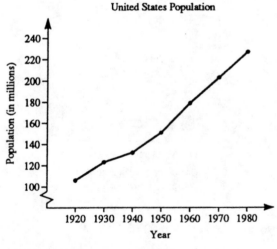

(b) The data falls into distinct categories and it is not continuous, so we use a bar graph.

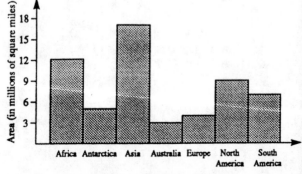

17. (a) Chicken (b) 10 mph (c) Cheetah (d) Yes
18. (a) Women (b) Approximately 2 years.
(c) Approximately 7.5 years.
19. Answers vary.
20. Answers vary.
21. Answers vary.
22. (a) Approximately $8400 (b) 14,000
(c) Approximately $7200 (d) Right after 2 years
23. (a) Asia (b) Africa (c) It is about $\frac{2}{3}$ as large.
(d) Asia and Africa (e) 5:16 (f) Approximately
58.6 million square miles
24.

Home Run Leaders

National League	1976–90		American League
	2	2	
9877761	3	22699	
9887000	4	00123569	
	2	5	1

1 | 3 | represents
31 home runs

| 3 | 2 represents
32 home runs

25. (a)

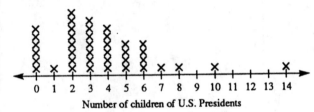

Number of children of U.S. Presidents

(b)

No. of Children	Tally	Frequency
0	JHT I	6
1	I	1
2	JHT III	8
3	JHT II	7
4	JHT I	6
5	IIII	4
6	IIII	4
7	I	1
8	I	1
9		0
10	I	1
11		0
12		0
13		0
14	I	1
		40

(c) 2

Problem Set 9-2

1. (a) Mean = 6.625, median = 7.5, mode = 8
(b) Mean = 13.$\overline{4}$, median = 12, mode = 12 (c) Mean $\doteq$ 19.9,
median = 18, modes = 18 and 22 (d) Mean = 81.4, median =
80, mode = 80 (e) Mean = 5.8$\overline{3}$, median = 5, mode = 5
2. (a) The mean, median and mode are all 80. (b) Answers
may vary.

3. 1500
4. 150 pounds
5. 78.$\overline{3}$
6. (a) $\bar{x} = 18.4$ years (b) 23.4 years (c) 28.4 years
(d) The mean in (b) is equal to the mean in (a) plus 5 years.
The mean in (c) is equal to the mean in (a) plus 10 years or
the mean in (b) plus 5 years.
7. Mode, answers vary.
8. Approximately 2.59
9. Approximately 215.45 pounds
10. $1880
11. (a) $41,275 (b) $38.000 (c) $38,000
12. (a) Balance beam-Olga(9.575); Uneven Bars-Lisa (9.85);
Floor-Lisa (9.925) (b) Lisa (29.20)
13. $19\frac{2}{3}$ mpg
14. 30 mph
15. $5\frac{4}{5}$ hr
16. 58 years old
17. (a) A (b) B and C (c) C
18. (a) Mean - 90; Median - 90; Mode - 90 (b) median or
Mode (c) Mean
19. (a) For example, 10, 30, 70, and 90. (b) Choose 4
numbers whose mean is 50. (c) The mean of the new numbers
is 50.
20. s $\doteq$ 7.3 cm
21. The mean increases by the number which has been added.
The standard deviation remains the same.
22. (a) s = 0 (b) Yes
23. (a) Approximately 76.81 (b) 76 (c) 71
(d) Approximately 156.82 (e) Approximately 12.52
24. 91
25. 96, 90, and 90
26. 2
27. No. To find the average speed we divide the distance
traveled by the time if takes to drive it. The first part of the trip
took $\frac{5}{30}$ or $\frac{1}{6}$ of an hour. The second part of the trip took $\frac{5}{50}$
or $\frac{1}{10}$ of an hour. Therefore, to find the average speed we
compute $\dfrac{10}{\frac{1}{6} + \frac{1}{10}}$ to obtain 37.5 mph.

28.

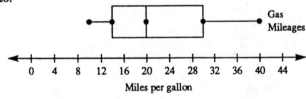

Miles per gallon

29. (a) A - $25, B - $50 (b) B (c) $80 at B
(d) Answers vary
30.

TEST SCORES

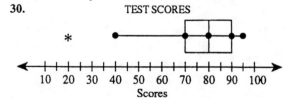

Scores

31. (a)

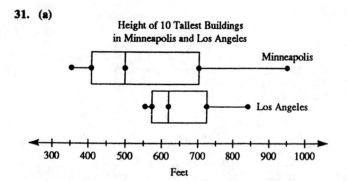

Height of 10 Tallest Buildings
in Minneapolis and Los Angeles

(b) There are no outliers

32. (a) (i) Increase by $1000 (ii) Increase by $1000
(iii) Increase by $1000 (iv) Increase by $1000 (v) Stays
the same **(b)** (i) Increase by 5% (ii) Increase by 5%

33. (a) (i) $\bar{x} = 5$, $m = 5$ (ii) $\bar{x} = 100$, $m = 100$ (iii) $\bar{x} = 307$,
$m = 307$ **(b)** The mean and median of an arithmetic sequence
are the same.

34.
$$v = \frac{(x_1 - \bar{x})^2 + (x_2 - \bar{x})^2 + \cdots + (x_n - \bar{x})^2}{n}$$
$$= \frac{(x_1^2 - 2\bar{x}x_1 + \bar{x}^2) + (x_2^2 - 2\bar{x}x_2 + \bar{x}^2) + \cdots + (x_n^2 - 2\bar{x}x_n + \bar{x}^2)}{n}$$
$$= \frac{(x_1^2 + x_2^2 + \cdots + x_n^2) - 2\bar{x}(x_1 + x_2 + \cdots + x_n) + n\bar{x}^2}{n}$$
$$= \frac{x_1^2 + x_2^2 + \cdots + x_n^2}{n} - \frac{2\bar{x}(x_1 + x_2 + \cdots + x_n)}{n} + \frac{n\bar{x}^2}{n}$$
$$= \frac{x_1^2 + x_2^2 + \cdots + x_n^2}{n} - 2\bar{x}^2 + \bar{x}^2$$
$$= \frac{x_1^2 + x_2^2 + \cdots + x_n^2}{n} - \bar{x}^2$$

35. (a) Everest, approximately 8500 m **(b)** Aconcagua,
Everest, McKinley

36. (a)

History Test Scores

5	5
6	48
7	2334679
8	0255567889
9	00346

7 | 2 represents
a score of 72

(b)

History Test Scores

Classes	Tallies	Frequency
55–59	I	1
60–64	I	1
65–69	I	1
70–74	IIII	4
75–79	III	3
80–84	II	2
85–89	JHT III	8
90–94	IIII	4
95–99	I	1

(c)

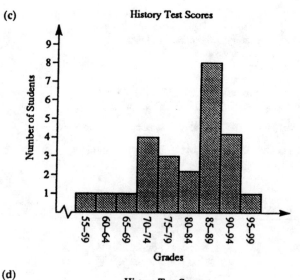

History Test Scores

(d)

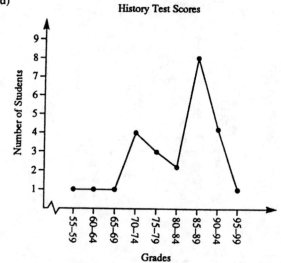

History Test Scores

(e) Approximately 115°

Brain Teaser (p. 470)

The mean speed for the total 6-mile run is 6 divided by the total
time it took to drive 6 miles. The total time is the sum of the
times spent on the first 3 miles, the next $1\frac{1}{2}$ miles, and the last
$1\frac{1}{2}$ miles. On the first 3 miles, he averaged 140 miles per hour.
Thus his time was $\frac{3}{140}$ hours. Similarly, the times on the next
two segments were $\frac{1.5}{168}$ hours and $\frac{1.5}{210}$ hours. His total time
was therefore $\frac{3}{140} + \frac{1.5}{168} + \frac{1.5}{210} = 0.0375$ hours. Consequently,
the mean speed was $\frac{6}{0.375} = 160$ miles per hour.

Brain Teaser (p. 473)

Let n be the sum of ages of the first seven people in the room.
Because the mean is 21, we have $n/7 = 21$, and $n = 147$. When Jeff
arrived, there were 8 people in the room with the sum of the

ges equal to 147+29 or 176. To find the effect of Mary's age n the mean, we add her age, 29, to the sum of the other ages the room, 176, and divide by 9, the number of people in the oom. Therefore the mean with Mary in the room is (176+29)/9 205/9 =22.8. When Elmer entered the room, the mean age ecame 30. If we let E be Elmer's age, then $(205+E)/10=30$, nd $E=95$. Therefore Elmer is 95 years old on his birthday.

Problem Set 9-3

. (a) 1020   (b) 1425   (c) 1.5, so 1 or 2 people
. 97.5%
. 0.68
. (a) verbal; 0.6; Quantitative, $0.8\overline{3}$; logical reasoning, 1
b) (i) Logical reasoning (ii) verbal (iii) Holly has a omposite score of $0.8\overline{1}$.
. 16%
. They are equal.
. (a) 47.5%   (b) 16%
. (a) 1.07%   (b) 95.54%   (c) 2.27%
. 1.4%
0. 0.84 (all values LESS than 125 oz.)
1. 8
2. 90
3. Between 60.5 in. and 70.5 in.
4. 50
5. 1600
6. (a)

High Jump Records

(graph with y-axis "Record (in.)" ranging 64 to 84, x-axis "Year" 1983 to 1993)

(b) Positive
17. (a) Negative   (b) Approximately 10   (c) 22 years old
18. (a) 74.17   (b) 75   (c) 65   (d) 237.37   (e) 15.43
19. 27.74
20. $76.\overline{6}$
21.

Men's Olympic
100 meter Run Times
1896-1964

```
1 0| 0 2 3 3 3 4 5 6 8 8 8 8
1 1| 0 0
1 2| 0          10| 0 represents
                    10.0 seconds
```

Problem Set 9-4

1. Answers vary.
2. Answers may vary. One possibility is that the temperature is always 25°C.
3. She could have taken a different number of quizzes during the first part of the quarter than the second part.

4. When the radius of a circle is doubled, the area is quadrupled, which is misleading since the population has only doubled.
5. The horizontal axis does not have uniformly-sized intervals and both the horizontal axis and the graph are not labeled.
6.. There were more scores above the mean than below, but the mean was affected more by low scores.
7. It could very well be that most of the pickups sold in the last 10 years were actually sold during the last 2 years In such a case most of the pickups have been on the road for only 2 years, and therefore the given information would not imply that the average life of a pickup is around ten years.
8. Answers vary; however, he is assuming that there are no deep holes in the river where he crosses.
9. The three dimensional drawing distorts the graph. The result of doubling the radius and the height of the can is to increase the volume by a factor of 8.
10. No labels so we can compare actual sales.
11. Answers vary.
12. (a) False, prices vary only by $30.   (b) False, the bar has 4 times the area but this not true of prices.   (c) True
13. Answers vary.
14. Answers vary.
15. Answers vary.

Chapter Test

1. If the average is 2.41 children, then the mean is being used. If the average is 2.5, then the mean or the median might have been used.
2. 23
3. (a) Mean = 30, median = 30, mode = 10
(b) Mean = 5, median = 5, modes = 3, 5, 6
4. (a) Range = 50, variance ≐ 371.43, standard deviation ≐ 19.27   (b) Range = 8, variance = 5.2, standard deviation = 2.28
5. (a)

Miss Rider's Class
Masses in Kilograms

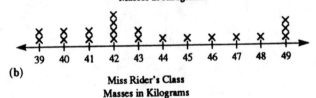

(b)

Miss Rider's Class
Masses in Kilograms

```
3 | 99
4 | 001122223345678999    4 | 0 represents
                              40 kg
```

(c)

Miss Rider's Class
Masses in Kilograms

Mass	Tally	Frequency
39	II	2
40	II	2
41	II	2
42	IIII	4
43	II	2
44	I	1
45	I	1
46	I	1
47	I	1
48	I	1
49	III	$\frac{3}{20}$

(d)

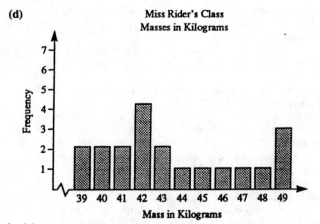

Miss Rider's Class
Masses in Kilograms

6. (a)

Test Grades

Classes	Tally	Frequency
61–70	JHT I	6
71–80	JHT JHT I	11
81–90	JHT II	7
91–100	JHT I	6
		30

(b) and **(c)** are on the same graph.

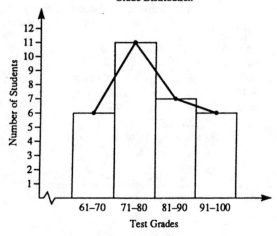

Grade Distribution

7.

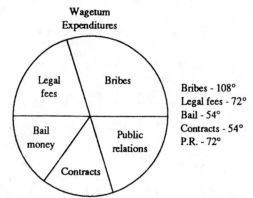

Wagetum
Expenditures

Bribes - 108°
Legal fees - 72°
Bail - 54°
Contracts - 54°
P.R. - 72°

8. The widths of the bars are not uniform and the graph has no title.

9. $2840

10.

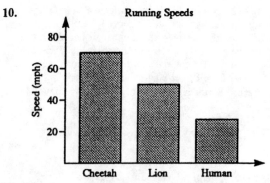

Running Speeds

11. (a)

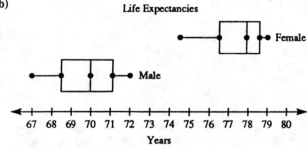

Life Expectancy
for Males and Females

Females		Males
	67	1446
	68	28
	69	156
	70	0049
	71	0223458
	72	
	73	
7	74	
9310	75	
86	76	
88532	77	
54332211	78	
7 |74| represents	79	|67| 1 represents
74.7 years old		67.1 years old

(b)

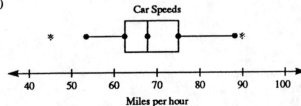

Life Expectancies

12. Larry was correct because his average was 3.26 while Moe's was $2.7\overline{3}$.

13. (a) 360   (b) none   (c) 350   (d) s $\doteq$ 108.22

14. (a) 67   (b) UQ = 74, LQ = 64

(c)

Car Speeds

Miles per hour

(d) 50%   **(e)** 30%   **(f)** No, there are fewer speeds close to 67 in the 3rd quartile than in the 2nd quartile.

15. (a) 25   (b) 475   (c) 0.16

16. 475

17. $1.\overline{6}$

18. Answers vary

19. (a) Positive   (b) 170 lb   (c) 67 in.   (d) 64 in.   (e) 50 lb

20. (a) Answers vary. (b) They show very popular shows during the ratings sweeps. Answers vary.

21. Answers vary.

CHAPTER 10

Problem Set 10-1

1. (a) $\overleftrightarrow{AB}$ (b) $\overline{AB}$ (c) $\overrightarrow{AB}$ (d) $\overset{\circ\!\to}{AB}$ (e) $\overleftrightarrow{AB} \parallel \overleftrightarrow{CD}$
(f) $\overset{\circ\!-\!\circ}{AB}$ (g) $\overleftrightarrow{AB} \perp \overleftrightarrow{CD}$ (h) $m(\angle ABC) = 30°$

2. (a) {C} (b) ∅ (c) {C} (d) {C} (e) $\overline{CE}$ (f) $\overrightarrow{AB}$
(g) $\overrightarrow{AB}$ (h) $\overleftrightarrow{AD}$

3. No. The symbol is a finite collection of points.

4. (a) ∅ (b) ∠E−BD−A (c) {C} (d) {A} (e) {A}
(f) {A} (g) Answers vary (h) $\overleftrightarrow{AC}$ and $\overleftrightarrow{DE}$ or $\overleftrightarrow{AD}$ and $\overleftrightarrow{CE}$
(i) Plane BCD or Plane BEA

5. (a) True (b) True (c) False (d) False (e) True (f) True
(g) False (h) False (i) False (j) True (k) True (l) True

6. Answers vary

7. 20 pairs

8. Answers vary

9. (a) Yes; otherwise a point of intersection of the two lines would also be a point of intersection of the two parallel planes.
(b) No; an example may be seen in the drawing in problem 4
(c) Yes if the planes were not parallel they would intersect in a line m and at least one of the given lines would intersect m and would then intersect plane α, which contradicts the fact that the given lines are parallel to α.

10. (a) 110° (b) 40° (c) 20° (d) 130°

11. (a) Approximately 36° (b) Approximately 120°

12. (a) (i) 41°31'10" (ii) 79°48'47" (b) (i) 54'
(ii) 15°7'48"

13. (a) 4 (b) 6 (c) 8 (d) 2(n - 1)

14. (a) 3 (b) 6 (c) 10
(d) $1+2+3+\cdots+(n-1)=n(n-1)/2$

15. (a)

Number of Intersection Points

		0	1	2	3	4	5
Number of lines	2	⟷	✕	Not Possible	Not Possible	Not Possible	Not Possible
	3					Not Possible	Not Possible
	4			Not Possible			
	5			Not Possible	Not Possible		
	6			Not Possible	Not Possible	Not Possible	

(b) n(n-1)/2

16. Three points determine a single plane, and a plane determines a level surface. Four points may not all lie in a plane and hence may not determine a level surface.

17. (a) No; if ∠BCD were a right angle, then both $\overleftrightarrow{BD}$ and $\overleftrightarrow{BC}$ would be perpendicular to $\overleftrightarrow{DC}$ and thus be parallel.

(b) No; the angle formed by $\overrightarrow{PD}$ and $\overrightarrow{PC}$ must have measure less than a right angle. Otherwise, $\overrightarrow{DP}$ would be parallel to either $\overleftrightarrow{DC}$ or $\overleftrightarrow{PC}$. This is impossible (c) Yes; use the definition of perpendicular planes.

18. (a) Yes (b) Yes (c) Yes

19. Answers may vary.

20. (a) 3 (b) 4 (c) 4 (d) 6

21. b, d, e, and g

22. $\overrightarrow{AB}$ begins at point A and extends in the direction of point B. $\overrightarrow{BA}$ begins at point B and extends in the direction of point A.

23. (a) No, Skew lines do not intersect so they cannot be perpendicular. (b) No, if each angle is greater than 90°, the sum of the 2 angles will be greater than 180° (c) No, if each angle is less than 90°, the sum of the 2 angles will be less than 180°.

24. No, if the planes are not parallel, they will intersect.

25. For line segments in the same plane to be parallel, they must be on parallel lines.

26. Extending the rays does not change the angle measure.

27. From the Denseness Property, we know that for any two points we can always find a point between them. Since this is true for any two points we see that there are an infinite number of points in a segment.

28. No, if the 4 points are collinear there is 1 line, if 3 are collinear, there are 4 lines, and if no 3 are collinear, there are 6 lines.

29. Suppose $\alpha \parallel \beta$ and γ intersects α in $\overleftrightarrow{AB}$, and γ intersects β in $\overleftrightarrow{CD}$. If $\overleftrightarrow{AB} \cap \overleftrightarrow{CD}$ is point Q, then Q is a point of both plane α and plane β. This cannot happen so $\overleftrightarrow{AB} \parallel \overleftrightarrow{CD}$.

30. Answers may vary.
   (a) TO ANGLE :SIZE
       FD 100 BK 100
       RT :SIZE FD 100
       BK 100 LT :SIZE
   END
   (b) TO SEGMENT :LENGTH
       FD :LENGTH BK :LENGTH
   END
   (c) TO PERPENDICULAR :LENGTH1 :LENGTH2
       FD :LENGTH1 BK :LENGTH1/2
       RT 90 FD :LENGTH2
       BK :LENGTH2 LT 90
       BK :LENGTH1/2
   END
   (d) TO PARALLEL :LENGTH1 :LENGTH2
       DRAW
           FD :LENGTH1 PENUP
           RT 90 FD 10 RT 90
           PENDOWN FD :LENGTH2
           PENUP HOME
           RT 180 PENDOWN
   END
(In LCSI, replace DRAW with CLEARSCREEN).

Brain Teaser (p. 506)

Each segment is determined by 2 points. Consequently the number of segments is equal to the number of ways that we can choose 2 points out of a possible 25 points with no regard for order, that is, a combination of 25 things taken 2 at a time.

$_{25}C_2 = 25!/2!23! = 25 \times 24/2 = 300$

Therefore 300 segments can be drawn.
The problem can also be solved using patterns built up from simpler cases or considering the problem geometrically.

Problem Set 10-2

1. (a) 1, 2, 3, 6, 7, 8, 9, 11, 12   (b) 1, 2, 7, 8, 9, 11
(c) 1, 2, 3, 6, 7, 8, 9,11   (d) 1, 2, 7, 8, 9,11   (e) 7, 8
(f) 1,2,9,11
2. D and O
3. (a) Outside   (b) Outside
4. (a) Yes   (b) No (Jordan Curve Theorem)
5. 8 (nonconvex quadrilateral)
6. (a) and (c) are convex; (b) and (d) are concave.
7. Answers may vary.
8. (d) and (e) are impossible because the measure of each angle of an equilateral triangle has measure 60°.
9. (a) 35   (b) 170   (c) 4850
10. (a) Isosceles and equilateral   (b) Isosceles   (c) Scalene
11. (a) False. To be isosceles, the triangle may have only 2 congruent sides, not necessarily 3.   (b) True   (c) True
(d) True   (e) True   (f) False. To be a regular quadrilateral a rhombus would have to be a square. Not all rhombi are squares.
(g) True   (h) False. A scalene triangle has no two sides congruent.   (i) True   (j) True   (k) False. All squares are rectangles.   (l) False. Some trapezoids are parallelograms, because the set of parallelograms is a proper subset of the set of trapezoids.   (m) True   (n) False. An isosceles trapezoid that is a square is also a kite   (o) False. See (n).
12. A square is a particular kind of rectangle in which all sides have equal measure. All squares are rectangles.
13. To be regular, all sides must be congruent but also all angles must be congruent. All angles are not congruent unless the rhombus is a square.
14. (a) and (b) represent rhombuses and rectangles.
15. (a) T, Q, R, H, G, I, F, J   (b) Y, Z, E   (c) W, D, A, Z, U, E
(d) Q, J, F, G, H   (e) Y

16.

8	2-3-3	isosceles
9	3-3-3	equilateral
	2-3-4	scalene
	1-4-4	isosceles
10	2-4-4	isosceles
	3-3-4	isosceles
11	1-5-5	isosceles
	2-4-5	scalene
	3-3-5	isosceles
	4-4-3	isosceles
12	4-4-4	equilateral
	2-5-5	isosceles
	3-4-5	scalene

17. Answers may vary
18. (a) Answers may vary.
        TO SQUARE :SIDE
          REPEAT 4 [FD :SIDE RT 90]
        END
    (b) Answers may vary.
        TO RECTANGLE :WIDTH :LENGTH
          REPEAT 2 [FD :WIDTH RT 90 FD
            :LENGTH RT 90]
        END
19. (a) 45   (b) n(n - 1)/2
20. ∅, 1 point, 2 points, ray
21. (a) {C}   (b) $\overline{BD}$ (c) $\overline{AB}$, $\overline{AC}$, and $\overline{AD}$ (d) {D}

22. (a) False. A ray has only one endpoint.   (b) True
(c) False. Skew lines cannot be contained in the single plane.
(d) False $\overleftrightarrow{MN}$ has a endpoint M and extends in the direction of point N; $\overleftrightarrow{NM}$ has endpoint N and extends in the direction of point M.   (e) True   (f) False. Their intersection is a line.

Brain Teaser (p. 529)
No, the Jordan Curve Theorem can be used to verify this.

Problem Set 10-3

1. (a) ∠1 and ∠2 are adjacent angles; ∠3 and ∠4 are vertical angles.   (b) ∠1 and ∠2 are vertical angles; ∠3 and ∠4 are adjacent angles.   (c) ∠1 and ∠2 are neither vertical nor adjacent angles.   (d) ∠1 and ∠2 are adjacent angles.
2. Answers may vary.
3. Answers may vary.
4. 20
5. (a) 60°   (b) 45°   (c) 60°   (d) 60°
6. (a) Yes; a pair of corresponding angles are 50° each.
(b) Yes; a pair of corresponding angles are 70° each.
(c) Yes; a pair of alternate interior angles are 40° each.
(d) Yes: a pair of corresponding angles are 90° each.
7. (a) No. Two or more obtuse angles will produce a sum of more than 180°.   (b) Yes. For example, each angle may have measure 60°.   (c) No. The sum of the measures of the three angles would be more than 180°.   (d) No. It may have an obtuse or a right angle as well.
8. (a) 70°   (b) 70°   (c) 65°   (d) 45°
9. (a) x = 40° and y = 50°   (b) x=18°   (c) x = 50° and y = 60°
(d) x=83°
10. (a) 60°   (b) 90°
11. 70° and 20°
12. 60°
13. (a) 360°   (b) 360°   (c) 360°
14. If the two distinct lines are both perpendicular, then the measure of ∠B and ∠ C are both 90°. This would force the sum of the measures of the angles of ∆ABC to be greater than 180°. This is impossible.
15. (a) 20   (b) 150°
16. (a) $5 \cdot 180° - 360° = 540°$ (b) The sum of the measures of the angles in all n triangles is 180n degrees. Subtracting the measures of all nonoverlapping angles whose vertex is P, we obtain $180n - 360° = (n-2)180°$
17. (a) There are 5 - 2 triangles which can be drawn from any vertex of the pentagon. Hence, there are (5 - 2)180 degrees in the sum of the angle measures of the interior angles of any convex pentagon.   (b) There are n - 2 triangles which can be drawn from any vertex of the n-gon. Hence, there are (n - 2)180 degrees in the sum of the angle measures of the interior angles of any convex polygon.
18. (a) True   (b) False   (c) False   (d) True   (e) False
19. (a) Equal
(b) $m(\angle 4) = 180° - m(\angle 3)$ (Straight angle)
           $= 180° - [180° - m(\angle 1) - m(\angle 2)]$
           $= m(\angle 1) + m(\angle 2)$
20. 60, 84, 108, 132, 156
21. Vertical angles are formed by two intersecting lines. In this case angle 1 is formed by a line and a ray.
22. No, regular hexagons fit because the measure of each vertex angle is 120° and 3 hexagons fit to form 360° and the plane can be filled. For a regular pentagon, the measure of each vertex angle is 108° and so pentagons cannot be placed together to form 360° and the plane cannot be filled.

23. 90°

24. Yes, because the sum of the angles in a triangle must be 180°. Hence, the measure of the third angle in each triangle must be 180° minus the sum of the measures of the two angles.

25 They must be supplementary.

26. 111°

27. $m(\angle 1) = 60°$, $m(\angle 2) = 30°$, $m(\angle 3) = 110°$,

28. 135°

29. Theorem 10-1(a) Supplements to the same angle, or congruent angles, are congruent.

Proof: **(a)** Let both $\angle 2$ and $\angle 3$ be supplements of $\angle 1$.

$$m(\angle 2) + m(\angle 1) = 180°$$
$$m(\angle 3) + m(\angle 1) = 180°$$
$$m(\angle 2) + m(\angle 1) = m(\angle 3) + m(\angle 1)$$
$$m(\angle 2) = m(\angle 3)$$
$$\angle 2 \cong \angle 3$$

(b) Let $\angle 3$ be the supplement of $\angle 1$, and $\angle 4$ be supplemental $\angle 2$, and $\angle 1 \cong \angle 2$.

$$m(\angle 3) + m(\angle 1) = 180°$$
$$m(\angle 4) + m(\angle 2) = 180°$$
$$m(\angle 3) + m(\angle 1) = m(\angle 4) + m(\angle 2)$$
$$\angle 1 \cong \angle 2 \text{ implies } m(\angle 1) = m(\angle 2)$$
$$m(\angle 3) + m(\angle 2) = m(\angle 4) + m(\angle 2)$$
$$m(\angle 3) = m(\angle 4)$$
$$\angle 3 \cong \angle 4$$

Theorem 10-1(b) Complements of the same angle, or congruent angles, are congruent. Proof. Proof is similar to the above.

30. If two lines are perpendicular to the same line, then congruent corresponding angles of 90° each are formed and hence the lines are parallel.

31.

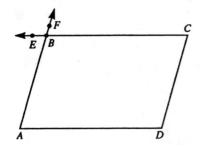

(a) $\qquad m(\angle A) = m(\angle FBC)$ (corresponding angles)

$m(\angle FBE) + m(\angle FBC) = 180°$ (supplementary angles)

$\qquad m(\angle FBE) = m(\angle ABC)$ (vertical angles)

Thus,

$\qquad m(\angle ABC) + m(\angle A) = 180°$ (substitution)

(b) $\qquad m(\angle A) = m(\angle ABE)$ (alternate interior angles)

$\qquad m(\angle ABE) = m(\angle C)$ (corresponding angles)

Hence,

$\qquad m(\angle A) = m(\angle C)$. Likewise $m(\angle B) = m(\angle D)$.

32. 83.5° or 83°30'

33. Answers may vary.

(a) TO PARALLELOGRAM :L :W :A
  REPEAT 2 [FD :L RT 180 - :A FD :W RT :A]
  END

(b) TO RECTANGLE :L :W
  PARALLELOGRAM :L :W 90
  END

(c) TO RHOMBUS :L :A
  PARALLELOGRAM :L :L :A
  END

(d) Execute PARALLELOGRAM 50 50 90.

(e) Execute RHOMBUS 50 90.

34. 6

35. No. The union of two rays will always extend infinitely in at least one direction

36. Answers may vary.

37. Answers may vary.

38. Sketches may vary, but the possibilities are the empty set, a single point, a segment, a quadrilateral, a triangle, a pentagon, and a hexagon. There are various types of quadrilaterals possible.

39. (a) A hexagon (b) A pentagon (c) Two intersecting segments or lines (d) A rectangle (e) A rhombus or square

40. (a) All angles must be right angles and all diagonals are the same length. (b) All sides are the same length and all angles are right angles. (c) Impossible because all squares are parallelograms.

Brain Teaser (p. 537)

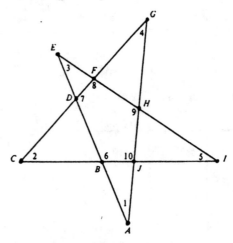

Denote the interior angles of the pentagon as show above. Summing the measures of the angles in the triangles AEH, CGJ, EIB, GAD, and ICF, respectively, we obtain:

$$m(\angle 1) + m(\angle 3) + m(\angle 9) = 180°$$
$$m(\angle 2) + m(\angle 4) + m(\angle 10) = 180°$$
$$m(\angle 3) + m(\angle 5) + m(\angle 6) = 180°$$
$$m(\angle 4) + m(\angle 1) + m(\angle 7) = 180°$$
$$m(\angle 5) + m(\angle 2) + m(\angle 8) = 180°$$

Thus $2[m(\angle 1) + m(\angle 2) + m(\angle 3) + m(\angle 4) + m(\angle 5)]$
$+ m(\angle 6) + m(\angle 7) + m(\angle 8) + m(\angle 9) + m(\angle 10)]$

$= 5 \cdot 180°$ Since $m(\angle 6) + m(\angle 7) + m(\angle 8) + m(\angle 9) + m(\angle 10)$
is the sum of the measures of the angles in a pentagon, this sum equals $(5 - 2) \ 180° = 3 \cdot 180°$. Hence,

$$2 \cdot [m(\angle 1) + m(\angle 2) + m(\angle 3) + m(\angle 4) + m(\angle 5)]$$
$$+ 3 \cdot 180° = 5 \cdot 180° \text{ and}$$
$$2 \cdot [m(\angle 1) + m(\angle 2) + m(\angle 3) + m(\angle 4) + m(\angle 5)] = 2 \cdot 180°.$$

Thus $m(\angle 1) + m(\angle 2) + m(\angle 3) + m(\angle 4) + m(\angle 5) = 180°$

The sum of the measures of the angles in any seven-pointed star is $3 \cdot 180° = 540°$. The sum of the measures of the angles in any n-pointed star (where n is odd) is $(n-4) \cdot 180°$.

Problem Set 10-4
1. (a) Quadrilateral pyramid   (b) Quadrilateral prism; possibly a trapezoidal prism   (c) Pentagonal pyramid
2. (a) A, D, R, W (b) $\overline{AR}$, $\overline{RD}$, $\overline{AD}$, $\overline{AW}$, $\overline{WR}$; $\overline{WD}$
   (c) $\triangle ARD$, $\triangle AWD$, $\triangle AWR$, $\triangle WDR$ (d) {R}
3. Answers vary.
4. (a) 5 (b) 4 (c) 4
5. (a) True (b) False (c) True (d) False (e) False
   (f) False (g) False (h) True
6. 3; Each pair of parallel faces could be considered as bases.
7. Answers vary.
8.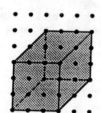

9. (a) Hexagonal pyramid   (b) Quadrilateral (square) pyramid
   (c) Cube (d) Rectangular prism   (e) Hexagonal prism
10. (a) iv (b) iii
11. (a) iv (b) ii
12. (a) i, ii, and iii   (b) ii, iii, iv

13.
Vertices per base	Diagonals per vertex	Total number of diagonals
4	1	4
5	2	10
6	3	18
7	4	28
8	5	40
.	.	.
.	.	.
.	.	.
n	(n - 3)	n(n - 3)

14. Both could be drawings of a quadrilateral pyramid. In part (a) we are directly above the pyramid and in part (b) we are directly below the pyramid.
15. All are possible.
16.

(a)

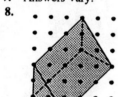
(b)

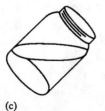
(c)

17. (a) (2) (b) (4)
18.

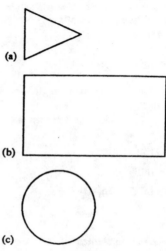
(a)

(b)

(c)

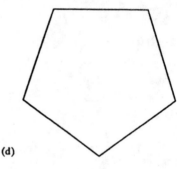
(d)

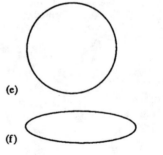
(e)

(f)

19. (a) $5 + 5 - 8 = 2$ (b) $8 + 6 - 12 = 2$ (c) $6 + 6 - 10 = 2$
20.
	Pyramid	Prism
(a)	n + 1	n + 2
(b)	n + 1	2n
(c)	2n	3n
(d)	(n + 1) + (n + 1) - 2n = 2	
	(n + 2) + 2n - 3n = 2	

21. (a) 6 (b) 48 (c) 11
22. (a) Yes (b) Yes
23. (a) A cone might be described as a many-side pyramid.
   (b) A cylinder might be described as a many-sided prism
22. (a) Yes, if the base is an n-gon, the number of edges is 3n. Thus, if 3n = 33, then n =11 and an 11-gon has exactly 33 edges.   (b) No, if the base of a pyramid is an n-gon, then the number of edges is 2n. Because 2n is even, the number of edges cannot be 33.
25. Parallelogram
26. $m(\angle BCD) = 60°$
27. 140°

28. (a) True (b) True (c) False; The triangle could be equilateral and have three acute angles.

29. (a) Right (b) The sum of the measures of the complementary angles is 90°; hence the measures of the third angle must be 90°, and the triangle is a right triangle.

Brain Teaser (p. 552)
Read Hoffer's article listed in Bibliography

Problem Set 10-5

1. (a), (b), (c), (e), (g), (h), and (j) are traversable.

(a)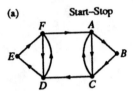

Path:
ABCACDEFDFA;
any point can be a
starting point.

(b)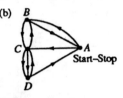

Path:
ABACBCDCDA;
any point can be a
starting point.

(c)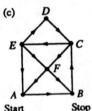

Start Stop

Path:
ABCFAEDCEFB;
only points *A* and *B*
can be starting points.

(e)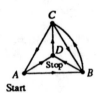

Start

Path:
ABCBDCAD;
only points *A* and *D*
can be starting points.

(g)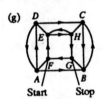

Start Stop

Path:
FADABCBGFEDCHEHG;
only points *F* and *G*
can be starting points.

(h)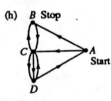

Path:
ACBCDCDAB;
only points *A* and *B*
can be starting points.

(j)

Path:
EFHKLNABDFGHLMNBCDE;
any point can be a
starting point.

2. All are possible if the starting and stopping points are not the same. If the traveling salesperson must start and return home, then it depends upon where home is.

3.

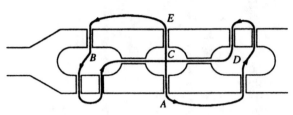

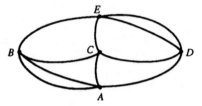

Path: *CEBABCADEDC*; any point can be a starting point.

4. (a)

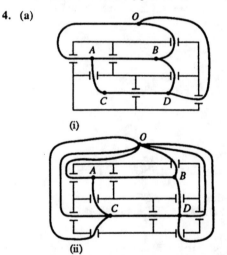

(i)

(ii)

(b) Network (i) is not traversable, since if has four odd vertices. Network (ii) has two odd vertices, so it is traversable, as shown.

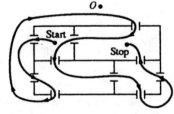

5. Yes. See figure.

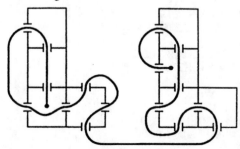

6. It is not possible.

7.

Network	R	V	A	R+V-A
(a)	6	6	10	2
(b)	6	4	8	2
(c)	6	6	10	2
(d)	4	4	6	2
(e)	5	4	7	2
(f)	8	8	14	2
(g)	9	8	15	2
(h)	6	4	8	2
(i)	7	7	12	2
(j)	8	12	18	2

8.

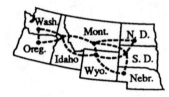

Since all vertices are even, the trip is possible. It makes no difference where she starts.

9. Answers vary, for example

10. The bridge could be built anywhere and we would have 2 odd vertices and thus the network is traversable.

*Problem Set 10-6

1. (a) TO RECTANGLE :LENGTH :WIDTH
   PARALLELOGRAM :LENGTH :WIDTH 90
   END
   (b) TO RHOMBUS :SIDE :ANGLE
   PARALLELOGRAM :SIDE :SIDE :ANGLE
   END

2. TO SQUARE :SIDE
   RHOMBUS :SIDE 90
   END

3. TO CUBE :SIDE
   REPEAT 3 [RHOMBUS :SIDE 60 RIGHT 120]
   END

4. (a) 60° (b) (360/7)° (c) 45° (d) 30°

5. Execute on the computer.

6. No; the methods of this section yield an equilateral triangle if a 6-pointed star is attempted.

7. Answers may vary.
   (a) TO HEXSTACK :SIDE
   REPEAT 3 [LEFT 30 HEXAGON :SIDE FD :SIDE RT
   60 FD :SIDE LT 60]
   END
   TO HEXAGON :SIDE
   REPEAT 6 [FD :SIDE RIGHT 60]
   END
   (b) TO HONEYCOMB :SIDE
   REPEAT 3 [HEXAGON :SIDE RT 120]
   END

8. Answers may vary
   TO THIRTY
   FD 100 BK 100 RT 30
   FD 100 BK 100 LT 30
   END

9. Answers may vary.
   (a) TO SEG
   RT 45 FD 50 BK 100
   FD 50 LT 45
   END
   (b) TO PAR
   PENUP FD 50 PENDOWN
   SEG
   END

10. It will draw a 30-gon that looks like a circle on the screen. It will have perimeter 120 units

11. Answers may vary.
   TO FILL.RECT :WID :LEN
   IF :WID < 0 STOP
   REPEAT 4 [FD :WID RT 90 FD :LEN RT 90]
   FILL.RECT :WID -1 :LEN -1
   HT
   END
(In LCSI , replace STOP with [STOP])

12. TO POLYGON :NUM :LEN
   REPEAT :NUM [FD :LEN RT 360/:NUM]
   END

13. Answers may vary.
   TO COUNT.ANGLES :NUMBER
   IF :NUMBER = 1 OUTPUT 0 STOP
   OUTPUT :NUMBER - 1 + COUNT.ANGLES
   :NUMBER -1
   END
(In LCSI replace IF :NUMBER = 1 OUTPUT 0 STOP with IF :NUMBER = 1 [OUTPUT 0 STOP].)

Chapter 10 Test

1. Answers may vary.

2. (a) $\overleftrightarrow{AB}$, $\overleftrightarrow{BC}$ and $\overleftrightarrow{AC}$ (b) $\overrightarrow{BA}$ and $\overrightarrow{BC}$ (c) $\overline{AB}$
(d) $\overrightarrow{AB}$ (e) $\overline{AB}$

3. (a) Answers may vary. (b) Planes APQ and BPQ
(c) $\overleftrightarrow{AQ}$ (d) No. $\overleftrightarrow{PQ}$ and $\overleftrightarrow{AB}$ are skew lines so that no single plane contains them.

4. Answers may vary.

5. Answers may vary.

6. (a) No. The sum of the measures of two obtuse angles is greater than 180°, which is the sum of the measures of the angles of any triangle. (b) No. The sum of the measures of the four angles in a parallelogram must be 360°. If all the angles are acute, the sum would be less than 360°.

7. 18°, 36°, 126°.

8. (a) Given any convex n-gon, pick any vertex and draw all possible diagonals from this vertex. This will determine n - 2 triangles. Because the sum of the measures of the angles in each triangle is 180°, the sum of the measures of the angles in the n-gon is (n - 2)180°. (b) 90 sides

9. (a) Answers may vary. (b) Euler's formula holds.

10. Answers may vary.

11. Answers may vary, but the possibilities are a point, a segment, a triangle, a quadrilateral, or an empty set.

12. 6

13. 35°8'35"

14. (a) 60° (b) 120° (c) 120°

15. 8

16. 48°

17. **(a)** (i), (ii), and (iv) are traversable.
(b)

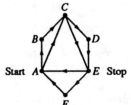

(i)

Path:
ABCDEFACEA;
any point can be usd
as a starting point.

(ii)

Path:
ABCDAEDBE;
points *A* and *E* are
possible starting points.

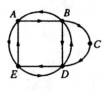

(iv)

Path:
BDEABAEDBCD;
points *B* and *D* are
possible starting points.

18. Answers may vary.
TO PERPENDICULAR :SEG1 :SEG2
FD :SEG1 RT 90
FD :SEG2
END

19. Answers may vary.
TO ISOS :LEG :ANGLE
HOME FD :LEG
RT 180 - :ANGLE
FD :LEG
HOME
END

CHAPTER 11

Problem Set 11-1

1. **(a)** BC > AC **(b)** m($\angle$A) > m($\angle$B) **(c)** The side of greater
length is opposite the angle of greater measure.
2. **(a)** Right **(b)** No triangle is possible.
3. **(b)** The triangle is unique by SSS. **(c)** The triangle
is unique by SSS. **(d)** There is no triangle because of the
Triangle Inequality **(e)** The triangle is unique by SSS.
(f) The triangle is unique by SAS. **(g)** The triangle is not
unique. **(h)** The triangle is unique by SAS. **(i)** The triangle
is unique by SAS.
4. 22 triangles
5. **(a)** Yes; SAS **(b)** Yes; SSS **(c)** No
6. The purpose of the diagonals is to form congruent
triangles. Triangles are rigid structures and hence make the gate
stronger. They also prevent the cows from squeezing through.
7. The lengths of the wires must be the same because they are
congruent parts of the congruent triangles formed.
8. Such a construction tells us that $\triangle$BDC $\cong$ $\triangle$BAC by SAS.
Therefore, DB = AB. By measuring DB, we know AB.
9.-10. Constructions

11. **(a)** $\triangle$ABC $\cong$ $\triangle$ABC $\triangle$ABC $\cong$ $\triangle$ACB
    $\triangle$ABC $\cong$ $\triangle$BAC $\triangle$ABC $\cong$ $\triangle$BCA
    $\triangle$ABC $\cong$ $\triangle$CAB $\triangle$ABC $\cong$ $\triangle$CBA
(b) Because $\triangle$ABC $\cong$ $\triangle$BCA , $\angle$A $\cong$ $\angle$B and $\angle$B $\cong$ $\angle$C.
Hence $\angle$A $\cong$ $\angle$B $\cong$ $\angle$C.
12. **(a)** $\overline{AD} \cong \overline{CD}$ **(b)** $\angle$ABD $\cong$ $\angle$CBD by definition of
angle bisector. $\overline{AB} \cong \overline{CB}$ is given. $\overline{BD} \cong \overline{BD}$. So
$\triangle$ABD $\cong$ $\triangle$CBD by SAS. Hence, $\overline{AD} \cong \overline{CD}$ by CPCTC. **(c)** 90°
(d) $\angle$ADB and $\angle$CDB are congruent by CPCTC (using part
(b)); $\angle$ADB and $\angle$CDB are congruent supplementary angles,
and therefore each must have a measure of 90°.
13. Right angles and obtuse angles.
14. **(a)** F is the midpoint of both diagonals. **(b)** We can
show $\triangle$ABD $\cong$ $\triangle$CBD by SSS and then $\angle$BDC $\cong$ $\angle$BDA by
CPCTC. $\triangle$AFD $\cong$ $\triangle$CFD by SAS, so $\overline{AF} \cong \overline{FC}$, thus F is the
midpoint of $\overline{AC}$. A similar argument will show $\overline{BF} \cong \overline{FD}$.
(c) 90° **(d)** From part (b), $\angle$AFD $\cong$ $\angle$CFD by CPCTC, but
are also supplementary. Hence, m($\angle$AFD) = 90°. A similar
argument is used for $\angle$BFA and $\angle$BFC.
15. **(a)** A parallelogram. **(b)** Let ABCD be the quadrilateral,
with E the intersection point of its diagonals. Show that
$\triangle$AED $\cong$ $\triangle$CEB and that $\triangle$BEA $\cong$ $\triangle$DEC. Use congruent
alternate interior angles to show $\overline{BC} \parallel \overline{AD}$ and $\overline{AB} \parallel \overline{CD}$.
16. **(a)** The angles formed by the diagonals of a rhombus are
right angles. **(b)** First show that $\triangle$ABO $\cong$ $\triangle$CDO and conclude
that $\overline{AO} \cong \overline{OC}$. Then show that $\triangle$ABO $\cong$ $\triangle$CBO by SSS. Hence,
conclude that $\angle$AOB $\cong$ $\angle$COB and consequently that each angle
is a right angle.
17. **(a)** A parallelogram. **(b)** Let $\overline{AB} \cong \overline{CD}$ and $\overline{BC} \cong \overline{AD}$.
Prove that $\triangle$ABC $\cong$ $\triangle$CDA and conclude that $\overline{BC} \parallel \overline{AD}$.
Similarly show $\triangle$ABD $\cong$ $\triangle$DCB and conclude that $\overline{AB} \cong \overline{DC}$.
18. By the definition of an isosceles triangle, $\overline{AB} \cong \overline{AC}$.
Since congruence is an equivalence relation, we have the
symmetric statement $\overline{AC} \cong \overline{AB}$. Also $\overline{BC} \cong \overline{CB}$. Hence by SSS,
$\triangle$BAC $\cong$ $\triangle$CAB and by CPCTC, $\angle$BAC $\cong$ $\angle$CAB.
19. Answers may vary.
TO EQUITRI :SIDE
REPEAT 3 [FD :SIDE RT 120]
END
20. Execute the procedure.
21. They produce basically the same result.
22. **(a)** A triangle is constructed because the computer does
not know the difference in an angle measure and a compass
heading. **(b)** In reality, no because no triangle has one angle
with measure 190°. **(c)** Add the following:
IF NOT (:ANGLE < 180) PRINT [NO TRIANGLE IS POSSIBLE.]
STOP
(In LSCI Logo use the following line:
IF NOT (:ANGLE < 180) [PRINT [NO TRIANGLE IS POSSIBLE.]
STOP].)

Problem Set 11-2

1. **(d)** Infinitely many triangles are possible.
2. **(a)** No; by ASA, the triangle is unique. **(b)** No, by AAS,
the triangle is unique. **(c)** No: by ASA. the triangle is unique.
(d) Yes; AAA does not determine a unique triangle.
3. **(a)** Yes; ASA **(b)** Yes; AAS **(c)** No, SSA does not assure
congruence. **(d)** No, AAA does not assure congruence.
4. When the parallel ruler is open at any setting. the distance
BD = DB. It is given that AB = DC and AD = BC. So

△ABD ≅ △CDB by SSS. Hence ∠ABD ≅ ∠CDB by CPCTC. ∠ABD and ∠CDB are alternate interior angles formed by $\overleftrightarrow{AB}$ and $\overleftrightarrow{DC}$ with transversal $\overleftrightarrow{BD}$, so $\overline{AB} \parallel \overline{DC}$.

5. One way is to make both legs of the ironing board the same length and fasten them together with a hinge at their centers. If one of these legs is attached to the board at a fixed spot and the other leg can be attached at various spots then the height of the ironing board can be adjusted. Since the legs form the diagonals of rectangle, the board will always be parallel to the floor. (It can be shown that a quadrilateral whose diagonals are the same length and bisect each other is a rectangle.) In most comercially available ironing boards the legs are designed to form diagonals of a trapezoid. The fact that the surface is always parallel to the floor follows from properties of similar triantgles discussed in section 11-5.

6. (a) Parallelogram (b) None (c) None (d) Rectangle (e) Rhombus (f) Square (g) Parallelogram

7. (a) True (b) True (c) True (d) True (e) True (f) False; A countererexample can be seen in a trapezoid in which two consecutive angles are right angles but the other two are not. (g) True (h) False; A square is both a rectangle and a rhombus. (i) False; A square can be a trapezoid. (j) True

8. (a) Answers may vary, (b) If a quadrilateral has three right angles, then the fourth must also be a right angle. (c) No: any parallelogram with a pair of right angles must have right angles as its other pair of angles and hence be a rectangle.

9. There are five possibilities: one parallelogram and four kites.

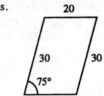

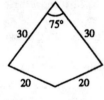

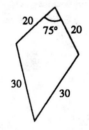

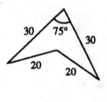

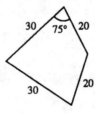

10. The triangle formed bv Stan's head, Stan's feet, and the opposite bank is congruent to the triangle formed by Stan's head, Stan's feet, and the spot just obscured by the bill of his cap. These triangles are congruent by ASA since the angle at Stan's feet is 90° in both triangles, Stan's height is the same in both triangles, and the angle formed by the bill of his cap is the same in both triangles. The distance across the river is approximately equal to the distance he paced off since these distances are corresponding parts of congruent triangles.

11. (a) $\overline{OP} \cong \overline{OQ}$ (b) ∠PDO ≅ ∠BQO; alternate interior angles formed by the transversal $\overleftrightarrow{DB}$ and parallel lines $\overleftrightarrow{DC}$ and $\overleftrightarrow{AB}$. ∠DPO ≅ ∠BQO because $\overleftrightarrow{PQ}$ is a transversal of $\overleftrightarrow{CD}$ and $\overleftrightarrow{AB}$. $\overline{DO} \cong \overline{BO}$; diagonals of a parallelogram bisect each other. △POD ≅ △QOB by AAS. $\overline{PO} \cong \overline{QO}$ by CPCTC.

12. (a) △ABC ≅ △ADC by SSS. Hence ∠BAC ≅ ∠DAC and ∠BCM ≅ ∠DCM by CPCTC. Therefore. $\overleftrightarrow{AC}$ bisects ∠A and ∠C. (b) The angles formed are right angles. By part (a), ∠BAM ≅ ∠DAM. Hence △ABM ≅ △ADM by SAS. ∠BMA ≅ ∠DMA by CPCTC. Since ∠BMA and ∠DMA are adjacent congruent angles, each must be a right angle. Since vertical angles formed are congruent, all four angles formed by the diagonals are right angles. (c) By part (b), $\overline{BM} \cong \overline{MD}$; CPCTC.

13. (a) The sides opposite congruent angles in an isosceles trapezoid are congruent. (b) The diagonals are congruent. (c) In isosceles trapezoid ABCD, draw $\overline{BX}$ and $\overline{CY}$ perpendicular to $\overline{AD}$.

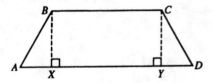

BCYX is a rectangle. (Why?) $\overline{BX} \cong \overline{CY}$; opposite sides of a rectangle are congruent.

△BAX ≅ △CDY; AAS. Thus $\overline{AB} \cong \overline{DC}$; CPCTC.

DABD ≅ DDCA; SAS. Thus $\overline{AC} \cong \overline{DB}$; CPCTC.

14. Construction. Answers may vary.

15. (a) Rhombus (b) Use SAS to prove that △ECF ≅ △GBF ≅ △EDH ≅ △GAH. (c) Parallelogram. (d) Suppose ADCB in part (a) is a parallelogram. Use SAS to show that △EDH ≅ △GBF and conclude that $\overline{EH} \cong \overline{GF}$. Similarly, show that △ECF ≅ △GAH and hence that $\overline{EF} \cong \overline{GH}$. Next use SSS to prove that △EFG ≅ △GHE. Now conclude that ∠GEH ≅ ∠EGF and consequently that $\overline{FG} \parallel \overline{EH}$. Similarlly, show that $\overline{EF} \parallel \overline{HG}$. (e) Parallelogram.

16. (a) The lengths of one side of each square must be equal. (b) The lengths of the sides of two perpendicular sides of the rectangles. (c) Answers vary. One solution is the lengths of two adjacent sides of the parallelograms and the angles between them.

17. (a) Use the definition of a parallelogram and ASA to prove that △ADB ≅ △CDB and △ADC ≅ △CBA. (b) Use a pair of triangles from (a). (c) Prove that △ABF ≅ △CDF (d) Extend $\overline{AB}$ and look for corresponding angles.

18. (b) (i) Two intersecting line segments (ii) Three segments that do not close into a triangle. (c) Add the following line:
IF NOT (ALLOF (:ANGLE1 + :ANGLE2 < 180) (:ANGLE1 > 0) (:ANGLE 2 > 0)) PRINT [NO TRIANGLE IS POSSIBLE.] STOP (In LSCI, use the following line:
IF NOT (AND (:ANGLE1 + :ANGLE2< 180) (:ANGLE1 > 0) (:ANGLE2 > 0)) [PRINT [NO TRIANGLE 1S POSSIBLE.] STOP])

19. (a) Answers may vary.
TO RHOMBUS :SIDE :ANGLE
REPEAT 2 [FD :SIDE RT (180 - :ANGLE) FD :SIDE
RT :ANGLE]
END
(b) They are congruent.
(c) TO SQ.RHOM :SIDE
RHOMBUS :SIDE 90
END
20. Answers may vary.
TO ISOSTRI :SIDE :ANGLE
HOME FD :SIDE
RIGHT (2* :ANGLE)
FD :SIDE RIGHT :ANGLE
HOME
21-22. Constructions
23. (a) Yes: SAS   (b) Yes: SSS   (c) No

Problem Set 11-3

1-4. Constructions
5.   Given $\angle BAC$, put one strip of tape so that an edge of the tape is along $\overrightarrow{AB}$ and another strip of the tape so that one of its edges is on $\overrightarrow{AC}$ as shown. Two edges of the strips of tape intersect in the interior of the angle at D. Connect A with D, $\overrightarrow{AD}$ is the angle bisector. Because the diagonals of a rhombus bisect its angles, this construction can be justified by showning that AEDF is a rhombus. (E and F are the points of intersection of the tops of the tape pieces and the opposite sides.) AEDF is a parallelogram (Why?). It remains to be shown that $\overline{AF} \cong \overline{AE}$. For that purpose, we show that $\Delta FAG \cong \Delta EAH$. We have $\overline{FG} \cong \overline{HE}$ because the two strips of tape have the same width, $\angle A \cong \angle A$, and the angles at H and G are right angles. Thus the triangles are congruent by AAS.

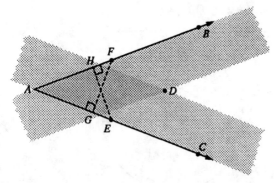

6. (d) The lines containing the allitudes meet at a point inside the triangle.   (e) The lines containing the altitudes meet at the vertex of the right angle.   (f) The lines containing the altitudes meet outside the triangle.
7. (a) The perpendicular bisectors meet at a point inside the triangle.   (b) The perpendicular bisectors meet at the midpoint of the hypotenuse of the right triangle.   (c) The perpendicular bisectors meet at a point outside the triangle.
8. (a) The perpendicular bisector of a chord of a circle contains the center of the circle.   (b) Choose an arbitrary chord $\overline{AB}$ on the circle with center 0. Then $\overline{OA} \cong \overline{OB}$ since both are radii. Construct the angle bisector of $\angle AOB$ and let P be the point of intersection with chord $\overline{AB}$. Then $\Delta AOP \cong \Delta BOP$ by SAS, and $\angle OPB$ is a right angle since it is both congruent and supplemenlary to $\angle OPA$. Since $\overline{AP} \cong \overline{PB}$ and $\angle OPB$ is a right angle, $\overline{OP}$ is the perpendicular bisector of

$\overline{AB}$, and therefore the perpendicular bisector of an arbitrary chord contains point O.   (c) Hint: Construct two non-parallel chords and find their perpendicular bisectors. The intersection of the perpendicular bisectors is the center of the circle.
9-10.   Constructions
11.   Answers may vary. One possibility is: Draw a line segment. (10¢)
Draw two intersecting arcs (20¢) to construct a perpendicular segment. (10¢)
With compass point at the intersection of the two segments, sweep a wide arc (10¢) intersecting both segments.
Maintain the same compass setting and measure an arc from each of these points to determine the fourth point. (20¢)
Draw the two segments to complete the square. (20¢)
The sum is 90¢.
12.   Construction

13.   (a) $\overrightarrow{PQ}$ is the perpendicular bisector of $\overline{AB}$.   (b) Q is on the perpendicular bisector of $\overline{AB}$ because $\overline{AQ} \cong \overline{QB}$. Similarly, P is on the perpendicular bisector of $\overline{AB}$. Because a unique line contains two points, the perpendicular bisector contains $\overrightarrow{PQ}$.

(c) $\overrightarrow{PQ}$ is the angle bisector of $\angle APB$; $\overrightarrow{QC}$ is the angle bisector of $\angle AQB$.   (d) Show that $\Delta APQ \cong \Delta BPQ$ by SSS; then $\angle APQ \cong \angle BPQ$ by CPCTC. Show that $\Delta AQC \cong \Delta BQC$ and conclude that, $\angle AQC \cong \angle BQC$.
14.   (b) Construct two perpendicular segments bisecting each other and congruent to the given diagonal.   (c) There is no unique rectangle. The endpoints of two segments bisecting each other and congruent to the given diagonal determine a rectangle. Since the segments may intersect at any angle, there are infinitely many such rectangles.   (d) Without the angle between the sides being given, there is no unique prarallelogram.   (e) Construct two perpendicular segments bisecting each other and congruent to the given diagonals.   (f) This is impossible because the sum of the measures of the angles would be greater than 180°.   (g) This is impossible because the fourth angle must be a right angle also.   (h) The kite would not be unique without knowing lengths of some sides.   (i) The kite would not be unique but would he a square.   (j) Consider ΔABC and the angle bisector $\overline{CD}$. Since $\overline{AC} \cong \overline{BC}$, then $\overline{CD} \perp \overline{AB}$. It is possible to construct ΔADC, since $\overline{AD}$ is half as long as the base and $m(\angle DAC) = 90° - 1/2 m(\angle ACB)$.

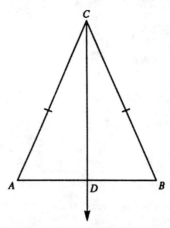

(k) There is no unique trapezoid unless two sides are designated as parallel; if this is the case, consider the trapezoid ABCD.

Through B, construct $\overline{BE} \parallel \overline{CD}$. It follows that $\overline{BE} \cong \overline{CD}$ (Why?) Also, AE = AD - ED = AD - BC. Hence, $\triangle ABE$ can be constructed by SSS. Now extend $\overline{AE}$ so that $\overline{ED} \cong \overline{BC}$ and through B draw $\overline{BC}$ parallel to $\overline{AE}$. The construction is not always possible. If the four given sides are such that $\triangle ABE$ cannot be constructed, the trapezoid cannot be constructed either.

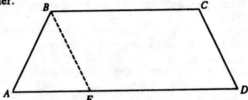

15-16. Constructions

17. (a) Since the triangles are congruent, the acute angles formed by the hypotenuse and the line are congruent. Since the corresponding angles are congruent, the hypotenuses are parallel (the line formed by the top of the ruler is the transversal). (b) Construction.

18. Make the edge of the ruler coincide with ℓ. Let one of the legs of the right triangle slide along the edge of the ruler until the other leg goes through P. The line along the edge containing P is the required perpendicular.

19. Let ℓ be the given line and P a point on ℓ. Through P draw any line k intersecting ℓ. That line forms $\angle 1$ with ℓ as shown. Construct $\angle 2$ congruent to $\angle 1$ so that the two angles are alternate interior angles. Line m (which contains a side of $\angle 2$) is parallel to ℓ.

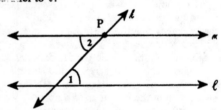

20. Answers may vary.
```
TO ALTITUDES
   REPEAT 3 [RT 30 FD 60 RT 90 FD 110 BK 130 FD 20 LT
      90 FD 60 RT 90]
END
```

21. Answers may vary.
(a)
```
TO ANGBIS :MEAS
   REPEAT 3 [FD 75 BK 75 RT :MEAS/2]
END
```
(b)
```
TO PERBIS :SIZE
   FD :SIZE/2 RT 90 FD :SIZE BK
   :SIZE/2 FD :SIZE RT 90 FD
   :SIZE/2
END
```
(c)
```
TO PARALLEL :SEG1 :SEG2
   FD :SEG1 PENUP RT 90
   FD 20 RT 90 PENDOWN
   FD :SEG2
END
```

22. $\triangle ABC \cong \triangle DEC$ by ASA. ($\overline{BC} \cong \overline{CE}$, $\angle ACB \cong \angle ECD$ as vertical angles, and $\angle C \cong \angle E$ as alternate interior angles formed by the parallels $\overline{AB}$ and $\overline{ED}$ and the transversal $\overleftrightarrow{EB}$.) $\overline{AC} \cong \overline{DC}$ by CPCTC.

23. Construction

24. (a) No (b) $\triangle LYC \cong \triangle UCY$ by SAS. $\overline{LY} \cong \overline{UC}$ is given; $\overline{YC} \cong \overline{CY}$. To show $\angle LYC \cong \angle UCY$, construct $\overline{UV} \parallel \overline{LY}$. Now LUVY is a parallelogram; $\overline{UV} \cong \overline{LY}$ and, by transitivity, $\overline{UV} \cong \overline{UC}$. $\angle LYC \cong \angle UVC$ (corresponding angles formed by $\overline{LY} \parallel \overline{UV}$ and transversal $\overleftrightarrow{YC}$). $\angle UVC \cong \angle UCV$ (base angles of isosceles triangle UVC). $\angle LYC \cong \angle UCY$ by transitive property. (2) $\triangle ULY \cong \triangle LUC$ by SAS. $\overline{LY} \cong \overline{UC}$ is given; $\overline{UL} \cong \overline{LU}$. To show $\triangle ULY \cong \triangle LUC$; use supplementary pairs of angles $\angle ULY$ & $\angle LYC$, $\angle LUC$ & $\angle UCY$ and $\angle LYC$ & $\angle UCY$ from part (1). (3) $\triangle LOY \cong \triangle UOC$ by SAS. $\overline{LY} \cong \overline{UC}$ is given. $\angle YLC \cong \angle CUY$ by CPCTC from part (1). $\angle LYU \cong \angle UCL$ by CPCTC from part (2).

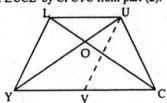

Problem Set 11-4

1. Consruction
2. No; the tangent line will intersect one circle in two points.
3. (a) 90° (b) 90° (c) 90° (d) An angle whose vertex is on a circle and whose sides intersect the circle in two points (determining a diameter) is a right angle. (e) In the drawing below, $\triangle AOC$ and $\triangle BOC$ are isosceles. (Why?) $\angle OAC \cong \angle OCA$ and $\angle OCB \cong \angle OBC$; base angles of an isosceles triangle are congruent.

Therefore, $m(\angle OAC) + m(\angle OCA) + m(\angle OCB) + m(\angle OBC)$
$= 2m(\angle OAC) + 2m(\angle OBC) = 180°$. Thus,
$m(\angle OAC) + m(\angle OBC) = 90°$. Hence $m(\angle ACB) = 90°$.

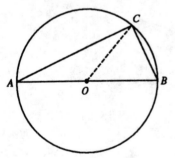

4. Construction
5. Hint: First inscribe a square in the given circle.
6. (c) Opposite angles are supplementary.
7. The center of the circle is at the intersection point of the diagonals.
8. No; it is only possible if the sides are equidistant from some point.
9. Hint. Draw a perpendicular from O to ℓ to obtain the radius of the circle.
10. Hint: Bisect the interior angles on the same side of the transversal. The center of the circle is the point of intersection of the angle bisectors.
11. (a) Isosceles (b) $m(\angle 1) + m(\angle 2) = m(\angle 3)$
(c) $m(\angle 1) = 1/2 m(\angle 3)$ (d) $\alpha = \frac{1}{2}\beta$

(e) $m(\angle 1) = m(\angle 2) = m(\angle 3)$

12. (a) 0, 1, or 2 depending on how the line is chosen.
(b) 0, 1, or infinitely many depending on how the plane is chosen.

13. (a) 270° **(b)** 180°

14. Given that $\overline{AB} \cong \overline{CD}$ (see the figure), prove that $\overline{OM} \cong \overline{ON}$. First prove that $\overline{AM} \cong \overline{MB}$ and $\overline{CN} \cong \overline{ND}$. Then show that $\triangle AOB \cong \triangle COD$. Hence conclude that $\angle A \cong \angle C$. Now prove that $\triangle AMO \cong \triangle CNO$ (by SAS). Consequently $\overline{OM} \cong \overline{ON}$.

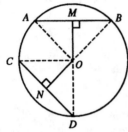

15. The radius r of the circle is half the distance between the parallel lines. The center of the circle is on line n parallel to the given lines and equidistant from these lines. The center of the required circle can be obtained by finding the point of intersection of line n with the circle whose center is at P and whose radius r.

16. Answers may vary. Newer versions of Logo have a FILL primitive.

    TO FILL.CIRCLE :RADIUS
      REPEAT 360 [FD :RADIUS BK :RADIUS RT 1]
    END

17. Answers may vary.
    TO DIAMETER
      REPEAT 360 [FD 1 RT 1]
      RT 90 FD 100
    END

18. $\overline{AB}$

19. $\angle ABC$

20. If $\angle A$ is not the right angle the triangles are congruent. If $\angle A$ is the right angle, the triangles are not necesarily congruent.

21. Yes; Use vertical angles to justify this result.

Brain Teaser (p. 611)

The following are two different size triangles with the given data. The triangles are similar but not congruent. (The ratio of the corresponding sides is $\frac{80}{100}$ or $\frac{4}{5}$.) Hence, the surveyor and the architect could both have been correct in their conclusions. One way for them to avoid their confusion is to specify which sides are opposite which angles.

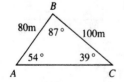 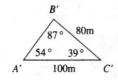

Problem Set 11-5

1. (a) Yes; AAA **(b)** Yes; sides are proportional and angles are congruent. **(c)** No **(d)** No **(e)** Yes; radii are proportional. **(f)** No **(g)** Yes; sides are proportional and angles are congruent.

2. This illustration is one possibility.

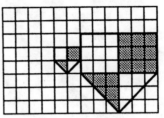

(a)

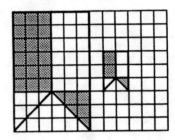

(b)

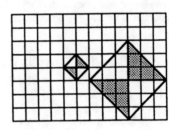

(c)

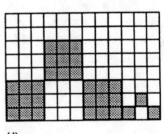

(d)

3. Yes; The scale factor is 1 and the angles are congruent.

4. (c) The triangles are similar if the corresponding sides are proportional.

5. (c) The triangles are similar if for example, if $\triangle ABC$ and $\triangle DEF$, we have AB/DE = AC/DF and $\angle A \cong \angle D$.

6. Answers may vary. **(a)** Two rectangles, one of which is a square and the other is not. **(b)** Two rhombuses, one of which is a square and the other is not but the sides are all the same length.

7. The ratio of the perimeters is the same as the ratio of the sides.

8. (a) (i) $\triangle ABC \sim \triangle DEF$ by AA **(ii)** $\triangle ABC \sim \triangle EDA$ by AA **(iii)** $\triangle ACD \sim \triangle ABE$ by AA **(iv)** $\triangle ABE \sim \triangle DBC$ by AA
(b) (i) 2/3 **(ii)** 1/2 **(iii)** 3/4 **(iv)** 3/4

9. (a) 7 **(b)** 24/7 **(c)** 3 **(d)** 96/13 m

10. Construction

11. Lay the licorice diagonally on the paper so it spans a number of spaces equal to the number of children. (See the figure.) Cut on the lines. Equidistant parallel lines will divide any transversal into congruent segments.

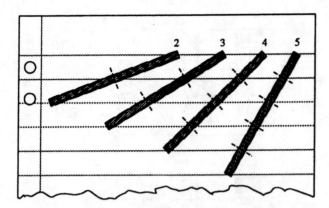

12. **(a)** (1) ΔABC ~ ΔACD by AA since ∠ADC and
∠ACB are right angles, and ∠A is common to both.
(2) ΔABC ~ ΔCBD by AA since ∠CDB and ∠ACB are
right angles and ∠B is common to both. (3) Using (1) and
(2), ΔACD ~ ΔCBD by the transitive property.
(b) (1) AC/AB = CD/CB = AD/AC (2) CB/AB = CD/AC =
DB/CB (3) AC/CB. = AD/CD = CD/DB

13. No; The maps are similar and even though the scales may
change, the actual distances do not.

14. 15 m

15. 900 cm

16. **(a)** In ΔABC let AB = BC and let $\overline{BD}$ be the angle
bisector of ∠B. Then $\overline{BD} \perp \overline{AC}$ (why?) and we have
$\alpha + \beta = 90°$. $\alpha = \beta$. Hence $\alpha = 45°$ and $2\beta = 90°$.
Consequently, the angles of the triangle are 45°, 45°, 90°. Next
suppose the angle bisector is the bisector of one of the base
angles. If the measure of each of the base angles is 2α then
ΔAEC is isosceles if and only if m(∠AEC) = 2α. Then in
ΔADC: $\alpha + 2\alpha + 2\alpha = 180°$ or $5\alpha = 180°$ Hence
$\alpha = 36°$ and $2\alpha = 72°$. Now m(∠B) = $180° - 2 \cdot 72° = 36°$. Hence
the angles of ΔADC are 72°, 72°, and 36°.

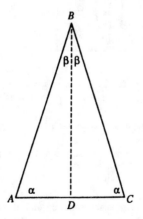

(b) In the first triangle, the angle bisector of the right angle
partitions the original triangle into two congruent isosceles
right triangles with base angles of 45°. The new triangles are
similar to the original triangle. In the second triangle, the
angle bisector of one of the 72° base angles partitions the
original triangle into two isosceles triangles which are neither
congruent nor similar to each other. One of the new triangles,
however, is similar to the original triangle.

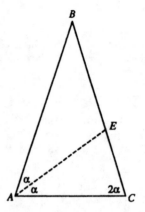

17. 232.62 inches or 19.38 feet

18. Place the projector so that the slide is 23 feet 9 inches
from the screen.

19. CF = 13 m, AE = 12 m.
Construct $\overline{BP}$ perpendicular to $\overline{CF}$ as shown. ΔCBP ≅ ΔDFE
by AAS because $\overline{BC} \cong \overline{FD}$ (opposite sides in a rectangle),
∠DEF ≅ ∠CPB (right angles), and from ∠FDE ≅ ∠CFD
(alternate interior angles between the parallels $\overleftrightarrow{CF}$ and $\overleftrightarrow{DE}$ and
the transversal $\overleftrightarrow{DF}$) and ∠CFD ≅ ∠BCP (alternate interior
angles between the parallels $\overleftrightarrow{FD} \parallel \overleftrightarrow{BC}$ and the transversal $\overleftrightarrow{CF}$)
it follows that ∠PDE ≅ ∠BCP. By CPCTC, $\overline{CP} \cong \overline{DE}$ and hence
CP = DE= 4 m. We have CF = PF + CP. Because ABPF is a
rectangle, PF = BA = 9 m, and hence CF = 9 + 4 =13 m. Now
$\overline{AF} \cong \overline{BP}$ (ABPF is a rectangle), $\overline{FE} \cong \overline{BP}$ (CPCTC in ΔCBP
and ΔDFE). Consequently $\overline{AF} \cong \overline{FE}$. Next show that
ΔABF ~ ΔEFD (by AA since ∠AFB and ∠FDE are
complements of ∠DFE and each triangle has a right angle.)
Consequently AB/EF = AF/ED or 9/EF = AF/4 or EF·AF = 36.
Because $\overline{EF} \cong \overline{AF}$, we have (EF)² = 36 or EF = 6. Because
AE = 2EF, AE = 12 m.

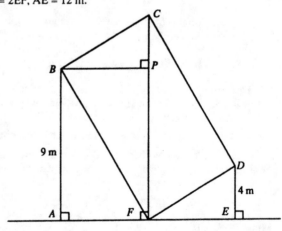

20. Answers may vary.
(a) TO RECTANGLE :LEN :WID
　　REPEAT 2 [FD :LEN RT 90 FD :WID RT 90]
　　END
　　TO SIM.RECT :LEN :WID
　　　RECTANGLE :LEN*2 :WID*2
　　END
(b) TO SIM.RECTANGLE :LEN :WID :SCALE
　　　RECTANGLE :LEN* :SCALE :WID* :SCALE
　　END

(c) TO PARALLELOGRAM :LEN :WID :ANGLE
   REPEAT 2 [FD :LEN RT 180– :ANGLE FD :WID RT
    :ANGLE]
   END
   TO SIM.PAR :LEN :WID :ANGLE :SCALE
   PARALLELOGRAM :LEN* :SCALE :WID* :SCALE
    :ANGLE
   END

21. Answers may vary.

(a) TO TRISECT :LEN
   REPEAT 3 [MARK FD :LEN/3]
   END
   TO MARK
   RT 90 FD 5
   BK 5 LT 90
   END

(b)   TO PARTITION :LEN :NUM
   REPEAT :NUM [MARK FD :LEN/:NUM]
   END

22. No; the image is two-dimensional while the original person is three-dimensional.

23. Construction

Brain Teaser (p. 615)
10 cm

Problem Set 11-6
Answers for the entire section may vary. Procedures are written only as possible answers.

1. TO SIMSQ :SIDE :K
   SQUARE :SIDE
   LEFT 90
   PENUP FD 50 PENDOWN
   SQUARE :SIDE* :K
   END
   TO SQUARE SIDE
   REPEAT 4 [FD : SIDE RT 90]
   END

2. TO RTISOS :HYPOT
   DRAW
   FD :HYPOT RT 135
   CHECK
   END
(In LCSI Logo, replace DRAW with CLEARSCREEN.)
   TO CHECK
   FORWARD 1
   SETHEADING TOWARDS 00
   IF ABS (HEADING - 225) < 2
    HOME STOP
   SETHEADING -135
   CHECK
   END
(In LCSI Logo, replace SETHEADING TOWARDS 00 with SETHEADING TOWARDS [0 0] and IF ABS (HEADING-225)<2 HOME STOP with IF ABS (HEADING-225<2) [HOME STOP].)
   TO ABS :VALUE
   IF :VALUE <0 OUTPUT-:VALUE ELSE
   OUTPUT :VALUE
   END
(In LCSI Logo, replace IF :VALUE<0 OUTPUT -:VALUE ELSE OUTPUT :VALUE with IF :VALUE <0 [OUTPUT -:VALUE] [OUTPUT :VALUE].)

3. TO TR130 :HYPOT
   DRAW
   FD :HYPOT/2 RT 120
   FD :HYPOT RT 120
   HOME
   END
(In LCSI Logo, replace DRAW with CLEARSCREEN.)

4. TO STAR :SIDE
   HEXAGON :SIDE
   REPEAT 6 [LT 60 FD :SIDE RT 120
    FD :SIDE]
   END
   TO HEXAGON :SIDE
    REPEAT 6 [FD :SIDE RT 60]
   END

5. TO ISOSCELES3 :ANGLE :HEIGHT
   DRAW
   PENUP FD :HEIGHT
   PENDOWN RT 90
   CHECKHEADR :ANGLE
   HOME
   PENUP FD :HEIGHT
   PENDOWN LT 90
   CHECKHEADL :ANGLE
   END
(In LCSI Logo, replace DRAW with CLEARSCREEN.)
   TO CHECKHEADR :ANGLE
   SETHEADING TOWARDS 00
   IF ABS (HEADING-(180+:ANGLE))<2
    HOME STOP
   SETHEADING 90 FD 1
    CHECKHEADR :ANGLE
   END
(In LCSI Logo, replace SETHEADING TOWARDS 00 with SETHEADING TOWARDS [0 0] and IF ABS (HEADING-(180+:ANGLE))<2 HOME STOP with IF (ABS HEADING-(180+:ANGLE))<2 [HOME STOP].)
   TO CHECKHEADL :ANGLE
   SETHEADING TOWARDS 00
   IF ABS (HEADING-(90+:ANGLE))<2
    HOME STOP
   SETHEADING -90 FD 1
    CHECK :ANGLE
   END
(In LCSI Logo, replace SETHEADING TOWARDS 00 with SETHEADING TOWARDS [0 0] and IF ABS (HEADING-(90+:ANGLE))<2 HOME STOP with IF (ABS HEADING-(90+:ANGLE))<2 [HOME STOP].)
   TO ABS :VALUE
   IF :VALUE<0 OUTPUT-:VALUE ELSE
    OUTPUT :VALUE
   END
(In LCSI Logo, replace IF :VALUE<0 OUTPUT-:VALUE ELSE OUTPUT :VALUE with IF :VALUE <0 [OUTPUT -:VALUE] [OUTPUT :VALUE].)

Chapter 11 Test
1. (a) $\triangle ADB \cong \triangle CDB$ by SAS
   (b) $\triangle GAC \cong \triangle EDB$ by SAS
   (c) $\triangle ABC \cong \triangle EDC$ by SAA
   (d) $\triangle BAD \cong \triangle EAC$ by ASA
   (e) $\triangle ABD \cong \triangle CBD$ by ASA or by SAS
   (f) $\triangle ABD \cong \triangle CBD$ by SAS

(g) $\triangle ABD \cong \triangle CBE$ by SSS

(h) $\triangle ABC \cong \triangle ADC$ by SSS; $\triangle ABE \cong \triangle ADE$ by SSS or SAS; $\triangle EBC \cong \triangle EDC$ by SSS or SAS

2. A parallelogram. $\triangle ADE \cong \triangle CBF$ by SAS. Hence, $\angle DEA \cong \angle CFB$. Since $\angle DEA \cong \angle EAF$ (alternate interior angles between the parallels $\overleftrightarrow{DC}$ and $\overleftrightarrow{AB}$ and the transversal $\overleftrightarrow{AE}$), it follows that $\angle EAF \cong \angle CFB$. Consequently, $\overline{AE} \cong \overline{AE}$. Also, $\overline{EC} \cong \overline{EC}$ (Why?), and therefore AECF is a parallelogram.

3. Construction

4. **(a)** x = 8; y = 5 **(b)** x = 6

5. Contruction

6. a/b = c/d because a/b = x/y and x/y = c/d

7. Hint: Find the intersection of the perpendicular bisector of $\overline{AB}$ and line ℓ.

8. **(a)** $\triangle ACB \sim \triangle DEB$ by AA. x = 24/5 **(b)** $\triangle ABC \sim \triangle ADE$ by AA. x = 55/6 and y = 4/3

9. **(a)** False; A chord has its endpoints on the circle. **(b)** False; A diameter intersects a circle in two points, and a tangent intersects it in only one point. **(c)** True **(d)** True **(e)** True.

10. 12 m high

11. **(a)** (iii) and (iv) **(b)** Any regular convex polygon can be inscribed in a circle.

12. 6 m

13. 256/5 m

14. **(a)** True in some cases and false in others: If the diagonals do not bisect each other, then it is not a square. Quadrilateral ABCD is not a square however its diagonals are perpendicular and congruent.

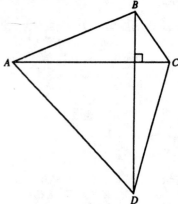

(b) Always true. The intersection of the perpendicular bisectors of the two non-parallel sides is also on the perpendicular bisector of the the bases and hence determlnes the center of the circle.

CHAPTER 12

Problem Set 12-1

1. **(a)** A translation **(b)** A translation

2.

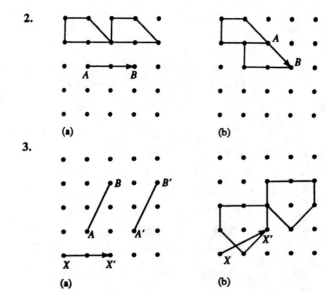

(a) **(b)**

3.

(a) **(b)**

4. Construction

5. Answers may vary.

6.

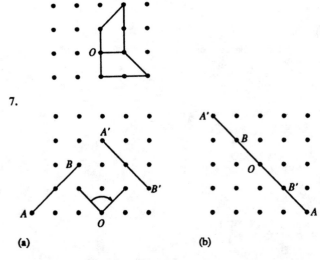

7.

(a) **(b)**

8. **(a)** Answers vary. SOS and I are examples. The following letters can be used:N, O, H, I, S, X, Z **(b)** 1, 8, 11, 69, 88, 96, 101, 111, 181, 609, 619, 689, 808, 818 906, 916, 986, 1001, 1111, 1691, 1961, 6009, 6119, 6699, 6889, 6969, 8008, 8118, 8698, 8968, 9696, 9966

9. Construction

10. Construction

11. Hint: Find the midpoint of $\overline{PP'}$. This is the center of the half-turn

12. **(b)** A rotation with center O through $\beta - \alpha$ **(c)** No **(d)** Yes

13. **(a)** A circle **(b)** The vertices A and B trace an identical path if and only if OA = OB. That is, if and only if O is on the perpendlcular blsector of $\overline{AB}$. Hence all points O for which two vertices trace an identical path are the points on the perpendicular bisectors of the sides of the triangle. **(c)** It follows from (b) that O must be on the perpendicular bisectors of all three sides. Hence O is the intersection of the perpendicular bisectors and is therefore the center of the circle that circumscribes ∆ABC. (O is determined by the intersection of any two perpendicular bisectors)

14. **(a)** Parallelogram. Under a half turn the image of a line is parallel to the line. (A half turn is an isometry and hence ∆ABC and its image ∆DCB are congruent by SSS, which implies that ∠ABC ≅ ∠DCB. Consequently $\overleftrightarrow{AB} \| \overleftrightarrow{CD}$). Thus $\overline{AB} \| \overline{CD}$ and $\overline{AC} \| \overline{DB}$ and therefore ABCD is a parallelogram.

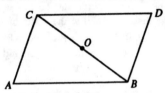

(b) Parallelogram. The image of $\overline{AB}$ is $\overline{FE}$ and hence $\overline{AB} \| \overline{EF}$. It seems that B, C, and F are collinear and A, D, and E are collinear. (B, C, F are collinear because $\overline{BC} \| \overline{AD}$ and $\overline{CF} \| \overline{AD}$.) Consequently $\overline{BF} \| \overline{AE}$ and ABFE is a parallelogram.

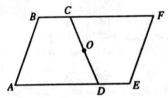

(c) Square. Because the image of A is C and the image of B is D, the image of ABCD is CDAB.

15. **(a)** ℓ is the same as ℓ. **(b)** ℓ' is parallel to ℓ.

(c) ℓ' is perpendicular to ℓ. **(d)** ℓ' intersects ℓ at 60°. (The smaller of the vertical angles formed by ℓ' and ℓ is 60°.)

16. **(a)** Hint: Find the image m', of line m under a half-turn with center P. This intersection of m and line ℓ is point A.
(b) No, it can be shown that AP = BP if and only if the distance from P to ℓ is the same as the distance from P to m. Hence the construction is possible if and only if P is equidistant from ℓ and m. Then any line through P will intersect ℓ and m in points A and B respectively so that $\overline{AB}$ is bisected by P.

17. **(b)**
```
TO SLIDE :DIRECTION :DISTANCE :SIDE
  EQUILATERAL :SIDE
  SETHEADING :DIRECTION
  FORWARD :DISTANCE
  PENDOWN
  SETHEADING 0
  EQUILATERAL :SIDE
END
TO EQUILATERAL :SIDE
  REPEAT 3[FORWARD :SIDE RIGHT 120]
END
```

18.
```
  TO ROTATE :A :SIDE
  SQUARE : S1 DE
  RIGHT :A
  SQUARE : S I DE
END
  TO SQUARE :SIDE
  REPEAT 4[FORWARD :SIDE RIGHT 90]
END
```

19. **(a)**
```
  TO TURN.CIRCLE :A
  CIRCLE
  LEFT : A
```

```
  CIRCLE
END
TO CIRCLE
  REPEAT 360 [FORWARD 1 RT 1]
END
```
To produce the desired transformation, execute TURN.CIRCLE 180. **(b)** To produce the desired transformation, execute TURN.CIRCLE 90.

Brain Teaser (p. 635)
Straight down. The transformation is a translation.

Problem Set 12-2
1.

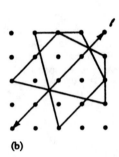

(a)   (b)

2. **(b)** Yes. Find A' and C', the images of A and C. Label the point of intersection of $\overline{AB}$ and line ℓ as point P; label the point of intersection of $\overline{BC}$ and line ℓ as point Q. Draw $\overleftrightarrow{A'P}$ and $\overleftrightarrow{C'Q}$. The intersection of these lines is B'.
3. Hint: Find the image of the center of the circle and one point on the circumference of the circle to determine the image of the circle.
4. **(a)** Yes, there are infinitely many such lines all of which contain the center of the circle. **(b)** Yes, there are two: the reflecting line is the perpendicular bisector of the segment, and the reflecting line is the line containing the segment.
(c) Yes, the reflecting line is the line containing the ray.
(d) Yes, there are four such lines: the perpendicular bisectors of the pairs of parallel sides, and the diagonals. **(e)** Yes, there are two such lines: the perpendicular bisectors of the pairs of parallel sides. **(f)** There are none. **(g)** Yes, there is one such line in a general isosceles triangle: the line that is the perpendicular bisector of the side that is not congruent to the other two. **(h)** Yes, there are three such lines: the perpendicular bisectors of each of the sides.
(i) There are none. **(j)** Yes, there is one such line; the line that is the perpendicular bisector of the parallel sides.
(k) Yes, there is one such line; the line that is the perpendicular bisector of the chord determined by the endpoints of the arc **(l)** Yes, there is one in a general kite: it is the diagonal determined by the vertices of the noncongruent angles.
(m) Yes, there are two, the diagonals. **(n)** Yes, there are six such lines: the perpendicular bisectors of the parallel sides and the three diameters determined by the vertices on the circumscribed circle. **(o)** Yes. there are n such lines.
5. Construction
6. The final image is the same as the original.
7. No, the final images are different
8. The final images are different in each case.
9. Construction.
10. **(a)** AHA, MOM, WOW, for example, but answers will vary **(b)** BOX, KID, BED, for example. but answers will vary. The letters B, C, D,E, H, I, K, O, X can be used. **(c)** 1, 8, 11, 88, 101, 181, 808, 818, 888, 1001, 1111, 1881, 8008, 8118, 8888.

11. (a) If AB = BC then the perpendicular biseclor of $\overline{AC}$ is the required line. Because a point is on the perpendicular bisector of $\overline{AC}$ if and only if it is equidistant from A and C, the image of B when reflected in $\overline{AC}$ is B and the image of A is C. Hence the image of $\triangle ABC$ is $\triangle CBA$.   (b) For equilateral triangles. From part (a) it follows that each of the three perpendicular bisectors of the sides will have the property.
12. Construction
13. (a) The images are the same.   (b) Yes
14. 1 to 2 is a rotation: 1 to 3 is a rotation; 1 to 4 is a translation; 1 to 5 is a rotation; 1 to 6 is a translation; 1 to 7 is a translation.
15. Construction
16. Reflect B in the line that contains side 1 to point B', then reflect B' in the line that contains side 2 to point B". Next reflect B" in the line that contains side 3, to point B'''. If the ball at A is shot at point B''', it will bounce as desired and hit the ball at B (Why?)

B''' •

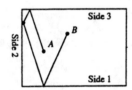

B'' •   •B'

17. Reflect A in road 1 and B in road 2. Connect the images by a straight line The intersection points with road 1 and road 2 are the desired locations for P and Q.
18. The angle of incidence is the same as the angle of reflection. With the mirrors tilted 45°, the object's image reflects to 90° down the tube; then 90° to the eyepiece. The two reflections "counteract" each other, leaving the image upright.
19. (a) ⁻150 degree rotation about the turtle's starting point. (b) Reflection about a vertical line containing the turtle's starting point.   (c) 45 degree rotation and slide.
20. (a) Answers may vary.   (b) The drawing produced in FIG3 is a reflection of the drawing produced by FIG1 through a horizontal line that contains the starting point of the turtle. (c) The drawing produced by FIG3 is a reflection to the drawing produced by FIG1 through a vertical line that contains the starting point of the turtle.
21. (a)
```
TO EQTRI : SIDE
  REPEAT 3 [FORWARD :SIDE RIGHT 120]
END
```
(b)
```
TO EQTR 12 : S I DE
  REPEAT 3 [FORWARD :SIDE LEFT 120]
END
```

(c) A reflection in a vertical line through the turtle's home
(d) A half-turn with the turtle's home as center.
22. H, I, N, O, S, X and Z
23. H, I, N, O, S, X and Z
24. Half-turn about the center of the letter O
25. (a) A rotation by any angle   (b) Reflections about lines containing diameters

Brain Teaser (p. 648)
Translate B towards A in the direction perpendicular to the banks of the river along the distance equal to the width of the river. Connect A with the image B'. The point P where $\overline{AB'}$ intersects the far bank is the point where the bridge should be built.

Problem Set 12-3
1. (a)The final images are congruent but not the same. (b) The final images are congruent but different if ℓ is not perpendicular to m. If $\ell \perp m$, the final images are the same.
2. (a) A translation from N to M. (b) A counterclockwise rotation by 75° about 0. (c) A clockwise rotation by 45° about A. (d) A glide reflection determined by reflection in m and a translation from B to A. (e) A reflection in n.
3. (a) (2, 1)   (b) (6,3)   (c) (7,4)   (d) (6,4)
4. If there is a size transformation such that the image of $\triangle ABC$ is $\triangle A'B'C'$ then the center O of the size transformation must be on each of the lines $\overleftrightarrow{AA'}$, $\overleftrightarrow{BB'}$, $\overleftrightarrow{CC'}$ Because the three lines can intersect in at most one common point there is only one possibility for the center. The scale factor of the size transformation is $\dfrac{OA'}{OA} = \dfrac{OB'}{OB} = \dfrac{OC'}{OC} = \dfrac{3}{4}$.
5. (a) A translation from C to B followed by a size transformation with center B and scale factor 2.   (b) A translation from C to E (which is equivalent to a translation by one unit vertically up followed by a translation 5 units horizontally to the right) followed by a size transformation with center E and scale factor 2.   (c) A 90° counterclockwise rotation about C followed by a size transformation with center C and scale factor 2.

(a)

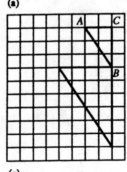

(b)

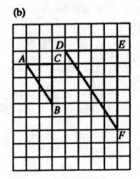

(c)

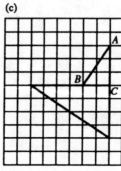

6.

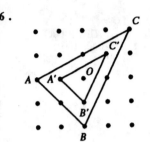

7. Answers may vary.

Problem Set 12-4

1. (a) Line, rotational and point symmetry (b) Line symmetry (c) Line symmetry (d) Line symmetry

2. Answers may vary.

3.

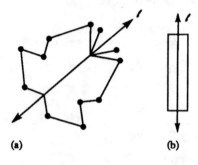

(a)   (b)

4. (a) (i) 4 (ii) None (iii) 2 (iv) 1

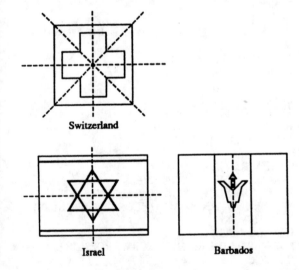

Switzerland

Israel   Barbados

5. (a) 1 vertical (b) 1 vertical (c) None (d) 1 vertical (e) 5 lines (f) 1 vertical

6. Sketches may vary. (a) Any scalene triangle (b) A nonequilateral isosceles triangle (c) Not possible (d) Any equilateral triangle

7. Sketches may vary

8. (a) Yes, a figure with point symmetry has 180 degree rotational symmetry. (b) Not necessarily. Counterexamples may vary. (c) Yes, figures may vary. (d) No to both questions. Counterexamples may vary. (e) Yes, see part (a).

9.

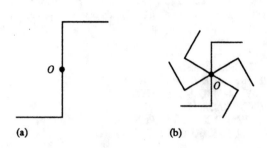

(a)   (b)

10. (a) 7 (b) 2 (c) 7 (d) 33

11.

```
TO TURN.SYM :S :N :A
  REPEAT :N [SQUARE :S RIGHT :A]
END
TO SQUARE :S
  REPEAT 4[FORWARD :S RIGHT 90
END
```

(a) Execute TURN.SYM 50 6 60 (b) Execute TURN.SYM 50 3 120 (c) Execute TURN.SYM 50 2 180 (d) Execute TURN.SYM 50 3 240 (e) Execute TURN.SYM 50 6 300

12.

```
TO TURN.SY :S :N :A
  REPEAT :N [EQTRI :S RIGHT :A]
END
TO EQTRI :S
  REPEAT 3 [FORWARD :S RIGHT 120]
END
```

(a) Execute TURN.SY 50 6 60 (b) Execute TURN.SY 50 3 120 (c) Execute TURN.SY 50 3 240 (d) Execute TURN.SY 50 6 300

13. Construction

14. Construction

Problem Set 12-5

1.

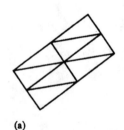

(a)

(b)

2. (1) Rotate the quadrilateral 180 degrees about the midpoint of each side. Repeat the process for each quadrilateral constructed in this way. (b) Yes

3. (a), (c), and (d) tessellate the plane.

4. (a) The dual is also a tessellation of squares. (b) The dual is a tessellation of triangles. (c) The dual is a tessellation of equilateral triangles.

5. Answers may vary.

6. (a)

```
TO TESSELSQUARE
  PENUP BACK 70 PENDOWN
  REPEAT 9 [SQUARE 20 FORWARD 20]
  PENUP BACK 180 RIGHT 90
  FORWARD 20 LEFT 90 PENDOWN
  REPEAT 9 [SQUARE 20 FORWARD 20]
END
  TO SQUARE :SIDE
  REPEAT 4 [FORWARD :SIDE RIGHT 90 ]
END
```

(b)

```
TO TESSELSQUARE
  PENUP BACK 70 PENDOWN
  REPEAT 9 [TRIANGLE 20 FORWARD 20]
  PENUP BACK 180 RIGHT 60
  FORWARD 20 LEFT .60 PENDOWN
  REPEAT 9 [TRIANGLE 20 FORWARD 20]
END
TO TRIANGLE :SIDE
  REPEAT 3 [FORWARD :SIDE RIGHT 120]
END
```

(c)

```
TO TESSELHEX
  PENUP BACK 70 LEFT 90 PENDOWN
  REPEAT 4 [HEXAGON 20 RIGHT 120 FORWARD 20
    LEFT 60 HEXAGON 20 FORWARD 20 LEFT 60]
END
TO HEXAGON :SIDE
  REPEAT 6 [FORWARD :SIDE RIGHT 60]
END
```

7.

```
TO TILESTRIP :S
  REPEAT 4 [TILE :S PENUP RIGHT 180 FORWARD 3* :S
    PENDOWN]
END
TO TILE :S
  RIGHT 180
  REPEAT 3 [REPEAT 4 [FORWARD :S LEFT 60] RIGHT
  120]
END
```

Problem Set 12-6

1.
```
TO WALL3 :XPT :YPT :SIDE
  DRAW
  SETUP :XPT :YPT
  WALLPAPER3 :YPT :SIDE
END
```
(In LSCI Logo replace DRAW with
CLEARSCREEN)
```
TO SETUP :XPT :YPT
  PENUP
  SETXY :XPT :YPT
  PENDOWN
END
```
(In LSCILogo, replace SETXY :XPT :YPT with SETPOS (LIST :XPT :YPT)
```
TO WALLPAPER3 :YPT :SIDE
  TRISTRIP :SIDE
  PENUP
  SETUP (:XPT + :SIDE* (SORT 3)/2) :YPT
  PENDOWN
  WALLPAPER3 :YPT :SIDE
END
```

```
TO TRISTRIP :SIDE
  IF XCOR + :SIDE>120 TOPLEVEL
  IF (ANYOF (XCOR<-120) (XCOR + :SIDE* (SQRT
  3)/2>120) (YCOR<-100)(YCOR + :SIDE>100))
  STOP
  TRIANGLE :SIDE
  FORWARD :SIDE
  RIGHT 60
  TRIANGLE :SIDE
  LEFT 60
  TRISTRIP :SIDE
END
```
(In LCSI Logo, replace IF XCOR + : SIDE > 120 TOPLEVEL with IF XCOR + :SIDE>120 [THROW "TOPLEVEL3]. Also replace IF (ANYOF (XCOR<-120) (XCOR + :SIDE*(SQRT 3)/2>120) (YCOR<-100) (YCOR + :SIDE>100)) STOP with IF (OR (XCOR<-120) (XCOR + :SIDE*(SQRT 3)/2>120) (YCOR <-100) (YCCR + :SIDE>100)) [THROW "TOPLEVEL].)
```
TO TRIANGLE :SIDE
  REPEAT 3[FORWARD :SIDE RIGHT 120]
END
```

2. The conditions are to keep the turtle from drawing off the screen It forces the boundaries to be as follows: $-120 < x < 120$ and $-100 < y < 100$.

3 .
```
TO WALL4 :XPT :YPT :SIDE
  DRAW
  SETUP :XPT :YPT
  WALLPAPER4 :YPT :SIDE
END
```
(In LCSI Logo , replace DRAW with
CLEARSCREEN)
```
TO SETUP :XPT :YPT
  PENUP
  SETXY :XPT :YPT
  PENDOWN
END
```
(In LCSI Logo replace SETXY :XPT :YPT with SETPOS (LIST :XPT : YPT.)
```
TO WALLPAPER4 :YPT :SIDE
  MAKE "X XCOR
  HEXSTRIP :SIDE
  PENUP
  SETUP (XCOR+ :SIDE* (SQRT 3)) :YPT
  PENDOWN
  WALLPAPER4 :YPT :SIDE
END
TO HEXSTRIP :SIDE
  IF XCOR+ :SIDE>120 TOPLEVEL
  IF (ANYOF (XCOR<-120) (XCOR+ :SIDE * (SQRT
    3))>120) (YCOR<-100) (YCOR+ :SIDE*3>100))
    STOP
  HEXAGON :SIDE
  FORWARD :SIDE RIGHT 60 FORWARD :SIDE LEFT 60
  HEXSTRIP :SIDE
END
```
(In LCSI Logo , replace IF XCOR + SIDE>120 TOPLEVEL with IF XCOR+ :SIDE> 120 [THROW "TOPLEVEL].
Also replace IF (ANYOF (XCOR< -120) (XCOR+ :SIDE*(SQRT 3)>120) (YCOR<-100) (YCOR+ :SIDE*3>100)) STOP with IF (OR (XCOR <-120) (XCOR+ :SIDE*(SQRT 3)>120) (YCOR <-100) (YCOR+ SIDE*3>100)) [STOP].)
```
TO HEXAGON :SIDE
  REPEAT 6[FORWARD :SIDE RIGHT 60]
END
```

4. Answers may vary.

5. Yes; once the figures fit between two parallel lines, then one could make a rubber stamp of the parallel lines and the drawings between them and stamp them all across the plane.

```
.   TO WALL5 :XPT :YPT :SIDE1 :SIDE2
      DRAW
      SETUP :XPT :YPT
      WALLPAPER5 :YT :SIDE1 :SIDE2
    END
(In LCSI Logo replace DRAW with CLEARSCREEN.)
    TO SETUP :XPT :YPT
      PENUP
      SETXY_:XPT :YPT
      PENDOWN
    END
(In LCSI Logo replace SETXY :XPT :YPT with SETPOS (LIST
XPT: YPT.)
    TO WALLPAPER5 :YPT :SIDE1 :SIDE2
      RECTANGLESTRIP :SIDE1 :SIDE2
      PENUP
      SETUP (XCOR+ :SIDE2) :YPT
      PENDOWN
      WALLPAPER5 :YPT :SIDE1 :SIDE2
    END
    TO RECTANGLESTRIP :SIDE1 :SIDE2
      IF XCOR+ :SIDE2>120 TOPLEVEL
      IF (ANYOF (XCOR<‾120) (XCOR+ :SIDE2>120)
        (YCOR<‾100) (YCOR + SIDE1 > 1 0 0 )) STOP
      RECTANGLE :SIDE1 :SIDE2
      FORWARD :SIDE1
      RECTANGLESTRIP :SIDE1 :SIDE2
    END
(In LCSI Logo replace IF XCOR+ :SIDE2>120 TOPLEVEL with
IF XCOR+ :SIDE2>120 [THROW "TOPLEVEL].Also replace IF
(ANYOF (XCOR<‾120) (XCOR+ :SIDE2>120) (YCOR<‾100)
(YCOR+ :SIDE1>100)) STOP with IF (OR (XCOR<‾120)
(XCOR+ :SIDE2>120) (YCOR <‾100) (YCOR+ :SIDE1>100))
[STOP].)
    TO RECTANGLE :SIDE1 SIDE2
      REPEAT 2[FORWARD :SIDE1 RIGHT 90 FORWARD
        :SIDE2 RIGHT 90]
    END
7 . TO WALL6 :XPT :YPT :SIDE
      DRAW
      SETUP :XPT : YPT
      WALLPAPER6 :YPT :SIDE
    END
(In LCSI Logo replace DRAW with CLEARSCREEN.)
    TO SETUP :XPT :YPT
      PENUP
      SETXY :XPT :YPT
      PENDOWN
    END
(In LCSI Logo, replace SETXY : XPT: YPT
with SETPOS (LIST : XPT :YPT).)
    TO WALLPAPER6 :YPT :SIDE
      CHEVRONSTRIP :SIDE
      PENUP
      SETUP (XCOR+ :SIDE) :YPT
      PENDOWN
      WALLPAPER6 :YPT :SIDE
    END
    TO CHEVRONSTRIP :SIDE
      IF XCOR+:SIDE>120 TOPLEVEL
      IF (ANYOF (XCOR‾:SIDE<‾120) (XCOR+ :SIDE>120)
        (YCOR‾:SIDE*(SQRT 2)/2<‾100)(YCOR –:SIDE>
        100))STOP
      CHEVRON :SIDE
      FORWARD :SIDE
```

```
      CHEVRONSTRIP :SIDE
    END
```
(In LCSI Logo, replace IF XCOR +: SIDE > 120 TOPLEVEL,
with IF XCOR+:SIDE>120 [THROW "TOPLEVEL], and replace
IF (ANYOF (XCOR- :SIDE<‾120) (XCOR+:SIDE>120) (YCOR
:SIDE*(SQRT 2)/2<‾100) (YCOR+:SIDE>100)) STOP with IF
(OR (XCOR- :SIDE<‾120) (XCOR+ :SIDE>120) (YCOR-
:SIDE*(SQRT 2)/2<‾100) (YCOR+:SIDE>100)) [STOP].)
```
    TO CHEVRON :SIDE
      FORWARD :SIDE RIGHT 135
      FORWARD :SIDE*(SQRT 2)/2 LEFT 90
      FORWARD :SIDE*(SQRT 2)/2 RIGHT 135
      FORWARD :SIDE RIGHT 45
      FORWARD :SIDE*(SQRT 2)/2 RIGHT 90
      FORWARD :SIDE*(SQRT 2)/2
      RIGHT 45
    END
```

Chapter 12 Test

1.

(a)

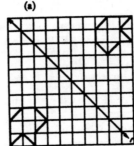

(b)

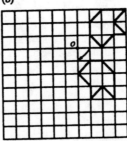

(c)

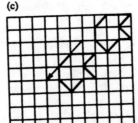

2. Construction
3. (a) 4 (b) 1 (c) 1 (d) None (e) 2 (f) 2
4. (a) Line and rotational (b) Line, rotational, and point
(c) Line
5. (a) Infinitely many (b) Infinitely many (c) 3 (d) 9
6. This answer depends totally upon how the letters are made, but generally we have the following: c has line symmetry; i has line symmetry, o has line, rotational, and point symmetry; s has rotational and point symmetry; t has line symmetry; v has line symmetry; w has line symmetry; x has line, rotational, and point symmetry; z has rotational and point symmetry.
7. The measure of each exterior angle of a regular octagon is $\dfrac{360°}{8}$ or 45°. Hence the measure of each interior angle is 180° - 45° or 135°. Because 135 ∤ 3 a regular octagon does not tessellate the plane.
8. Either point of intersection of the perpendicular bisector of $\overline{AB}$ and the circle may be C.
9. Hint: $\overline{BC}$ formed by the midpoints of $\overline{A'B'}$ and $\overline{A'C'}$.
10. In each part half turn about X.
11. (a) Rotation by 120° about the center of the hexagon.
(b) A reflection in the perpendicular bisector of $\overline{BY}$.
12. Reflection in $\overset{\leftrightarrow}{SO}$.
13. If ΔSER was the image of ΔHOR under a succession of isometries with a size transformation then ΔSER would be similar to ΔHOR which in turn would imply that ER/OR = SR/HR.
However, the last equation is false because $\dfrac{ER}{OR} = \dfrac{2}{3}$ and $\dfrac{SR}{HR} = \dfrac{5}{5}$.
This contradiction implies that ΔSER is not the image of ΔHOR under any succession of isometries with size transformation. Notice that in a similar way we could show that ΔSER is not the image of ΔOHR under such transformations.
14. Answers vary. One way is to apply the following transformation to ΔPIG in succession: reflection in $\overline{PG}$, reflection in the line through I perpendicular to $\overline{PG}$, a translation by 7 units horizontally to the left, followed by a size transformation with center B and scale factor 2.

CHAPTER 13

Problem Set 13-1
1. (a) 9 mm, or 0.9 cm (b) 9 mm, or 0.9 cm (c) 80 mm, or 8 cm
(d) 5 mm, or 0.5 cm (e) 7 mm, or 0.7 cm (f) 49 mm, or 4.9 cm
(g) 73 mm, or 7.3 cm (h) 52 mm, or 5.2 cm.
2. (a) 2 7/9 (b) 14,400 (c) 100 (d)31
3. Answers vary.
4. (a) 98 (b) 9.8
5. (a) Centimeters (b) Millimeters (c) Centimeters
(d) Centimeters (e) Centimeters (f) Meters (g) Centimeters
(h) Centimeters
6. (a) Inches (b) Inches (c) Feet (d) Inches (e) Inches
(f) Yards (g) Feet (h) Inches
7. (a) 0.35, 350 (b) 163,1630 (c) 0.035, 3 5 (d) 0.1, 10
(e) 200, 2000
8. (a) 10.00 (b) 0.77 (c) 10.00 (d) 15.5 (e) 195.0 (f) 8.100
(g) 40.0
9. 6 m, 5218 mm, 245 cm, 700 mm, 91 mm, 8 cm.
10. Answers vary.
11. (a) 8 cm (b) 12 cm (c) 9 cm (d) 20 cm

12 (a) 1 cm (b) 0 17 m (c) 0.262 km (d) 3000 m (e) 0.03 m
(f) 170 m (g) 3500 cm (h) 0.359 m (i) 0.1 cm (j) 64.7 cm
(k) 1 mm (l) 5000 m (m) 5130 cm
13. (a) AB + BC > AC (b) BC + CA > AB (c) AB + CA > BC
14. (a) Can be (b) Cannot be (c) Cannot be
15. Answers vary.
16. Answers vary.
17. (a) The maximum perimeter is attained when longer sides are part of the perimeter, for example,

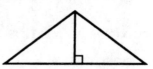

(b) The minimum perimeter is attained when the longer sides are not part of the perimeter, for example, the original rectangle.
18. (a) Answers vary (b) 8 squares (c) 20 squares
19. (a) 6 cm (b) 3/π m (c) 0.335/π m (d) 46 cm
20. (a) 6π cm (b) 6π cm (c) 4 cm (d) 6π² cm
21. Answers vary.
22 πr
23. Answers vary.
24. (a) 2:1 (b) They're the same (c) If ΔABC ~ ΔA'B'C', with
A'B'/AB = r, then $\dfrac{\text{perimeter } ΔAB'C'}{\text{perimeter } ΔABC} = \dfrac{r(AB+BC+AC)}{(AB+BC+AC)} = r$.
25. (a) About $9.5 \cdot 10^{12}$ km (b) About $4.1 \cdot 10^{13}$ km
(c) About $6.9 \cdot 10^{8}$ k, or about 78,000 years (d) 2495 hours, or about 104 days
26. (a) 3096 (b) 1032 (c) Approximately Mach 4.04
27. (50 + 6π) ft
28. (a) 6 foot longs (b) 10,560 foot longs
29. Answers vary.
30. Answers vary.
31.

Perimeter	Minimum Area	Maximum Area
4	1	1
6	2	2
8	3	4
10	4	6
12	5	9
14	6	12
16	7	16
18	8	20
20	9	25
22	10	30
24	11	36
26	12	42
2n	n-1	*

* Let q be the whole number quotient when 2n is divided by 4. If 2n is a multiple of 4, then the maximum area is q^2; otherwise it is q(q+1).

Brain Teaser (p. 697)

The tallest person on earth could walk under the wire. Suppose the two concentric circles below represented the earth and the lengthened wire.

$\overline{OA}$ and $\overline{OB}$ are the radii of the respective circles and have lengths r and r + x. Since the circumference of the earth plus 20 m equals the circumference of the lengthened wire, we have $2\pi r + 20 = 2\pi(r + x)$.

Consequently, $x = \frac{10}{\pi}$, or approximately 3.18 m.

Problem Set 13-2

1. (a) cm^2, in^2 (b) cm^2, in^2 (c) cm^2, in^2 (d) m^2, yd^2
(e) m^2, yd^2 (f) km^2, mi^2
2. Answers vary.
3. (a) $0.588\ m^2$, $58,800\ mm^2$ (b) $0.000192\ m^2$, $1.92\ cm^2$
(c) $15,000\ cm^2$, $1,500,000\ mm^2$ (d) $0.01\ m^2$, $10,000\ mm^2$
(e) $0.0005\ m^2$, $500\ mm^2$
4. Answers vary.
5. (a) $444.4\ yd^2$ (b) $0.32\ mi^2$ (c) 6400 acres
(d) $130,680\ ft^2$
6. (a) $4900\ m^2$ (b) 98 (c) 0.98 ha
7. (a) 3 sq. units (b) 3 sq. units (c) 2 sq. units (d) 5 sq. units
(e) 6 sq. units (f) 4 1/2 sq. units
8. They all check; i.e., I + 1/2B - 1 = A
9. (a) $20\ cm^2$ (b) $900\ cm^2$, or $0.09\ m^2$ (c) $7.5\ m^2$
(d) $39\ cm^2$ (e) $600\ cm^2$
10. Answers vary.
11. (a) $9\ cm^2$ (b) $96\ cm^2$ (c) $(2\sqrt{21} - 2\sqrt{5})\ cm^2$
(d) $20\ cm^2$ (e) $84\ cm^2$ (f) $105\ cm^2$
12. (a) (i) $1.95\ km^2$ (ii) 195 ha (b) (i) $0.63\ mi^2$ (ii) 402.89 acres (c) Answers vary.
13. (a) True (b) Don't know (c) Don't know (d) Don't know
14. (a) $75\ cm^2$ (b) If a>b, then dropping perpendiculars to the lower base from the endpoints of the upper base forms isosceles right triangles whose legs are (a-b)/2. Then using the formula for the area of a trapezoid, $A = 1/2(a + b)\ ((a-b)/2) = (a^2 - b^2)/4$
15. (1/2)ab
16. (a) $405.11 (b) $550
17. (a) $25\pi\ cm^2$ (b) $(8/3)\pi\ cm^2$ (c) $(18/5)\pi\ cm^2$
(d) $(9/2)\pi\ cm^2$ (e) $100\ cm^2$
18. 1200 tiles
19. 8 bags of seed
20. (a) (i) 12, 10 (ii) 14, 10 (iii) 62, 22 (b) (i) 9, 5 (ii) 42, 12
(c) 2(n + 1) (d) n-1
21. (a) $24\sqrt{3}\ cm^2$ (b) $9\sqrt{3}\ cm^2$
22. (a) $16\pi\ cm^2$ (b) $r = s\sqrt{\pi}$
23. (a) $2\pi\ cm^2$ (b) $(\pi/2 + 2)\ cm^2$ (c) $2\pi\ cm^2$
(d) $(50\pi - 100)\ cm^2$ (e) $(400 - 100\pi)\ cm^2$ (f) $1/4\ \pi r^2$
(g) $(1/8)\ \pi r^2$ (h) $(1/16)\ \pi r^2$
24. $7\pi\ m^2$
25. (a) About 21.46% (b) (i) Same as (a) (ii) Same as (a)
26. (a) Rotate the shaded region $180°$ clockwise about point E. The area of the triangle is the same as the area of the parallelogram. Thus, $A = (h/2)\cdot b$ (b) Paper cutting exercise

27. (a) 4:9; $A_1/A_2 = S_1^2/S_2^2$, and $S_1/S_2 = 2/3$; hence,
$A_1/A_2 = (2/3)^2 = 4/9$ (b) 4:9 (Hint: $A = d^2/2$ where d is the length of a diagonal.)
28. (a) 4:1 (b) The former is the square of the latter
(c) Answers vary.
29. (a) Answers vary. (b)28.3 in.
30. Rectangle; A = bh
31. The new figure is a parallelogram that has twice the area of the trapezoid. The area of the parallelogram is A = (1/2)(AB + DC)h, where h is the height of the parallelogram. Thus the area of the trapezoid is (1/2) (AB + DC)h.
32. P should be connected to the point that is 2 units above P and 1 1/2 units to the right of P.
33. Answers vary.
34. $(320 + 64\pi)\ m^2$
35. 1 in.
36. Draw altitudes $\overline{BE}$ and $\overline{DF}$ of triangles BCP and DCP, respectively.
$\triangle ABE \cong \triangle CDF$ by AAS. Thus $\overline{BE} \cong \overline{DF}$. Because $\overline{CP}$ is a base of $\triangle BCP$ and $\triangle DCP$, and because the heights are the same, the areas must be equal .
37. (a) 10 (b) 104 (c) 0.35 (d) 40 (e) 8000 m (f) 6.504
38. (a) $(2\pi + 4)$ cm (b) $(5\pi + 6)$ cm
39. Answers vary.

Brain Teaser (p. 714)

(1) 64 (2) 65 (3) Although the pieces look like they should fit together, they do not really. To see this, assume the pieces do fit. We then obtain the figure.

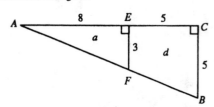

Since $\triangle AEF \sim \triangle ACB$, we have $\frac{8}{13} = \frac{3}{5}$ which is a contradiction.

This implies that pieces like those in the figure cannot fit together in order to form a triangle. In order for the pieces to fit together, the measure of $\overline{EF}$ must be given as: $\frac{8}{13} = \frac{EF}{5}$; hence EF = $\frac{40}{13} = 3\frac{1}{13}$.

Since $3\frac{1}{13}$ is close to 3, the discrepancy is small and the pieces only appear to fit. Other pieces which appear to fit should be analyzed.

Problem Set 13-3

1. (a) 6 (b)$2\sqrt{2}$ (c) 5a (d) 12 (e)$(s\sqrt{3})/2$ (f) $2\sqrt{2}$
(g) 9 (h) 13 (i)$2\sqrt{2}$ (j) $3\sqrt{5}$ (k) $3\sqrt{3}$ (l) 5/3
2. $6\sqrt{5}$, $12\sqrt{5}$
3. (a) No (b) Yes (c) Yes (d) Yes (e) Yes (f) Yes
4. $\sqrt{450}$, or $15\sqrt{2}$ cm
5. (a) x = 8, y = $2\sqrt{3}$ (b) x = 4, y = 2
6. $20\sqrt{13}$ km
7. About 2622 mi

8. $\sqrt{125}$ mi or about 11.2 mi

9. Answers vary.

10. $6\sqrt{6}$ ft, or about 14.7 ft

11. (a) $37.5\sqrt{3}$ cm^2 (b) $(3r^2\sqrt{3})/2$ m^2

12. 9.8 m

13. (a) $(s^2\sqrt{3})/4$ (b) $s^2/2$.

14. Approximately 1.5 m

15. 12.5 cm; 15 cm

16. $c\sqrt{3}/4$

17. $c/\sqrt{2}$, or $(c\sqrt{2})/2$

18. Answers vary.

19.

A-13-4

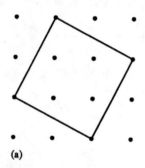

(a)

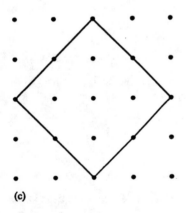

(b) Not possible

(c)

(d) Not possible (e) Not possible

20. ΔACD $\sim$ ΔABC;AC/AB = AD/AC implies b/c = x/b which implies $b^2 = cx$; ΔBCD $\sim$ ΔABC; AB/CB = CB/DB implies c/a = a/y which implies $a^2 = cy$;

$$a^2 + b^2 = cx + cy = c(x+y) = cc = c^2$$

21. The area of the trapezoid is equal to the sum of the areas of the three triangles. Thus,

$$1/2(a+b)(a+b) = 1/2ab + 1/2ab + 1/2c^2$$
$$1/2(a^2 + 2ab + b^2) = ab + 1/2c^2$$
$$a^2/2 + ab + b^2/2 = ab + c^2/2$$

Subtracting ab from both sides and multiplying both sides by 2, we have $a^2 + b^2 = c^2$. The reader should also verify that the angle formed by the two sides of length c has measure 90°.

22. Yes

23. Answers vary.

24. The area of the large square is equal to the sum of the areas of the smaller square and the four triangles. Thus,

$$(a+b)^2 = c^2 + 4(ab/2)$$
$$a^2 + 2ab + b^2 = c^2 + 2ab$$
$$a^2 + b^2 = c^2$$

25. Answers vary.

26. 8 cm

27. The problem is a little unclear, since we don't know precisely what her tactic will be in sawing the diagonal board. Will she saw it straight across, or will she hone it into a 90° point so it fits perfectly onto the gate? If we assume the former, we get 8-$\sqrt{34}$, or approximately 2.17 ft.

28. $90\sqrt{2}$ ft or about 127.28 ft

29. The longest piece of straight spaghetti will be $\sqrt{116}$ in., or approximately 10.77 in.

30. 0.032 km, 322 cm, 3.2 m, 3.020 mm.

31. (a) 33.25 cm^2 (b) 30 cm^2 (c) 32 m^2

32. (a) 10 cm, 10π cm, 25π cm^2 (b) 12 cm, 24π cm, 144π cm^2
(c) $\sqrt{17}$ m, $2\sqrt{17}$ m, $2\pi\sqrt{17}$ m (d) 10 cm, 20 cm, 100π cm^2

33. 25/π m^2

Brain Teaser (p. 724)

The room can be thought of as a box, which can be opened up so that A and C lie on the same plane. Then the shortest path is the line segment connecting A and C.

Thus AC = $\sqrt{2^2 + 6^2} = \sqrt{40} = 2\sqrt{10}$ m

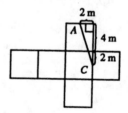

Problem Set 13-4

1. (a) 96 cm^2 (b) 216π cm^2 (c) 236 cm^2 (d) 64π cm^2
(e) 24π cm^2 (f) 90 cm^2 (g) 5600 ft^2 (h) 1500π ft^2
(i) $(32\pi + 16\pi\sqrt{5})$ cm^2

2. 2.5 L

3. 2688π m^2

4. 162,307,600π km^2

5. 4:9

6. (a) They have equal lateral surface areas (b) The one with radius 6.

7. $(108\sqrt{21} + 216\sqrt{3})$ m^2

8. Answers vary.

9. (a) The surface area is multiplied by 4 (b) The surface area is multiplied by 9 (c) The surface area is multiplied by k^2

10. (a) Lateral surface area is tripled (b) Lateral surface area is tripled (c) It is 9 times the original area.

11. Answers vary.

42. (a) 44 (b) 42 (c) Answers vary. (d) Answers vary.

43. Answers vary.

44. Answers vary.

45. Answers vary.

46. (a) $1.5\pi\,m^2$ (b) $2.5\pi\,m^2$

47. (a) $202.5\,cm^2$ (b) 7.08 cm

48. Answers vary.

49. 720 ft by 162 ft

20. $(100 + 100\sqrt{17})\,cm^2$

21. (a) $100\pi(1 + \sqrt{5}\,cm^2$ (b) $1350\pi\,cm^2$ (c) $2250\pi\,cm^2$

22. (a) Approximately 42 cm (b) Approximately 73 cm

23. 15.2 cm

24. $(6400\pi\sqrt{2} + 13{,}600\pi)\,cm^2$

25. $375\pi\,cm^2$

26. (a) 100,000 (b) 1.3680 (c) 500 (d) 2,000,000 (e) 1
(f) 1,000,000

27. $10\sqrt{5}$ cm

28. $20\sqrt{5}$ cm

29. (a) 240 cm; $2400\,cm^2$ (b) $(10\sqrt{2} + 30)$ cm, $75\,cm^2$

30. Length of side = 25 cm Diagonal $\overline{BD}$ is 30 cm.

Brain Teaser (p. 734)
The cone and the flattened region obtained by slitting the cone along a slant height are shown below.

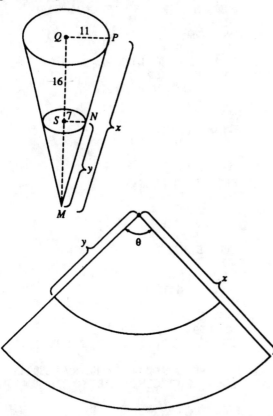

To construct the flattened ring we need to find x, y, and θ.

Because $\Delta MQP \sim \Delta MSN$ we have $\dfrac{16 + MS}{MS} = \dfrac{11}{7}$. Hence MS

= 28cm. In ΔMSN we have $28^2 + 7^2 = y^2$ or $y \doteq 28.86$.

In ΔPQM : $x^2 = 11^2 + 44^2$ or x· 45.35 cm.

To find θ we roll the sector with radius y and central angle θ into the cone whose base is 7cm and whose slant height is y. Hence

$2\pi y \cdot \dfrac{\theta}{360} = 2\pi \cdot 7$ or $\theta = \dfrac{7\cdot 360}{28.86} \doteq 87°\ 19'$.

Brain Teaser (p. 734)
The cylinder with circumference of base 17 in. and height of 10 in. holds the most popcorn.

Problem Set 13-5
1. (a) 8000 (b) 0.0005 (c) 0.000675 (d) 3,000,000 (e) 7
(f) 2000 (g) 0.00857 (h) 675 (i) 345.6 (j) 0.69

2. Answers vary.

3. (a) $64\,cm^3$ (b) $120\,cm^3$ (c) $216\,cm^3$ (d) $50\,cm^3$
(e) $21\pi\,cm^3$ (f) $432\pi\,cm^3$ (g) $(4000/3)\pi\,cm^3$ (h) $22{,}800\,ft^3$
(i) $(20{,}000/3)\pi\,ft^3$ (j) $76{,}200\,ft^3$ (k) $(256/3)\pi\,cm^3$

4. (a) 2000, 2, 2000 (b) 0.5, 0.5, 500 (c) 1500, 1.5, 1500
(d) 5000, 5, 5 (e) 0.75, 0.75, 750 (f) 4.8, 4.8, 4800

5. (a) 200.0 (b) 0.320 (c) 1.0 (d) 5.00

6. $1680\pi\,mm^3$

7. 8/27

8. It is multiplied by 8

9. (a) 2000, 2, 2 (b) 6000, 6, 6 (c) 2 dm, 4000, 4 (d) 2.5 dm, 7500, 7.5

10. $253{,}500\pi$ L

11. 64 to 1

12. 1.62 L

13. 2,500,000 L

14. 32.4 L

15. π mL

16. (a) 25π L (b) 127.32 km

17. No, it's only a third of the volume for 1/2 the price.

18. Answers vary.

19. Larger; The volume of the larger melon is 1.728 times the volume of the smaller, but is only 1 1/2 times as expensive.

20. $16\,m^3$

21. They're equal.

22. Approximately 2.2 cm

23. About 21.5%

24. (a) Answers vary (b) Infinitely many. Because V = 100 = $(1/3)a^2h$, where a is a side of the square base, then $300 = a^2h$. This equation has infinitely many solutions.

25. $(2/3)\sqrt{2/(5\sqrt{5})}\,m^3$, or approximately $0.28\ m^3$

26. (a) $512{,}000\,cm^3$ (b) Vol. $= (y - 2x)^2 x$

27. Let two square pyramids have sides and heights of s, h, and s_1 and h_1. If pyramids are similar, then $s/s_1 = h/h_1 = r$. Hence
$V/V_1 = \left((1/3)s^2h\right)/\left((1/3)s_1^2h_1\right) = (s/s_1)^2 \cdot (h/h_1) = r^2 r = r^3$.

28. Answers vary.

29. Approximately $45.90\,in^2$.

30. Answers vary.

31. $128\ ft^3$

32. It won't hold the cream at 10 cm tall; it would have to be 20 cm tall.

33. It is approximately 0.8 times the original radius.

34. (a) $15{,}600\,cm^2$ (b) $(100 + 200\sqrt{2})\,cm^2$
(c) $(1649 + (81\sqrt{3})/2)\,m^2$, or about $1719.1\ m^2$

35. (a) 340 cm (b) $6000\,cm^2$

36. $2\sqrt{2}\ m^2$

37. 62 cm

Problem Set 13-6

1. (a) Kilograms or tons (b) Kilograms (c) Grams
(d) Tons (e) Grams (f) Grams (g) Tons
(h) Kilograms, or grams (i) Grams or kilograms
2. (a) Milligrams (b) Kilograms (c) Milligrams
(d) Grams (e) Grams (f) Milligrams
3. (a) 15 (b) 8 (c) 36 (d) 0.072 (e) 4.230
(f) 3.007 (g) 5750 (h) 5.750 (i) 30 (j) 41.6
(k) 1.56 (l) 3.1 (m) 60.8
4. (a) No (b) Possibly (c) Yes (d) Yes (e) Yes
5. 16 kg
6. $2.32
7. 2¢
8. Answers vary.
9. (a) $-12°$ C (b) $-18°$ C (c) $-1°$ C (d) $38°$ C (e) $100°$ C
(f) $-40°$ C
10. (a) No (b) No (c) No (d) Yes (e) No (f) Yes (g) Yes
(h) Chilly (i) Hot
11. (a) $50°$ F (b) $32°$ F (c) $86°$ F (d) $212°$ F (e) $414°$ F
(f) $-40°$F
12. (a) $(20 + 6\pi)$ cm; $(48 + 18\pi)\,\mathrm{cm}^2$ (b) 40π cm; $100\pi\ \mathrm{cm}^2$
(c) 50 m; 80 m^2
13. (a) 35 (b) 0.16 (c) 400,000 (d) 5,200,000 (e) 5200
(f) 0.0035
14. (a) Yes (b) No (c) Yes (d) No
15. $\sqrt{61}$ km
16. (a) $12{,}000\pi\ \mathrm{cm}^3$; $2400\pi\ \mathrm{cm}^2$
(b) $42{,}900\ \mathrm{cm}^3$; $(6065 + 40\sqrt{5314})\ \mathrm{cm}^2$

Problem Set 13-7

1. (a) It draws a circle five times. The circumference is 1/5 of the
circumference of CIRCLE 1 (b) It draws the same size circle as
CIRCLE 1 but draws it to the left.
2.　　TO FCIRCLE :N :S
　　　　REPEAT :N [FD :S RT 360/:N]
　　　　END
3. (a)　　TO ARC :S :D
　　　　　REPEAT :D [FD :S RT 1]
　　　　　END
　　(b)　　TO ARCRAD :R :D
　　　　　REPEAT :D [FD 2*3.14159*:R/360 RT 1]
　　　　　END
4. Answers vary
5. (a)　　TO CIRCS :RAD
　　　　　HT
　　　　　CIRCLE :RAD
　　　　　ARCRAD :RAD/2 180
　　　　　LARCRAD :RAD/2 180
　　　　　END
　　　　　TO CIRCLE :R
　　　　　　VCIRCLE 2*3.14159*:R/360
　　　　　END
　　　　　TO VCIRCLE :S
　　　　　　REPEAT 360 [FD :S RT 1]
　　　　　END
　　　　　TO ARCRAD :R :D
　　　　　　REPEAT :D [FD 2*3.14159*:R/360 RT 1]
　　　　　END
　　　　　TO LARCRAD :R :D
　　　　　　REPEAT :D [FD 2*3.14159*:R/360 LT 1]
　　　　　END
　　(b)　　TO EYES :RAD

HT
CIRCLE :RAD
CIRCLE :RAD/2
CIRCLE :RAD/4
LCIRCLE :RAD
LCIRCLE :RAD/2
LCIRCLE :RAD/4
ARCRAD (:RAD + 0.6*:RAD) 90
LT 180
LARCRAD (:RAD + 0.6*:RAD) 90
RT 180
LARCRAD (:RAD + 0.6*:RAD) 90
HT
END
TO LCIRCLE :RAD
　LVCIRCLE 2*3.14159*:RAD/360
END
TO LVCIRCLE :S
　REPEAT 360 [FD :S LT 1]
END
(c)　TO SEMIS :R
　　　ARCRAD :R 180
　　　RT 90 FD :R*2 RT 90
　　　ARCRAD :R/2 180
　　　RT 180
　　　ARCRAD :R/2 180
　　　END
　　　TO ARCRAD R :D
　　　　REPEAT :D [FD 2*3.14159*:R/360 RT 1]
　　　END
(d)　TO CONCIRC :R
　　　HT CIRCLE :R
　　　PU LT 90 FD :R/2 RT 90 PD
　　　CIRCLE :R + :R/2
　　　PU LT 90 FD :R/2 RT 90 PD
　　　CIRCLE :R*2
　　　END
　　　TO CIRCLE :R
　　　　VCIRCLE 2*3.14159*:R/360
　　　END
　　　TO VCIRCLE :S
　　　　REPEAT 360 [FD :SRT 1]
　　　END
(e)　TO FRAME :SIZE
　　　SQUARE :SIZE
　　　FD :SIZE/2
　　　CIRCLE :SIZE/2
　　　END
　　　TO SQUARE :S
　　　　REPEAT 4 [FD :S RT 90]
　　　END
6.　　TO SYMBOL :R
　　　PU LT 90 FD 140 RT 90 PD
　　　REPEAT 3 [CIRCLE :R PU RT 90 FD 9*:R/4 LT 90
　　　　PD]
　　　PU LT 90 FD :R*45/8 LT 90 FD :R RT 180 PD
　　　REPEAT 2 [CIRCLE :R PU RT 90 FD 9*:R/4 LT 90
　　　　PD]
　　　HIDETURTLE
　　　END
　　　TO CIRCLE :R
　　　HT
　　　VCIRCLE 2*3.14159*:R/360
　　　ST
　　　END
　　TO VCIRCLE :S

```
    REPEAT 360 [FD :S RT 1]
    END
7.   TO FLOWER :RAD
       REPEAT 6 [PETAL :RAD 60 RT 60]
     END
     TO PETAL :RAD :DEG
       HT ARCRAD :RAD :DEG
       RT 180 - :DEG
       ARCRAD :RAD :DEG
       RT 180 - :DEG
       ST
     END
     TO ARCRAD :R :D
       REPEAT :D [FD 2*3.14159*:R/360 RT 1]
     END
8.   TO DIAMCIRC :R
       REPEAT 360 [FD 2*3.14159*:R/360 RT 1]
       RT 90
       FD 2*:R
     END
9.   TO MASTERCARD :W
       CARD 3*:W 5*:W
       PU FD 3*:W/2 RT 90 FD :W LT 90 PD
       CIRCLES :W
     END
     TO CARD :W :L
       REPEAT 2 [FD :W RT 90 FD :L RT 90]
     END
       TO CIRCLES :R
       CIRCLE :R PU
       RT 90
       FD :R
       LT 90 PD
       CIRCLE :R
     END
     TO CIRCLE :R
       VCIRCLE 2*3.14159*:R/360
     END
     TO CIRCLE :S
       REPEAT 360 [FD :S RT 1]
     END
```
10. 0.416666

Chapter 13 Test

1. (a) 50,000, 5000, 50   (b) 3200, 3.2, 0.0032   (c) 26,000,000,
260,000, 260   (d) 190,000, 19,000, 0.19
2. (a) Millimeters   (b) Centimeters   (c) Millimeters
(d) Kilometers   (e) Centimeters   (f) Meters
3. Answers vary.
4. 16
5. (a) 8 1/2 cm^2 (b) 6 1/2 cm^2 (c) 7 cm^2
6. 252 cm^2
7. Answers vary.
8. (a) $54\sqrt{3}$ cm^2 (b) 36π cm^2
9. (a) 12π cm^2 (b) $(12 + 4.5\pi)$ cm^2 (c) 24 cm^2
(d) 64.5 cm^2 (e) 178.5 m^2 (f) 4π cm^2
10. (a) Yes   (b) No
11. (a) SA $= 32(2 + \sqrt{13})$ cm^2 ; Vol $= 128$ cm^3
(b) SA $= 96\pi$ cm^2 ; Vol $= 96\pi$ cm^3 (c) SA $= 100\pi$ m^2 ;
Vol $= (500\pi)/3$ m^3 (d) SA $= 54\pi$ cm^2 ; Vol $= 54\pi$ cm^3
(e) SA $= 304$ m^2 ; Vol $= 320$ m^3
12. 65π m^3

13. Answers vary.
14. (a) Metric tons   (b) 1 cm^3 (c) 1 g   (d) Same volume   (e) 25
(f) 2000   (g) 51,800   (h) 10,000,000   (i) 50,000   (j) 5.830
(k) 25,000   (l) 75,000   (m) 52.813   (n) 4.8
15. (a) 16.7   (b) 0.54   (c) 1089   (d) 2176   (e) 486   (f) 1382.4
(g) 60.8   (h) 3.06   (i) 82.4   (j) 35
16. $h_1{}^3 / h_2{}^3 = V_1 / V_2$
17. (a) 6000 kg   (b) 1.557 m   (c) $r = \sqrt[3]{(9/(4\pi))}$ m
18. (a) L   (b) kg   (c) g   (d) g   (e) kg   (f) t   (g) mL
19. (a) Unlikely   (b) Likely   (c) Unlikely   (d) Unlikely
(e) Unlikely
20. (a) 2000   (b) 1000   (c) 3   (d) 0.0042   (e) 0.0002

CHAPTER 14

Problem Set 14-1
1. Answers vary.
2. (a) A(2, 2); B(5, 0); C(4, ⁻3); D(0, ⁻3); E(⁻2, ⁻3); F(⁻4, 0); G(⁻4,
3);.H(0, 3)   (b) (2, ⁻3) answers may vary
3. (a) I   (b) III   (c) II   (d) IV   (e) Between I and II
4. Quadrant I = {(x, y,)|x > 0 and y > 0}
Quadrant II = {(x, y,)|x < 0 and y > 0}
Quadrant III = {(x, y)|x < 0 and y < 0}
Quadrant IV = {(x, y)|x > 0 and y < 0}
5. D(4, ⁻2)
6. Answers vary

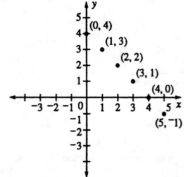

7. (a) P(3, 4); Q(6, 1)   (b) M(⁻1, ⁻1); N(⁻1, 4)
8. (a) P'(2, ⁻2); Q'(2, ⁻5); R'(4, ⁻2)   (b) P'(⁻2, 2); Q'(⁻5, 2); R'(⁻2,
4) (c) P'(4, 2); Q'(4, 5); R'(6, 2)
9. (a) (0, ⁻1), (1, 0), (2, ⁻4), (⁻2, ⁻4), (⁻2, 4), (2, 4)
(b) (0, 1), (⁻1, 0), (⁻2, 4), (2, 4), (2, ⁻4), (⁻2, ⁻4)
(c) (⁻1, 0), (0, 1) (⁻4, 2), (⁻4, ⁻2), (4, ⁻2), (4, 2)
(d) (0, ⁻1), (⁻1, 0), (⁻2, ⁻4), (2, ⁻4), (2, 4), (⁻2, ⁻4)
(e) (0, ⁻3), (1, ⁻4), (2, 0), (⁻2, 0), (⁻2, ⁻8), (2, ⁻8)
10. (a) A' (⁻2, ⁻5); B' (2, ⁻6); C' (5, ⁻1)
(b) A' (2, 5); B' (⁻2, 6); C' (⁻5, 1)
(c) A' (2, ⁻5); B' (⁻2, ⁻6); C' (⁻5, ⁻1)
11. (a) (⁻2, ⁻4)   (b) (⁻a, ⁻b)
12. A'(0, 1); B'(2, 2); C'(1, 3); D'(⁻1, 3); E'(b, a)
13. (a) (a-b, 0)   (b) (⁻b, a)
14. (a) 4   (b) 4   (c) 5   (d) 5   (e) $\sqrt{52}$, or $2\sqrt{13}$ (f) 5
(g) $\sqrt{365}/4$, or approx. 4.78   (h) Approx. 3.89   (i) 5
(j) $\sqrt{68}$, or $2\sqrt{17}$
15. $10 + \sqrt{10}$
16. The sides have lengths $\sqrt{45}$, $\sqrt{180}$, and $\sqrt{225}$. Since
$\left(\sqrt{45}\right)^2 + \left(\sqrt{180}\right)^2 = \left(\sqrt{225}\right)^2$, the triangle is a right triangle

17. $AB = 5 = BC$

18. $x = 9$ or $^-7$

19. (a) $(0, 5)$ (b) $(4.5, ^-2)$ (c) $(2, ^-1.2)$ (d) $(1, 0)$

20. $(^-7, 11)$

21. (a) $(^-2, 3), (2, 1), (0, 4)$ (b) $\sqrt{37}, 4, \sqrt{61}$

22. (a) $(x-3)^2 + (y+2)^2 = 4$ (b) $(x+3)^2 + (y+4)^2 = 25$

(c) $(x+1)^2 + y^2 = 4$ (d) $x^2 + y^2 = 9$

23. (a) Exterior (b) Interior (c) Exterior (d) Exterior
(e) Exterior (f) Interior (g) Exterior (h) On the circle

24. $x^2 + y^2 = 34$

25. (a) $(x-4)^2 + (y+3)^2 = 25$ (b) $(x-4)^2 + (y+3)^2 = 2$

26. $(x+2)^2 + (y+2)^2 = 52$

27.

(a)

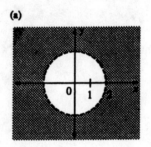

(b)

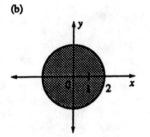

(c)

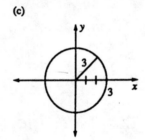

(d)

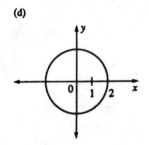

(e) This equation has no graph or the graph is the empty set.
(f) Same as (d)

28. $(x - 29/10)^2 + y^2 = (29/10)^2$

29. Answers vary.

30. Let A, B, and C have coordinates $(^-1, 5), (0, 2)$ and $(^-1, 1)$.
$AB = \sqrt{10}$; $BC = \sqrt{10}$; $AC = \sqrt{40} = 2\sqrt{10}$, so $AB + BC = AC$,
since $\sqrt{10} + \sqrt{10} = 2\sqrt{10}$. Consequently, A, B, and C are collinear.

31. If M is equidistant from the vertices, M has coordinates $(a/2, b/2)$. $BM = \sqrt{(a/2)^2 + (b - b/2)^2} = \sqrt{(a/2)^2 + (b/2)^2}$ (=
$\sqrt{((a^2 + b^2)/4)}$, or $\sqrt{a^2 + b^2}/2$

$AM = \sqrt{(a/2)^2 + (b/2)^2} = \sqrt{((a^2 + b^2)/4)} = \sqrt{a^2 + b^2}/2$.
Therefore,

$AM = BM \cdot OM = \sqrt{(a/2)^2 + (b/2)^2} = \sqrt{a^2 + b^2}/2$.

$\therefore OM = AM = BM$

32. H, at Home

33. 1/25

Problem Set 14-2

1.

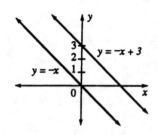

2. Answers vary.

3.

(a)

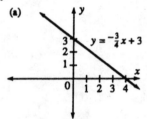

(b)

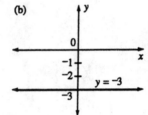

(c)

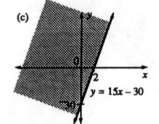

(d)

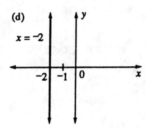

(e)

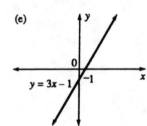

(f)

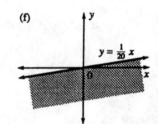

4.

	x intercept	y intercept
(a)	4	3
(b)	None	-3
(c)	2	-30
(d)	-2	None
(e)	1/3	-1
(f)	0	0

5.

(a)

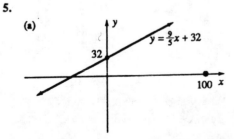

(b)

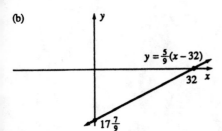

$$y = \tfrac{5}{9}(x - 32)$$

$17\tfrac{7}{9}$

(e)

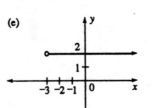

(f)

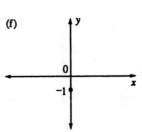

(c) Answers vary.

25. (a) x = 3 (b) y = 2 (c) y = 5 (d) x = ⁻4

5. (a) y= 1/3x (b) y = ⁻x + 3 (c) y = ⁻4x/3 + 4 (d) y = 3/4x + 7/4 (e) y = 1/3x (f) y = x
7. (a) 1/3 (b) 1/9 (c) 0 (d) No slope (e) 20,000
(f) 1 if a ≠ b
8. (a) y = ⁻x - 1 (b) y = 1/2x (c) y = 1 (d) x = 2 (e) y = x - 1/2
(f) y = 0
9. (a) y = ⁻1/2x - 3/2 (b) y = 2/3x - 1 1/3 (c) y = ⁻3
(d) y = ⁻5/7x - 40/7
10. (a) Parallel (b) Parallel (c) Parallel (d) Not parallel
11. (a) y = ⁻2x - 1 (b) y = ⁻2/3x + 5/3 (c) x = ⁻2 (d) y = 3
(e) x = ⁻2 (f) y=3 (g) y = ⁻x +1 (h) y = ⁻3/2x
12. (a) Perpendicular (b) Parallel (c) Perpendicular
(d) Neither
13. √1616 ft, or 4√101 ft
14. The slopes of $\overline{AB}$ and $\overline{CD}$ are each 4 which implies
$\overline{AB} \parallel \overline{CD}$ The slopes of $\overline{CB}$ and $\overline{AD}$ are each 1/2 which implies
$\overline{CB} \parallel \overline{AD}$. Thus, ABCD is a parallelogram.
15. All three determine a line of slope 3.
16. x - intercept = a; y - intercept = b
17. (a) y = ⁻3x - 1 (b) y = ⁻3x + 1 (c) y=1/3x - 1/3
18. (a) y = ⁻x (b) y = ⁻2/3x + 8/3
19. (a) Yes (b) No
20. $M_{\overline{OB}} = 1$; $M_{\overline{CA}} = ⁻1$;
Because $M_{\overline{OB}} \cdot M_{\overline{CA}} = (1)(⁻1) = ⁻1$, the lines are perpendicular.
The midpoint of $\overline{OB}$ is ((a+0)/2, (a+0)/2) = (a/2, a/2). The
midpoint of $\overline{AC}$ is ((a+0)/2, (a+0)/2) = (a/2, a/2). Thus, $\overline{OB}$ and
$\overline{AC}$ bisect each other.
21. Answers vary.
22. (a) x = ⁻2; y is any real number. (b) x is any real; y = 1
(c) x > 0 and y < 0; x and y are real numbers.
23. Perimeter = 12 units   Area = 8 sq units
24. (a)

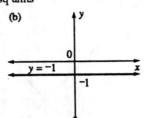

x = ⁻3

(b)

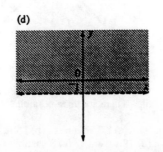

y = ⁻1

(c)

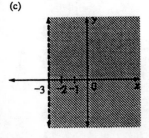

(d)

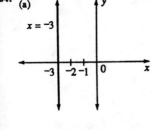

26

(a)

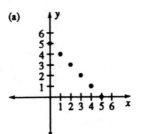

(b)

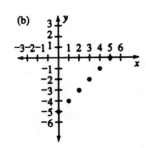

(c)

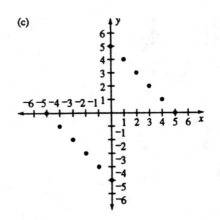

27.

(a)

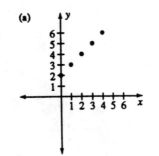

(b)

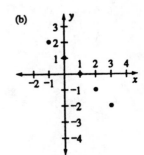

(c)
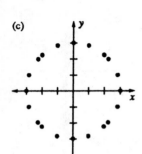

(d)
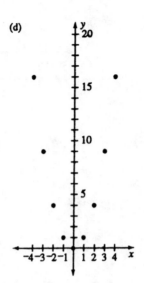

(e)
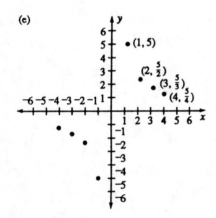

28. **(a)** $\{(x, y) \mid {}^-1 \le x \le 1 \text{ and } {}^-1 \le y \le 1\}$

(b) $\{(x, y) \mid x \le 1 \text{ and } y \le 1\}$

(c) $\{(x, y) \mid {}^-1 \le x \le 2 \text{ and } -1 \le y \le 1\}$

(d) $\{(x, y) \mid x \ge 0 \text{ and } y \le 1\}$

29. **(a)** $x = 3$ **(b)** $x = {}^-3$ **(c)** $y = 3$

30.

(a)
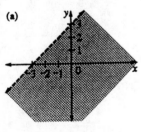

(b)
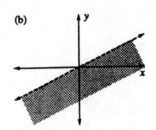

(c)
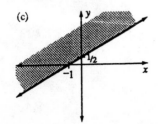

(d)
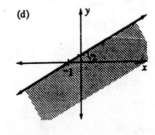

31.

(a)
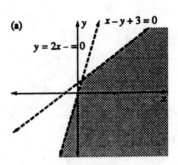

(b)
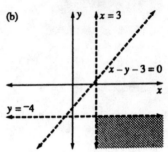

(c)
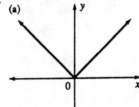

32. **(a)** $y = {}^-x$ **(b)** $y = {}^-x$ **(c)** $x = 0$ **(d)** $y = {}^-x$ **(e)** $y = x$
(f) $y = x - 3$ **(g)** $y = x + 3$ **(h)** One is reflection of the other in the x-axis **(i)** One is reflection of the other in the x-axis.

33. **(a)** $y = {}^-x + 1$ **(b)** $y = {}^-x - 1$ **(c)** $y = x + 1$ **(d)** $y = x + 1$

34.

(a)
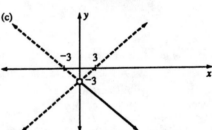

(b)

(c)
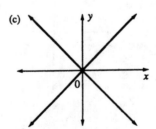

35. Answers vary.

36. **(a)** $y = {}^-8$ **(b)** $x = {}^-7$

37. **(a)** Answers vary; (3, -2) and (7, -2) **(b)** Answers vary; (-2, -2) and (8, 10).

38. There are three possible locations for D; (4, -8), (12, 0) or (0, 12)

39. **(a)** 3/2 sq. units **(b)** 15 sq. units **(c)** 15/2 sq. units
(d) 12 sq. units **(e)** 3 sq. units

Problem Set 14-3

1. (a) Answers vary; (0, ⁻5/3); (5/2, 0); (1, ⁻1); (2, ⁻1/3)

(b)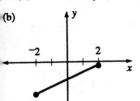

(c)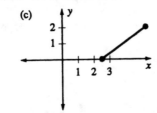

2. (a) (2, 5), unique solution **(b)** No solution **(c)** (1,⁻5), unique solution **(d)** No solution **(e)** (0, 0), unique solution **(f)** (4/11, 1/11), unique solution

3. Answers vary.

4. Answers vary.

5. (a) Unique solution **(b)** No solutions **(c)** Infinitely many solutions; same line **(d)** Unique solution

6. Equations of Lines $y = 8x - 40$; $y = -4/7x + 40/7$; $y = 1/2x$; Unique Common Solution (16/3, 8/3)

7. $y = 1/3x - 4$ and $y = -1/2x - 4$

8. 8 1/6 sq units

9. (a) (17/7, 17/7) **(b)** Slope $\overline{AB}$ = 5/2; Slope of altitude from C to $\overline{BA}$ = ⁻2/5; Then the equation of the altitude through point C is $y = -2/5x + 17/5$. Substituting $x = 17/7$ gives $y = 17/7$ and so the third altitude does pass through point P.

10. 55/72 and ⁻1/72

11. 4000 gal of gasoline and 1000 gal of kerosene

12. 133 1/3 lb cashew nut granola and 66 2/3 lb golden granola

13. 50 L of 60% solution and 100 L of 90% solution

14. $20,000 and $60,000, respectively

15. (a) $2000 **(b)** 6% annual interest or 0.5% per month.

16. Width = 60 in.; length 75 in.

17. 17 quarters; 10 dimes

18. Answers vary.

19. The altitudes $\overline{AU}$ and $\overline{BV}$ intersect at P as shown. Note that $m_{\overleftrightarrow{AU}} = -1/m_{\overline{BC}} = -(b-a)/c$. Hence the equation of $\overleftrightarrow{AU}$ is $y = (-(b-a)/c) \cdot x$. Because $\overleftrightarrow{BV}$ is a vertical line which goes through B its equation is $x = b$. Solving these two equations simultaneously, we get $x = b$, $y = (-(b-a)/c)b$ as the coordinates of P. To show that the altitudes are concurrent we find the equation of the line containing the altitude through C perpendicular to $\overline{AB}$. The slope of $\overline{AB}$ is c/b. Hence the equation of the line containing the altitude is $y = (-b/c)(x - a)$. This altitude goes through P because the coordinates of P, $x = b$, $y = (-(b-a)/c)b$ satisfy the equation $y = -(b/c)(x - a)$.

20. (a) is equation **(b)** not an equation **(c)** is not an equation **(d)** is an equation

21. (a) Slope ⁻5/6, y-intercept 7/6 **(b)** Slope ⁻4/3, y-intercept 2/5 **(c)** Slope 3.75, y-intercept 1.85 **(d)** Slope 0, y-intercept 4

22. (a) $y = 9/10x + 17/5$ **(b)** $y = 5/3x + 1/3$ **(c)** $y = -8$

23.

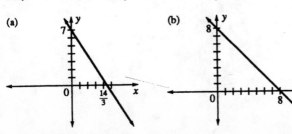

24. (a) 1/2 **(b)** ⁻1/2 **(c)** 0 **(d)** undefined, no slope

25. $y = 2$

(c)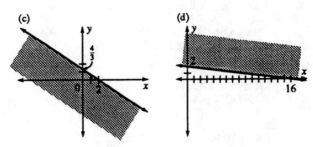

(d)

Brain Teaser (p. 801)

Let x be the number of minute divisions the hour hand has crossed since 3:00 P.M. and y be the number of minutes the minute hand moved since 3:00 P.M. Since the minute hand is 12 times faster than the hour hand, we have $y = 12x$. Since the position of the hands is reversed at the end of the meetings, the minute hand moved $15 + x$ minutes after 6:00 P.M., and the hour hand passed across $y - 30$ minute divisions. Consequently, we have $15 + x = 12(y - 30)$. The solution to the two equations is $\left(\dfrac{375}{143}, \dfrac{12 \cdot 375}{143}\right)$, which translates into approximately 28 seconds past 3:31 P.M. for the starting time and approximately 37 seconds after 6:17 P.M. for the ending time.

Problem Set 14-4

1. The answer will vary depending upon the version of Logo used.

2. The figures generated by the MEDIAL.TRI procedure are similar.

3.
```
TO AXES
   SETXY 0 120
   SETXY 0 (-120)
   SETXY 0 0
   SETXY 130 0
   SETXY -130 0
   SETXY 0 0
END
```
(In LCSI, use SETPOS LIST instead of SETXY.)

4. There are three possible squares that can be constructed.

5.
```
TO FILL.RECT
   REPEAT 50 [SETY 30 SETY 0 RT 90 FD 1 LT 90]
END
```

6.
```
TO CCIRCLE :XCEN :YCEN :RAD
   PU SETXY :XCEN :YCEN
   FD :RAD RT 90
   PD
   CIRCLE :RAD
END
TO CIRCLE :R
   VCIRCLE 2*3 · 14159*:R/360
END
TO VCIRCLE :S
   REPEAT 360 [FD :S RT 1]
END
```

7.
```
TO QUAD :X1 :Y1 :X2 :Y2 :X3 :Y3 :X4 :Y4
   PU SETXY :X1 :Y1 PD
   SETXY :X2 :Y2
   SETXY :X3 :Y3
   SETXY :X4 :Y4
   SETXY :X1 :Y1
END
```
(In LCSI, use SETPOS LIST instead of SETXY.)

8. (a) Use the QUAD procedure from problem 7 and the following:

```
TO MEDIAL.QUAD :X1 :Y1 :X2 :Y2 :X3 :Y3 :X4 :Y4
    QUAD :X1 :Y1 :X2 :Y2 :X3 :Y3 :X4 :Y4
    MIDPOINT :X1 :Y1 :X2 :Y2
    MIDPOINT :X2 :Y2 :X3 :Y3
    MIDPOINT :X3 :Y3 :X4 :Y4
    MIDPOINT :X4 :Y4 :X1 :Y1
    MIDPOINT :X1 :Y1 :X2 :Y2
END
TO MIDPOINT :X1 :Y1 :X2 :Y2
    SETXY (:X1 + :X2)/2 (:Y1 + :Y2)/2
END
```

(In LCSI, use SETPOS LIST instead of SETXY.)

(b) The medial quadrilateral is a parallelogram.

9. Use the QUAD procedure from problem 7 and the following:

```
TO MEDIAL.QUADS :NUM :X1 :Y1 :X2 :Y2 :X3 :Y3 :X4
    :Y4
    IF :NUM = 0 STOP
    QUAD :X1 :Y1 :X2 :Y2 :X3 :Y3 :X4 :Y4
    MEDIAL.QUADS :NUM - 1 (:X1 + :X2)/2 (:Y1 + :Y2)/2
        (:X2 + :X3)/2 (:Y2 + :Y3)/2 (:X3 + :X4)/2 (:Y3 +
        :Y4)/2 (:X4 + :X1)/2 (:Y4 + :Y1)/2
END
```

(In LCSI, replace STOP with [STOP] and use SETPOS LIST instead of SETXY.)

```
10.    TO SAS :S1 :A :S2
        BK :S1
        RT :A
        FD :S2
        HOME
       END
```

```
11.    TO R.ISOS.TRI :LEN
        FD :LEN
        RT 90
        FD :LEN
        RT 135
        FD (SORT 2)*:LEN
       END
12.    TO CIRC5O
        PU
        SETXY (-20) (-40)
        PD
        REPEAT 360 [FD 2*3.14159*:R/360 RT 1]
       END
```

(In LCSI, use SETPOS LIST instead of SETXY.

```
13.    TO GENCIRC :X :Y :R
        PU
        SETXY :X :Y
        PD
        REPEAT 360 [FD 2*3.14159*:R/360 RT 1]
       END
```

(In LCSI, use SETPOS LIST instead of SETXY.

```
14.    TO MEDIAL.TRIS :NUM :X1 :Y1 :X2 :Y2 :X3 :Y3
        IF :NUM = 0 STOP
        TRI :X1 :Y1 :X2 :Y2 :X3 :Y3
        MEDIAL.TRIS :NUM -1 (:X1 +:X2)/2 (:Y1 + :Y2)/2 (:X2
            + :X3)/2 (:Y2 + :Y3)/2 (:X3 + :X1)/2 (:Y3 + :Y1)/2
       END
       TO TRI :X1 :Y1 :X2 :Y2 :X3 :Y3
        PU
        SETXY :X1 :Y1
        PD
```

```
        SETXY :X2 :Y2
        SETXY :X3 :Y3
        SETXY :X1 :Y1
       END
```

(In LCSI, replace STOP with [STOP] and use SETPOS LIST instead of SETXY.)

Chapter 14 Test

1. 16

2. (i) Equations of line through all three points: $y = 3/4x - 1$ (ii)

Distance between A(4, 2) and B(0, -1) is $\sqrt{3^2 + 4^2} = 5$

Distance between A(4, 2) and C(-4, -4) = $\sqrt{6^2 + 8^2} = 10$

Distance between B(0, -1) and C(-4, -4) = $\sqrt{3^2 + 4^2} = 5$

3.

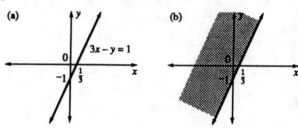

(a)   (b)

(c)

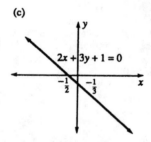

4. (a) $y = -4/3x - 1/3$ **(b)** $x = -3$ **(c)** $y = 3$

5. (a) $y = 4/3x + 7/3$ **(b)** $y = 5$ **(c)** $(3/4, 5)$

6. $y = 3/2x - 1/3$

7. Answers vary.

8. 80 regular and 30 deluxe

9. (a) $(1, -1/2)$. **(b)** $(-7, 3)$

10.

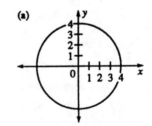

(a)   (b)

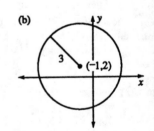

(c)

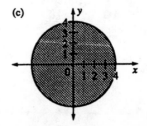

11. $(x+3)^2 + (y-4)^2 = 25$

12.

(a)

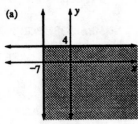

(b)

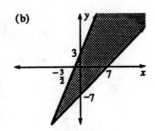

13. 9 red and 3 black

14. 275 freshmen and 500 sophomores

15. Hoover, 15,957,537; Roosevelt, 22,521,525

16. (a) (5/2, 3/2) (b) The equation of a third perpendicular is: y - 2 = x - 3. The point in (a) is on the perpendicular bisector because

$(3/2) - 2 = (5/2) - 3$ (c) $\sqrt{(5/2-0)^2 + (3/2-0)^2} = \sqrt{34/2}$

$\sqrt{(5/2-1)^2 + (3/2-4)^2} = \sqrt{34/2}$

$\sqrt{(5/2-5)^2 + (3/2)^2} = \sqrt{34/2}$

(d) $(x-5/2)^2 + (y-3/2)^2 = 34/4$

17. (3/2, 3/2)

18. $(2/5)\sqrt{5}$

19. $(2/5)\sqrt{5}$

20. (a) (5, 3) (b) (3, 8) (c) None (d) $\sqrt{13}$ (e) 7
(f) 10

APPENDIX-I

Problem Set A-I

1. (a), (b), (d), (e) and (g)

2. (a) $X\wedge 2 + Y\wedge 2 - 3*Z$ (b) $24*34/2\wedge 3$

(c) $A+B-C\wedge 2/D$ (d) $(A+B)(C+D)$

(e) $15/(A*(2*B\wedge +5))$

3. (a) 7 (b) 7 (c) 6 (d) 3 (e) 16 (f) ⁻44

4. (a) 35,200,000 (b) 0.0000193 (c) ⁻0.000001233 (d) ⁻7402

5. Answers may vary depending upon the computer used.

6. (a)
```
5     REM WE INPUT THE VALUE OF
      THE VARIABLE X
10    INPUT X
20    LET Y = 13*X ^ 5 - 27/X + 3
30    PRINT "WHEN X = ";X;", Y ="; Y
40    END
```
(b) (i)
```
RUN
? 1.873
WHEN X = 1.873, Y = 288.247015
```
(ii)
```
RUN
? 7
WHEN X = 7, Y = 218490.143
```

7. (a)
```
10    REM THIS PROGRAM CONVERTS
      DEGREES FAHRENHEIT
20    REM TO DEGREES CELSIUS
30    PRINT "THE NUMBER OF
      DEGREES FAHRENHEIT IS " ;
40    INPUT F
50    LET C = 5/9*(F - 32)
60    PRINT F; " DEGREES
      FAHRENHEIT = ";C;" DEGREES
      CELSIUS"
70    END
```

(b) (i)
```
THE NUMBER OF DEGREES
FAHRENHEIT IS? 212
212 DEGREES FAHRENHEIT =
 100 DEGREES CELSIUS
```
(ii)
```
THE NUMBER OF DEGREES
FAHRENHEIT IS? 98.6
98.6 DEGREES FAHRENHEIT =
37 DEGREES CELSIUS
```
(iii)
```
THE NUMBER OF DEGREES
FAHRENHEIT IS? 68
68 DEGREES FAHRENHEIT =
20 DEGREES CELSIUS
```
(iv)
```
THE NUMBER OF DEGREES
FAHRENHEIT IS? 32
32 DEGREES FAHRENHEIT = O
DEGREES CELSIUS
```
(v)
```
THE NUMBER OF DEGREES FAHRENHEIT
IS? -40
-40 DEGREES FAHRENHEIT =
-40 DEGREES CELSIUS
```
(vi)
```
THE NUMBER OF DEGREES FAHRENHEIT
IS? -273
-273 DEGREES FAHRENHEIT =
-169.444444 DEGREES CELSIUS
```

8.
```
10    THIS PROGRAM FINDS THE VOLUME OF A
      RIGHT RECTANGULAR PRISM
20    PRINT "TYPE THE LENGTH, WIDTH, AND
      HEIGHT SEPARATED BY COMMAS"
30    INPUT L,W,H
35    REM V IS THE VOLUME OF THE PRISM
40    LET V = L*W*H
50    PRINT "THE VOLUME OF A BOX WITH
      LENGTH ";L;", WIDTH ";W;
60    PRINT " AND HEIGHT ";H;" IS"; V
70    END
TYPE THE LENGTH WIDTH AND HEIGHT
SEPARATED BY COMMAS.
? 8,5,3
THE VOLUME OF A BOX WITH LENGTH 8,
WIDTH 5 AND HEIGHT 3 IS 120
```

9. (a)
```
PRINT 100*1.18 ^ 25
6266.8628
```
(b)
```
5     REM N IS THE NUMBER OF YEARS THE
      MONEY IS INVESTED
10    INPUT N
15    REM B IS THE BALANCE
20    LET B = 100*1.18 ^ N
30    PRINT "AFTER ";N;" YEARS, THE
      BALANCE IS $";B
40    END
```
(The balance in (b) is the same as in (a).)

10. Answers may vary depending upon the computer used.

11. (a) HEY YOU OUT THERE
(b) HEY YOU OUT THERE
HEY YOU OUT THERE
HEY YOU OUT THERE
HEY YOU OUT THERE
HEY YOU OUT THERE
HEY YOU OUT THERE
HEY YOU OUT THERE

Outputs are different because of the placement of the PRINT statement being outside the loop in (a) and inside the loop in (b).

12. (a)
```
10    FOR N = 1 TO 20
10    PRINT 2*N
30    NEXT N
40    END
```

(b)
```
10    FOR N = 1 TO 20
20    PRINT 2*N " ";
30    NEXT N
40    END
```

13.
```
5     REM THIS PROGRAM COMPUTES THE SUM OF
      THE SQUARES OF THE
6     REM FIRST 100 POSITIVE INTEGERS
7     REM N IS A POSITIVE INTEGER
10    FOR N = 1 TO 100
15    REM Y IS USED TO ACCUMULATE
20    LET Y = Y + N*N
30    NEXT N
40    PRINT Y
50    END
5050
```

14.
```
10    PRINT "THIS PROGRAM IS TO PRACTICE
      MULTIPLYING."
20    PRINT "TYPE THE TWO NUMBERS TO BE
      MULTIPLIED";
21    PRINT "SEPARATED BY A COMMA."
25    REM A AND B REPRESENT THE NUMBERS
      TO BE MULTIPLIED
26    REM X INITIALIZES A COUNTER
27    REM C REPRESENTS THE PRODUCT OF
      A AND B
28    LET X = O
30    INPUT A, B
35    LET X = X + 1
40    PRINT "AFTER THE QUESTION MARK, TYPE
      THE PRODUCT."
50    PRINT A;"*";B;"=";
60    INPUT C
70    IF A*B > C THEN 100
80    PRINT "SORRY, TRY AGAIN."
90    GOTO 40
100   PRINT "VERY GOOD. DO YOU WANT TO
      MULTIPLY OTHER NUMBERS?"
110   INPUT D$
120   IF D$ = "YES" THEN 20
130   PRINT "THE NUMBER OF ATTEMPTED
      EXERCISES WAS ";X
140   END
```

15. The output is given below.
```
1     4     5
1     5     6
2     4     6
2     5     7
3     4     7
3     5     8
```

16.
```
5     REM THIS PROGRAM WILL DETERMINE IF A
      POSITIVE INTEGER IS PRIME
6     REM N REPRESENTS A POSITIVE INTEGER
7     REM A REPRESENTS AN INTEGER BETWEEN 1
      AND N
8     REM Y REPRESENTS THE QUOTIENT N/A
10    INPUT N
15    IF N = 1 THEN 60
16    IF N = 2 THEN 80
20    FOR A =2 TO N - 1
30    LET Y = N/A
40    IF Y = INT(Y) THEN 60
50    NEXT A
55    GOTO 80
60    PRINT N;" IS NOT A PRIME."
70    GOTO 90
80    PRINT N;" IS NOT A PRIME."
```

```
90    END
```

17.
```
10    REM THIS PROGRAM CONVERTS DEGREES
      FAHRENHEIT
20    REM TO DEGREES CELSIUS
25    REM F REPRESENTS A NUMBER OF DEGREES
      FAHRENHEIT
26    REM C REPRESENTS A NUMBER OF DEGREES
      CELSIUS
30    PRINT "DEGREE FAHRENHEIT", "DEGREE
      CELSIUS"
40    FOR F = -40 TO 220 STEP 10
50    LET C = 5/9*(F - 32)
60    PRINT F, ,C
70    NEXT F
80    END
```

18.
```
10    REM THIS PROGRAM CALCULATES THE AREA
20    REM AND THE CIRCUMFERENCE OF A CIRCLE
25    REM R IS THE RADIUS; C IS THE
      CIRCUMFERENCE; A IS THE AREA
30    PRINT "WHAT IS THE RADIUS";
40    INPUT R
50    LET A = 3.14159*R^2
60    LET C = 2*3.14159*R
70    PRINT "RADIUS","AREA","CIRCUMFERENCE"
80    PRINT R,A,C
90    END
```

19.
```
10    REM THIS PROGRAM CALCULATES N!
15    REM N IS A NATURAL NUMBER
16    REM T IS USED TO ACCUMULATE PRODUCTS
17    REM A IS USED AS A COUNTER
20    PRINT "WHAT IS THE VALUE OF N";
30    INPUT N
40    LET T = 1
50    FOR A = 1 TO N
60    LET T = T*A
70    NEXT A
80    PRINT "N","N!"
90    PRINT N,T
100   END
```

20.
```
10    REM LAURA'S LOTTERY
11    REM P IS THE PRIZE
12    REM A IS THE AMOUNT ACCUMULATED
13    REM N IS A COUNTER
14    REM P IS THE DIFFERENCE IN A AND $10000
15    LET N = O
20    LET P = 50000
30    LET A = P*(1 + .15)
40    LET N = N + 1
50    LET P = A - 10000
60    IF P <= 0 THEN 80
70    GOTO 30
80    PRINT "YOU'RE OUT OF MONEY."
90    PRINT "IT LASTED ";N - 1;" YEARS."
100   END
YOU'RE OUT OF MONEY. IT LASTED 9 YEARS.
```

21.
```
10    REM SUM OF CUBES EQUALS SQUARES OF
      SUM OF INTEGERS
15    REM N IS AN INTEGER
16    REM Y IS THE CUBE OF N
17    REM K IS TO ACCUMULATE THE SUM OF
      CUBES
18    REM Z IS TO ACCUMULATE THE SUM OF THE
      NUMBERS
19    REM S IS TO SQUARE Z
20    PRINT "1^3 + 2^3 +...+ N^3","(1 + 2 + 3 +...+ N)^2"
25    LET K = 0
```

```
26    LET Z = 0
30    FOR N = 1 TO 10
40    LET Y = N ∧ 3
50    LET K = K + Y
60    LET Z = Z + N
70    LET 5 = Z ∧ 2
80    PRINT K,,S
90    NEXT N
100   END
```

22.
```
10    REM THIS PROGRAM COMPUTES THE SUM OF
      THE
20    REM FIRST 1000 ODD NATURAL NUMBERS
21    REM A IS A NATURAL NUMBER
22    REM N DETERMINES ODD NATURAL
      NUMBERS
23    REM Y ACCUMULATES THE SUM OF THE ODD
      NATURAL NUMBERS
24    LET Y = 0
30    FOR A = 1 TO 1000
40    LET N = 2*A - 1
50    LET Y = Y + N
60    NEXT A
70    PRINT "THE SUM OF THE FIRST 1000 ODD
      NATURAL ";
80    PRINT "NUMBERS IS ";Y
90    END
```

23.
```
10    REM HARMONIC SERIES
11    REM K IS A COUNTER
12    LET K = 0
13    REM Y ACCUMULATES THE SUM
14    LET Y = 0
20    PRINT "HOW ANY TERMS DO YOU WANT";
30    INPUT N
40    LET K = K + 1
50    LET Y = Y + 1/K
60    IF K>= N THEN 80
70    GOTO 40
80    PRINT "THE VALUE OF THE FIRST ";N;" TERMS
      OF THE ";
90    PRINT "HARMONIC SERIES IS ";Y
100   END
HOW MANY TERMS DO YOU WANT? 100
THE VALUE OF THE FIRST 100 TERMS OF THE
HARMONIC SERIES IS 5.187377
```

24.
```
10    REM PLASTIC CARD COMPANY BILLS
11    REM 01 IS THE AMOUNT FOR FIRST METHOD
12    REM 02 IS THE AMOUNT FOR SECOND
      METHOD
13    REM 03 IS THE AMOUNT FOR THIRD METHOD
20    PRINT "WHAT IS THE CUSTOMER ID NUMBER";
30    INPUT I
40    PRINT "WHAT IS THE BILL";
40    INPUT B
60    LET 01 = B - 5/100*B
70    LET 02 = B
80    LET 03 = B + 2/100*B
90    PRINT "ID#","OPTION 1","OPTION 2","OPTION 3"
100   PRINT 1,01,02,03
110   END
```

25.
```
10    REM TABLE OF CUBES AND CUBE ROOTS
11    REM N IS A NATURAL NUMBER
20    PRINT "NUMBER","CUBE","CUBE ROOT"
30    FOR N = 1 TO 20
40    PRINT N,N^3,N^(1/3)
60    NEXT N
70    END
```

26.
```
10    REM THIS PROGRAM PRINTS INTEREST
      COMPOUNDED DAILY
15    REM N IS A COUNTER
16    REM B IS THE AMOUNT ACCUMULATED
17    LET N = 0
20    LET N = N + 1
30    LET B = 1000*(1 + 5/36500)^N
40    IF B > 5000 THEN 60
50    GOTO 20
60    PRINT "AFTER ";N;" DAYS, THE
      BALANCE EXCEEDS $5000."
70    END
AFTER 11750 DAYS, THE BALANCE EXCEEDS $5000.
```

27.
```
5     REM THIS PROGRAM PRINTS FIBONACCI
      NUMBERS
10    REM X IS THE FIRST TERM
11    REM Y IS THE SECOND TERM
12    REM A COUNTS THE TERMS AFTER THE THIRD
13    REM Z FINDS SUCCESSIVE TERMS
14    PRINT "HOW MANY TERMS OF THE SEQUENCE
      DO YOU WANT";
15    INPUT N
20    LET X = 1
30    PRINT X; " "
40    IF N = 1 THEN 140
50    LET Y = 1
60    PRINT Y; " ";
70    IF N = 2 THEN 140
80    FOR A = 3 TO N
90    LET Z = X + Y
100   LET X = Y
110   LET Y = Z
120   PRINT Z; " "
130   NEXT A
140   END
HOW MANY TERMS OF THE SEQUENCE DO YOU
WANT? 10
1 1 2 3 5 8 13 21 34 55
```

28.
```
10    REM THIS PROGRAM OUTPUTS BATTING
      AVERAGES
11    REM K COUNTS THE PLAYERS
12    REM A IS THE BATTING AVERAGE
13    REM R IS THE BATTING AVERAGE IN
      THOUSANDTHS
15    LET K = 0
20    PRINT "HOW MANY PLAYERS ARE THERE";
30    INPUT N
40    PRINT "PLAYER #"."# OF BATS","# OF
      HITS","BATTING AVERAGE"
50    LET K = K + 1
60    PRINT "AFTER THE QUESTION MARK, TYPE
      THE # OF AT BATS,"
70    PRINT "THE # OF HITS OF PLAYER ";K;"
      SEPARATED BY COMMAS."
80    INPUT B, H
90    LET A = H/B
100   LET R = INT(1000~A)
105   LET R = R/1000
110   PRINT K,B,H,R
120   IF K < N THEN 50
130   END
```

29.
```
10    REM THIS PROGRAM DOUBLES SALARY
11    REM D COUNTS DAYS
12    REM S COMPUTES SALARY FOR DAY
13    REM T ACCUMULATES SALARY
14    LET T = 0
```

```
20    FOR D = 1 TO 15
30    LET S = 2^(D - 1)
35    IF D = 15 THEN 60
40    LET T = T + S
50    NEXT D
60    PRINT "THE DIFFERENCE OF THE 15TH DAY'S
      SALARY AND"
70    PRINT " THE TOTAL FOR 14 DAYS IS ";S - T
80    END
```
THE DIFFERENCE OF THE 15TH DAY'S SALARY AND
THE TOTAL FOR 14 DAYS IS 1

30.
```
10    REM THE SUM OF TWO SQUARES
11    REM X AND Y REPRESENT POSSIBLE
      NUMBERS
12    REM Z IS THE SUM OF X^2 AND Y^2
20    FOR X = 1 TO 6
30    FOR Y = 1 TO 6
40    LET Z = X^2 + Y^2
50    IF X >= Y THEN 70
60    IF Z < 40 THEN 100
70    NEXT Y
80    NEXT X
90    GOTO 120
100   PRINT Z;"=" ;X;"^2 +";Y;"^2"
110   GOTO 70
120   END
```

$5 = 1^2 + 2^2$
$10 = 1^2 + 3^2$
$17 = 1^2 + 4^2$
$26 = 1^2 + 5^2$
$37 = 1^2 + 6^2$
$13 = 2^2 + 3^2$
$20 = 2^2 + 4^2$
$29 = 2^2 + 5^2$
$25 = 3^2 + 4^2$
$34 = 3^2 + 5^2$

APPENDIX II

Problem Set AII-1

1.
(a)

(b)

(c)

(d)

(e) 0   (f)   (g)

2.   The answer may vary depending upon the type of computer being used.

3.

(a) 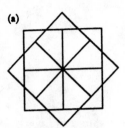   (b)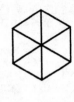

(c)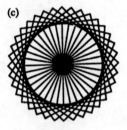

4.   Answers may vary.
(a)   TO RECT
       REPEAT 2 [FORWARD 30 RIGHT 90
       FORWARD 60 RIGHT 90]
      END
(b)   TO FLAG '
       FORWARD 40
       REPEAT 2 [FORWARD 20 RIGHT 90
       FORWARD 40 RIGHT 90]
      END
(c)   TO HAT
       REPEAT 2 [FORWARD 60 RIGHT 90 FORWARD 30
            RIGHT 90]
       PENUP LEFT 90 FORWARD 30 PENDOWN
       REPEAT 2[LEFT 90 FORWARD 6 LEFT 90
            FORWARD 90]
      END
(d)   TO T
       FORWARD 60 LEFT 90
       FORWARD 30 BACK 60
      END
(e)   TO RHOMBUS
       RIGHT 20
       REPEAT 2[FD 40 RT 70 FD 40 RT 110]
      END
(f)   TO CENTER.SQUARE
       REPEAT 4[FORWARD 70 RIGHT 90]
       RIGHT 45 PENUP
       FORWARD 35 LEFT 45
       PENDOWN
       REPEAT 4[FORWARD 20 RIGHT 90]
      END
5.   Answers may vary.
      TO LOGO
       PENUP LEFT 90 FORWARD 90 RIGHT 90
       PENDOWN L
       SPACE O
       SPACE G
       SPACE O
      END
      TO L
       FORWARD 40 BACK 40
       RIGHT 90 FORWARD 20
       BACK 20 LEFT 90
      END

```
TO O
  REPEAT 2[FORWARD 40 RIGHT 90 FORWARD 25
    RIGHT 90]
END
TO G
  FORWARD 40 RIGHT 90 FORWARD 25
  PENUP RIGHT 90 FORWARD 20
  PENDOWN
  RIGHT 90 FORWARD 10 BACK 10
  LEFT 90 FORWARD 20 RIGHT 90
  FORWARD 25 RIGHT 90
END
TO SPACE
  PENUP RIGHT 90
  FORWARD 35 LEFT 90
  PENDOWN
END
```

6.   Answers may vary
```
TO SQUARE1
  REPEAT 4[FORWARD 50 RIGHT 90]
END
TO TRIANGLE1
  REPEAT 3[FORWARD 50 RIGHT 120]
END
```
(a)
```
TO SQUARE.PILE
  REPEAT 4[SQUARE1 RIGHT 90]
END
```
(b)
```
TO DIAMOND
  RIGHT 30 TRIANGLE1
  RIGHT 60 FORWARD 50 RIGHT 120
  TRIANGLE1
END
```
(c)
```
TO RECT1
  REPEAT 2[FORWARD 60 RIGHT 90 FORWARD 30
    RIGHT 90]
END
TO RECT.SWIRL
  RIGHT 30
  REPEAT 4[RECT1 LEFT 90]
END
```
(d)
```
TO TRI.SWIRL
  REPEAT 3[TRIANGLE1 RIGHT 120]
END
```
(e)
```
TO STAR
  RIGHT 30
  REPEAT 4[TRIANGLE1 RIGHT 60 FORWARD 50
    RIGHT 30]
END
```
(f)
```
TO FLAG1
FORWARD 10
  REPEAT 2[FORWARD 5 RIGHT 90 FORWARD 8
    RIGHT 90]
END
TO FLAG.TOP
  SQUARE1
  FORWARD 50 RIGHT 30
  TRIANGLE1
  FORWARD 50 LEFT 30
  FLAG1
END
```
7.   Answers may vary.
(a)
```
TO SQUARE.FACE
  SQUARE 60
  FORWARD 5 PENUP RIGHT 90
  FORWARD 25
  LEFT 90 PENDOWN
```

```
  SQUARE 10 PENUP FORWARD 18
  PENDOWN RIGHT 30
  TRIANGLE 10
  PENUP LEFT 30 FORWARD 15 LEFT 90
  FORWARD 10
  RIGHT 90 PENDOWN
  SQUARE 10 PENUP RIGHT 90
  FORWARD 20 LEFT 90 PENDOWN
  SQUARE 10
END
TO SQUARE :S
  REPEAT 4[FORWARD 5 RIGHT 90]
END
TO TRIANGLE :S
  REPEAT 3[FORWARD :S RIGHT 120]
END
```
(b)
```
TO BUILD.SQR :S
  SQUARE :S
  SQUARE :S + 10
  SQUARE :S + 20
  SQUARE :S + 30
  SQUARE :S + 40
END
```
(c)
```
TO TAIL :S
  SQUARE :S
  FORWARD :S RIGHT 90 FORWARD :S LEFT 90
  SQUARE :S/2
  FORWARD :S/2 RIGHT 90 FORWARD S/2 LEFT 90
  SQUARE :S/4
END
```
(d)
```
TO TOWER :S
  SQUARE :S
  FORWARD :S RIGHT 90 FORWARD :S/4 LEFT 90
  SQUARE :S/2
  FORWARD :S/2 RIGHT 90 FORWARD :S/8 LEFT 90
  SQUARE :S/4
END
```
8.
```
TO DOG
  FULLSCREEN
  PENUP BACK 50 LEFT 90 FORWARD 50 RIGHT 90
  PENDOWN
  BODY BACK 50
  LEG PENUP RIGHT 90 FORWARD 90 LEFT 90
  PENDOWN
  LEG RIGHT 90 FORWARD 10 LEFT 90
  FORWARD 100
  TAIL LEFT 90 FORWARD 100 RIGHT 90 BACK 20
  HEAD FORWARD 20 EAR
  PENUP LEFT 90 FORWARD 25 RIGHT 90
  FORWARD 15 PENDOWN
  EYE PENUP BACK 30 LEFT 90 FORWARD 15
  RIGHT 90 PENDOWN
  NOSE
END
TO BODY
  REPEAT 2[FORWARD 50 RIGHT 90 FORWARD 100
    RIGHT 90]
END
TO LEG
  REPEAT 2[FORWARD 50 RIGHT 90 FORWARD 10
    RIGHT 90]
END
TO TAIL
  REPEAT 2[FORWARD 30 RIGHT 90 FORWARD 10
    RIGHT 90]
END
```

```
TO HEAD
  REPEAT 2[FORWARD 50 LEFT 90 FORWARD 40
    LEFT 90]
END
TO EAR
  REPEAT 2[FORWARD 30 LEFT 90  FORWARD 15
    LEFT 90]
END
TO EYE
  REPEAT 4[FORWARD 5 RIGHT 90]
END
TO NOSE
  REPEAT 2[FORWARD 15 LEFT 90 FORWARD 5
    LEFT 90]
END
TO KITE
  LEFT 45
  REPEAT 4[FORWARD 40 RIGHT 90]
  RIGHT 45
  REPEAT 3[BACK 20 K.TAIL RIGHT 60]
  BACK 20
END
TO K.TAIL
  RIGHT 60
  REPEAT 3[FORWARD 10 RIGHT 120] LEFT 120
  REPEAT 3[FORWARD 10 LEFT 120]
END
```

10. (a)
```
TO RECT :L :W
REPEAT 2[FORWARD :L RIGHT 90 FORWARD :W
  RIGHT 90]
END
```
(b) Use the RECT procedure from part (a).
```
TO FLAG :S
  FORWARD :S
  RECT :S/3 :S/2
END
```
(c)
```
TO HAT :S
  RECT :S :S/2
  PENUP LEFT 90 FORWARD :S/2
  PENDOWN
  REPEAT 2[LEFT 90 FORWARD :S/10 LEFT 90
    FORWARD :S + :S/2]
END
```
(d)
```
TO T :S
  FORWARD :S LEFT 90
  FORWARD :S/2 BACK :S
END
```
(e)
```
TO RHOMBUS :S :A
  REPEAT 2[FORWARD :S RIGHT (180 - :A) FORWARD
    :S RIGHT :A]
END
```
(f)
```
TO CENTER.SQUARE :S
  SQUARE :S
  RIGHT 90
  PENUP FORWARD :S/3 LEFT 90 FORWARD :S/3
  PENDOWN
  SQUARE : S / 3
END
TO SQUARE :S
  REPEAT 4[FORWARD :S RIGHT 90]
END
```
11.
```
TO BLADES :S
  REPEAT 12[FORWARD :S PARALLELOGRAM :S*3/2
    :S 30 RIGHT 30]
END
```

```
TO PARALLELOGRAM :S1 :S2 :A
  REPEAT 2[FORWARD :S1 RIGHT :A FORWARD :S2
    RIGHT (180 - :A)]
END
```
12.
```
TO RECTANGLES :S
  LEFT 90
  REPEAT 4[RECTANGLE :S/3 :S RIGHT 90 FORWARD
    :S/3]
END
TO RECTANGLE :S1 :S2
  REPEAT 2[FORWARD :S1 RIGHT 90 FORWARD :S2
    RIGHT 90]
END
```

Brain Teaser (p. 846)
```
TO TEASER
  LEFT 45 FORWARD 70.7
  LEFT 135 FORWARD 50
  REPEAT 3[LEFT 90 FORWARD 50]
  REPEAT 2[RIGHT 120 FORWARD 50]
  RIGHT 75 FORWARD 70.7
END
```

Problem Set AII-2
1. Type the procedures on the computer.
2. Type procedures on the computer.
3. Answers may vary.
(a)
```
TO STRETCH :S
  IF :S<5 STOP
  SQUARE :S
  FORWARD :S RIGHT 90
  FORWARD :S LEFT 90
  STRETCH :S-10
END
```
(In LCSI, replace IF :S<5 STOP with IF :S <5 [STOP])
(b)
```
TO TOWER :S
  IF :S<5 STOP
  SQUARE :S
  FORWARD :S RIGHT 90 FORWARD :S/4
  LEFT 90 TOWER :S/2
END
```
(In LCSI, replace IF :S<5 STOP with IF :S <5 [STOP])
(c)
```
TO PISA :S :A
  IF :S<5 STOP
  SQUARE :S
  FORWARD :S LEFT :A
  PISA :S*0.75 :A
END
```
(In LCSI, replace IF :S<5 STOP with IF :
S <5 [STOP])
(d)
```
TO CONSQRS :S
  IF :S<5 STOP
  SQUARE :S
  PENUP FORWARD :S/3 RIGHT 90
  FORWARD :S/3
  LEFT 90 PENDOWN
  CONSQRS :S/3
END
```
(In LCSI, replace IF :S<5 STOP with IF :S <5 [STOP])
(e)
```
TO ROW.HOUSE :S
  IF :S<5 STOP
  HOUSE :S
  SETUP :S
  ROW.HOUSE :S/ 2
END
```
(In LCSI, replace IF :S<5 STOP with IF :S <5 [STOP])

```
    TO HOUSE :S
      SQUARE :S
      FORWARD :S
      RIGHT 30 TRIANGLE :S
      LEFT 30
    END
    TO SETUP :S
      BACK :S RIGHT 90
      FORWARD :S LEFT 90
    END
(f) TO TRI.TOWER :S
      IF :S<5 STOP
      RIGHT 30 TRIANGLE :S
      SETUP : S
      TRI.TOWER :S/2
    END
    (In LCSI, replace IF :S<5 STOP with IF :S <5 [STOP])
    TO TRIANGLE :S
      REPEAT 3[FORWARD :S RIGHT 120]
    END
    TO SETUP :S
      FORWARD :S LEFT 120
      FORWARD :S/4 RIGHT 90
    END
    TO NEST.TRI :S
      IF :S<10 STOP
      RIGHT 30 TRIANGLE :S
      FD :S/2 RIGHT 30
      NEST.TRI :S/2
    END
    (In LCSI, replace IF :S<10 STOP with IF :S <10 [STOP])
    TO TRIANGLE :S
      REPEAT 3[FORWARD :S RIGHT 120]
    END
```

5. Answers may vary.

6. Type the procedure on computer.
7. Answers may vary.

```
    TO SPIN.SQ :S
      IF :S<5 STOP
      SQUARE :S
      RIGHT 20
      SPIN.SQ :S-5
    END
    (In LCSI, replace IF :S<5 STOP with IF :S <5 [STOP])
    TO SQUARE :S
      REPEAT 4[FORWARD :S RIGHT 90]
    END
```

8. Answers may vary, for example, STAR 0 30

```
    TO STAR :N :S
      IF :N=6 STOP
      FORWARD :S*(SQRT 2)/3 LEFT 45
      PENDOWN
      SQUARE :S PENUP RIGHT 45 BACK :S*(SQRT 2)/3
      RIGHT 60 PENDOWN
      STAR :N+1 :S
    END
    (In LCSI, replace IF : N=6 STOP with IF :N=6 [STOP].)
    TO SQUARE :S
      REPEAT 4[FORWARD :S RIGHT 90]
    END
```

9. Answers may vary.

```
    TO SQ.TOWER :S
      IF :S<5 STOP
      SQUARE :S FORWARD :S SQ.TOWER :S/2
      SQUARE :S FORWARD :S
    END
    (In LCSI, replace IF :S<5 STOP with IF :S <5 [STOP])
    TO SQUARE :S
      REPEAT 4[FORWARD :S RIGHT 90]
    END
```